BLAENAVON

FROM IRON TOWN TO WORLD HERITAGE SITE

In Memory of
Marion Knight 1937-1992
and
Beatrice Knight 1970-2014

BLAENAVON

FROM IRON TOWN TO WORLD HERITAGE SITE

by

Jeremy Knight

Logaston Press

LOGASTON PRESS
Little Logaston Woonton Almeley
Herefordshire HR3 6QH
logastonpress.co.uk

First published by Logaston Press 2016
Copyright text © Jeremy Knight
Copyright illustrations © as acknowledged

ISBN 978 1 910839 01 0

Typeset by Logaston Press
and printed and bound in Poland by
www.lfbookservices.co.uk

CONTENTS

ACKNOWLEDGEMENTS

This book could not have been written without the generous help of many kind friends and others, among them Jonathan Berry, Dan Bish, Oliver Blackmore Marion Blockley, Steve Clarke, Susan Fiander-Woodhouse (Blaenavon Cheese Co.), Viscount Grimston, Robert Prothero Jones (Big Pit), Jeremy Lowe, Neil Philips, John Owen, Laura Smyth (English Folk Dance and Song Society), Yolanda Stanton, Peter Wakelin, Diane Williams, Pru Williams and Alison Hargeaves at Blaenavon ironworks; Homie Younessi; the ever helpful staff of Gwent Archives, particularly the County Archivist Tony Hopkins, Kai Michael and Howard Humphries and of Newport Reference Library Monmouthshire Collection. Martin Lawler very generously allowed me the use of his unpublished research and fieldwork, and I am particularly grateful to John Bennet and Harry Thornton of the Rugeley Historical Society for much information regarding the activities of the Hill and Hopkins families there, photographs of buildings associated with them and a copy of Harry Thornton's article on Rugeley ironmasters. Calvin Rees read and commented on Chapter 7. Simon Hardy's and Nathan Matthews fine photographs speak for themselves, Francis Keen kindly allowed use of his painting on page 51 (photographed by Nathan Matthews), and Jeremy Lowe allowed me to reproduce some photographs of housing in Blaenavon. Illustrations not otherwise acknowledged are from the author's slide collection. Tony Hopkins of Gwent Archives produced the map of Blaenavon of the 1880s, stitched together from four separate sheets, and used on pages *xii-xiii*. At Logaston Press, Andy Johnson's rigorous and constructive editing did much to improve my text. My greatest debt however is to Marion and to Annie. The former was my co-partner in much of the research here presented, which was hers as much as mine, whilst Annie, by her patient support and wise advice, has enabled the work that we did then to be brought to fruition.

INTRODUCTION: A LEASE OF THE HILLS

'History is made without knowing of its making'
Jean Paul Sartre, quoted in Fernand Braudel *The Identity of France*

The town of Blaenavon is surrounded by seven square miles of high moorland, with a complex of remains of early industry: coal and ironstone mines and levels, quarries, tramways, ponds and water leats and much else. Of these, the ironworks is preserved as an industrial monument under the care of Cadw and open to the public. Big Pit, one of a great number of collieries in the area that produced coal for sale (as opposed to for use in the ironworks), is now the National Coal Museum of the National Museum of Wales, with a wealth of buildings and exhibits, including underground tours. Its history is only covered here in the context of the history of the wider town and landscape.

For a World Heritage site, Blaenavon, in its bowl of the north Monmouthshire hills, is a secret place, still able to give the visitor a sense of discovery and surprise. The most easterly town of the south Welsh ironfield, it is almost within walking distance of the villages of rural Monmouthshire and from the high moorland of the Blorenge above, the hills of the Brecon Beacons form a backdrop to the view across the Usk Valley. Blaenavon belongs with the *Border Country* of Raymond Williams' novel rather than with the colliery towns of the Rhondda or west Glamorgan, which have a different culture and history.

From Pontypool, the traveller goes northward up the valley of the Afon Llwyd, passing through Pontnewynydd, a huddle of houses in the valley bottom, once the terminus of the Monmouthshire Canal. Beyond is Abersychan, with a milepost for the Blaenavon tramway outside a shop and roads leading off to vanished ironworks at Varteg, British and Golynos. Above Abersychan the valley is green and sylvan, in a landscape that reminded 18th-century travellers of parts of Switzerland. There is still native woodland and a few whitewashed farms remain. In Cwmafon what had been a large brewery building was converted by Quakers to a remarkable self-help enterprise during the depression of the 1930s, while a row of whitewashed, slate-roofed cottages of Forge Row lie next to the residence of the teetotal ironmaster and pioneer sociologist George Kenrick. An incline plane brought pig iron from his Varteg furnaces high on the hill above down to the forges at Cwmafon where it was converted to more profitable bar iron.

Coming to Blaenavon from the opposite direction, from Abergavenny in the Usk Valley, the traveller sees a different landscape. From the cluster of ironmasters' houses around the church of Llanfoist, a road winds steeply through woodland to the high bare moorland plateau of the Blorenge, with its industrial landscape dotted with tramways, spoil heaps and the remains of early metal extraction, before dropping down to the ironworks at Blaenavon.

Not long after the ironworks had passed into state care, I was in the Gwent County Record Office, then in Cwmbran, examining the early leases from Lord Abergavenny that had brought Blaenavon into being. One of these bore on the outside a note in pencil added long ago in some solicitor's office: 'A Lease of the Hills'. Whether this referred to the uplands in which the works had been built ('Lord Abergavenny's Hills') or to the three successive Thomas Hill ironmasters I am not certain, but it seemed an almost metaphysical, if unintended, pun. A lease after all has a finite time span.

The Duke of Wellington once said that no one could write the history of a battle any more than one could write the history of a ball. Anyone attempting to write about Blaenavon must feel the same, for similarly it is not one story but many, and often the story of people who do not figure in conventional histories. The culture of choirs, chapels, benefit societies and amateur sport was home grown. At first glance, this might seem to have little in common with the business history of the successive iron companies that, under various names, operated the ironworks, collieries and steel plant, the lives of the businessmen who controlled those companies, or the vagaries of Victorian economic history. Yet it was these that shaped that society and determined its prosperity or poverty. Combining these into a single thread is not easy, but it is essential if the story of this remarkable town is to be told.

Conditions in Blaenavon and its geographical position created a society significantly different from the industrial monoculture of areas like the Glamorgan coalfield. The outcropping bands of ironstone and coal along the northern escarpment of the uplands could be exploited by horizontal levels driven into the hillside, worked under a sub-contract system by small contractors little different from rural builders and craftsmen like the Brute family of masons from the Monmouthshire Breconshire borders, from which one of their number – Aaron Brute, mason, coal owner and Calvinistic Methodist theologian – came. These levels were often worked by family groups, male and female. Whilst conditions underground for women and children rightly shocked the Victorian conscience, many Blaenavon women had their own views. When the Company belatedly ended the illegal practice of women working underground, some of them staged a noisy protest outside the Company offices, claiming that their families would suffer.

In contrast, the deep mines of areas like the Rhondda required both a radically greater input of capital and far tighter work discipline for safety reasons. This more regimented and socially divided society reflected itself in political terms. The tradition that Blaenavon men did not take part in the Chartist rising of 1839 may or may not be true. There is no way of knowing and certainly many Abersychan men were involved – but even as folk myth it reflects an outside view of a society less receptive to political militancy than some of its neighbours.[1]

My first chapter tries to explain why Blaenavon was built where it was and when it was. The history of ironmaking in the county is followed from medieval bloomery furnaces through charcoal-fired blast furnaces, often part of a landed estate, to the highly capitalised multiple coke-fired and steam-blown blast furnaces of whose first generation Blaenavon is the only survivor. My second chapter considers what was at Blaenavon before the coming of the ironmasters, the landscape history of the seven square miles of the Blaenavon historic landscape and the uses made of it by small farmers and coal and ironstone miners. My third chapter deals with how Blaenavon came into being between 1789 and 1836 under three generations of ironmasters named Thomas Hill, and looks at the community which this enterprise created. The story of Blaenavon is then continued down to 1870, as it struggled to hold its place in a rapidly changing and increasingly competitive industry in the face of an awkward geographical location and a chronic lack of capital. I then look in more detail at the daily experience of living and working in Blaenavon from the starvation years of the 1840s onwards, with child labour, the experiences of working women and migrant labourers, the truck shops which were said to provide a man with his cradle and coffin and half starve him between, and the self-help culture of pubs and benefit societies. Next, I look at how religion – Nonconformist, Anglican and Roman Catholic – reflected that society and how a traditional largely Welsh-speaking Calvinist chapel culture coped with a new English influx affecting how, and in what language, God was worshipped.

The story of two of Blaenavon's most notable people, Sidney Gilchrist Thomas and his cousin Percy Carlyle Gilchrist, covered in Chapter 8, in many ways bridges two halves of Blaenavon's history. In a parliamentary debate on Bletchley Park, scene of the wartime code-breaking operations, a peer remarked that what Ironbridge was to the industrial revolution, Bletchley was to the computing age.[2] She might have added that Blaenavon played a similar role in the age of steel. Their experiments (in which Percy may have played a larger part than he is often credited with) helped convert an iron age into a steel age, with far reaching consequences worldwide. Their story is not without irony. Sidney was a radical liberal, a teetotaller and pacifist. Much of his motivation was to enable his mother to continue her charitable work. Yet the work of the two cousins, at Blaenavon and elsewhere, helped make the First World War technologically possible. At its outbreak, 60% of German steel production was still made by the 'Thomas process'.

My three final chapters deal with Blaenavon's often troubled history in late Victorian times and the two halves of the 20th century. Amid continuing industrial decline, Blaenavon, like the rest of Britain, experienced social and political change and industrial unrest. Though it escaped the worst horrors of two world wars, the town was far from unaffected.

Monmouthshire industrial communities have a long tradition of able local historians, from Edmund Jones 'The Old Prophet' at Aberystruth in 1789 to Arthur Gray-Jones at Ebbw Vale, E.J. Davies at Blaenavon, Evan Powell and Oliver Jones at Tredegar and Cliff Knight at Pillgwenlly in Newport – to name only some. Blaenavon itself has a tradition of historical writing going back to its miner historian Lewis Browning in 1906. Much of its older buildings and townscape have disappeared in recent years. A guide to this lost world is to be found in the three volumes of photographs collected over the years by Malcolm Thomas and John Lewis. Recently, Blaenavon has seen a remarkable communal enterprise in oral history and social history by the Blaenavon History Group of the Workers Educational Association (WEA) and the Blaenavon Community Heritage Museum. They have produced two volumes of lasting value: *Funeral to Festival,* a history of Blaenavon in the first half of the 20th century, and an account of Blaenavon and its people during the First World War.

My first awareness of the Monmouthshire iron industry came at the age of 12, when my grandfather Alf Knight, a railwayman in Newport Docks, brought me samples of the various types of imported iron ore that passed through the docks. Though I went to school in Pontypool and had friends from Blaenavon, I did not visit the town until I returned to Wales from London in 1967 and began exploring the industrial monuments of the south Wales valleys. David Morgan Rees of the National Museum and Douglas Hague of the Welsh Royal Commission introduced me to former ironworking sites and happily I was just in time to see the older housing of places like Blaenavon before they were swept away. I worked in the south Wales valleys both as an Ancient Monuments Inspector dealing, among other things, with industrial monuments, and as an adult education lecturer and came to know many local historians who were generous with their knowledge and help.

When the ironworks passed into state care in 1976, what is now Cadw faced formidable problems. The most urgent was the need to conserve the crumbling, often heat-damaged and dangerous structures, very different from the ruined abbeys and castles with which Cadw normally dealt. The aim was to conserve them and eventually make them suitable for public display. My own main interests lay in much earlier periods – late Roman and earlier medieval – but as a medievalist I had learnt from Inspectorate colleagues like Arnold Taylor and Stuart Rigold the importance of dating and interpreting structures from the available documentation, and of studying them against a wider historical background than the immediate monument.

There was thus a need to study both the existing remains and the extensive documentation for the ironworks and for the town so as to inform this process of conservation. I put together a small research team, largely the same group of people with whom I had earlier excavated Montgomery Castle in mid Wales. This research was carried out, both in record offices and libraries and in Blaenavon itself, by Marion Knight, Martin Lawler, James Hawes and myself. Local newspapers, particularly the *Monmouthshire Merlin* and *Pontypool Free Press*, contained much about the town, sometimes documenting structures in the ironworks. The *Merlin* often carried articles headed 'The Works' giving detailed information on the current situation. Since this fragile resource is now mostly only available on line, if at all, I have given full citations.

One problem in writing of Monmouthshire is the conflict between the Anglicised place name forms in current use and the correct Welsh versions, particularly between v and f – Blaenavon and Varteg as against Blaenafon and Y Farteg. I have used the former versions since these were the forms in use throughout the history of the ironworks, including in contemporary quotations. Where the latter use the correct Welsh forms, I have of course retained them. Similarly, some readers may be unfamiliar with the pre-1971 coinage and such terms as 'half a crown' or 'three and sixpence' (3s 6d). I have therefore always turned such terms into actual shillings and pence without trying to give any decimal equivalents.

Sections of this book are revised versions of articles which have appeared elsewhere. Parts of Chapters 2 and 4 were in the *Monmouthshire Antiquary* 23 (2007) and 4, 1-2 (1970); part of Chapter 3 in *Bulletin of the Board of Celtic Studies* 28 (1970) and Chapter 5 in *Monmouthshire Antiquary* 16 (2000). In all cases, the text has been substantially revised.

The significance of Blaenavon extends far wider than the town itself, or its place in 19th-century British industry and society. Its re-invention of itself at the end of the 20th century for post-industrial leisure and tourism and its re-colonisation by small craft- or food-based enterprises is something it shares with many other post-industrial towns in western and northern Britain. The town motto, borrowed from the 19th century family of ironmasters the Kennards, is apt: *At Spes not Fracta* – But Hope is not Broken.

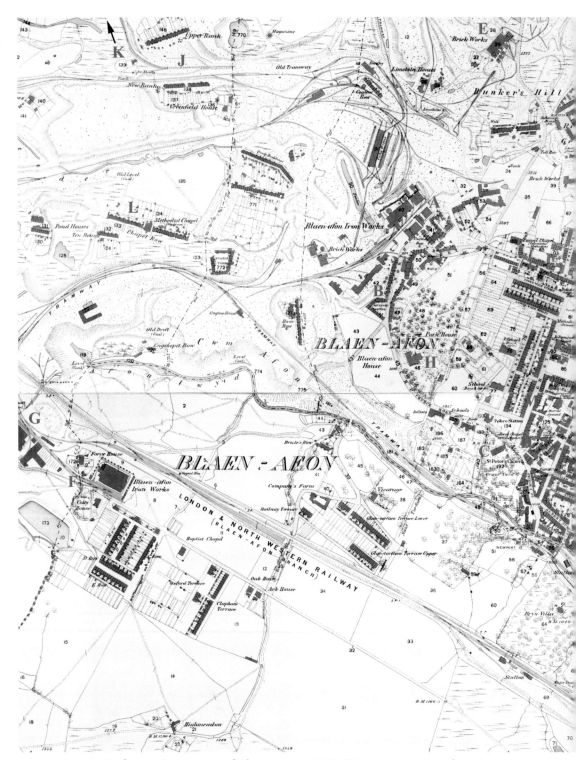

An Ordnance Survey map of Blaenavon c.1880. (Courtesy Gwent Archives)
A: Blaenavon Ironworks   B: Shepherd Square & North Street
C: St Peter's Church & Church School   D: Workmen's Hall

E: Upper Brickyard   F: Forgeside Works   G: Big Pit

H: Blaenavon House (the ironmaster's residence)   J: Upper and Lower New Rank

K: Hill's Pit   L: Chapel Row   M High Street   N: Broad Street

BLAENAVON TIME LINE

1325	Coal and ironstone mines on the Blorenge	1827	Death of Thomas Hill II Thomas Hill III resident partner
1584	Richard Hanbury digging ironstone on the Blorenge	1830	Death of King George IV
1709	Abraham Darby smelts iron ore with coke at Ironbridge	1831	Friendly Society of Coal Mining (Trade Union) opens short-lived branch
1786	Hanbury lease due to expire	1833	Thomas Hill III tries to sell ironworks
1787	Thomas Hill and Benjamin Pratt agree to lease Thomas Hopkins taken into partnership	1836	Blaenavon sold to Blaenavon Iron and Coal Company (1836-1864) William Unwin Sims, Chairman James Ashwell, Managing Director
1789	Hill, Hopkins and Pratt sign lease Site of ironworks bought from Lewis Robert Lewis Furnaces nos.1-3 built	1836-41	Water balance tower built Forgeside furnaces begun
1789-91	Office (Stack) Square built	1837	Death of King William IV Queen Victoria comes to the throne
1792	Nantyglo ironworks built	1838	Cinder Pit disaster
1794	Death of Benjamin Pratt Samuel Hopkins resident partner	1839	Death of William Unwin Sims Chartist Rising in Newport James Hodder, first Police Sergeant
1796	Monmouthshire Canal completed	1840	Church Sunday School opens
1799	Revd William Coxe and Sir Richard Colt Hoare visit Blaenavon	1841	James Ashwell resigns Harry Scrivenor, Manager R.W. Kennard, Chairman Forgeside furnaces left unfinished
1799	Rock Chapel founded		
1800	Boulton and Watt steam engine bought	1841-44	'The Hungry Forties'
1805	St Peters Church built Battle of Trafalgar	1841	Childrens Employment Commission
		1842	Act prohibiting women and children under 10 from working underground
1805-6	Furnaces nos.4 and 5 added	1844	Richard Johnson, Manager Thomas Dyne Steel, Assistant Manager Hill's Pit and Garn yr Erw collieries built First railway locomotives at Blaenavon
1812	Brecon and Abergavenny Canal reaches Llanfoist		
1815	Death of Samuel Hopkins Thomas Hill II managing partner Battle of Waterloo		
1816	Sarah Hopkins founds Church Endowed School (now Visitor Centre)	1846-47	'Railway Mania' and slump
		1847	English Baptist Church (Moriah) opens Bethlehem Congregationalist Church built (rebuilt 1864)
1816-17	Hills Tramroad and Garnddyrys Forge built		
1819	Penuel replaces Rock Chapel	1849	Women prevented from working underground at Blaenavon
1820	Death of King George III		
1822	Old Horeb Baptist Church founded	1849-50	Coke ovens built above furnaces, replacing open heaps
1824	Death of Thomas Hill I		
1825	Blaenavon-Abergavenny Toll Road (B4246) opens Ebenezer Baptist Church founded	1850	Dyne Steel incline built
		1852	Railway built from Newport to Pontypool

BLAENAVON TIME LINE

1854	Railway reaches Blaenavon
	Crimean War starts
1857	Kennard begins programme of modernisation
	British (Nonconformist) School opens
1859	Forgeside furnaces completed
	Rifle Volunteer Company formed
1860	Rail Mill opens on Forgeside
	New blast engine and no.6 furnace in ironworks
1861	Bible Christian Chapel opens
1862	Tyre Mill opens on Forgeside
	Town Hall built
	Kennard sells works and retires to Crumlin Hall
1863	New Horeb Baptist Church opens
1865	Arthur J. Munby visits Blaenavon
1866	Mutual Improvement Society started with reading room and library
	Blaenavon and Brynmawr Railway built
1868	Election riot
	English Congregational Chapel opens
1870	Death of R.W. Kennard
	Blaenavon Iron and Steel Company founded (1870-78)
	Roman Catholic school open next to St Felix's Church
1871	Cricket Club founded
	Wesleyan Methodist school opens
1872-75	Coal strikes (Thomas Halliday Amalgamated Association of Miners)
1872	Blaenavon gets piped water
1874	Streets of Blaenavon lit by gas
1876	Percy Carlyle Gilchrist appointed works chemist
1877	Blaenavon Rugby Football Club plays its first game
1878	Sidney Gilchrist Thomas announces Basic Bessemer process
	Failure of Blaenavon Iron and Steel Company
	Blaenavon Company Ltd founded
	King Street Baptist Church opens
1882	Bessemer steelworks open on Forgeside

1883	Workmens Institute opens in Lion Street
1885	Death of Sidney Gilchrist Thomas
	New Methodist church built in Park Street
1889	Blaenavon Co-operative Society founded
1889-91	Dowlais steelworks moves from Merthyr to Cardiff (East Moors)
1890	American McKinley tariff hits South Welsh steel industry
1893	St Pauls and St Johns Anglican churches built
1895	Workmens Hall opens
1898	South Wales Miners Federation founded
1901	Death of Queen Victoria
1906	Lewis Browning publishes *A Brief History of Blaenavon*
1910	Death of King Edward VII
1911	New Otto-Higenstock coke ovens open on Forgeside
	Nos.4 and 5 furnaces demolished
1914	War declared
1915	Second Battle of Ypres; heavy casualties to 2nd Monmouthshires
1916	Battle of the Somme; 38th Welsh Division at Mametz Wood
1918	Armistice
	Thomas Griffiths elected Labour M.P. for Pontypool
1919	Sankey Report on coal industry
1920	Mining Industry Act: penny levy on coal ('The magic penny')
1921	William Henry Taylor publishes *The Cheated Death*
	Recreation ground opened on Forgeside
1922	First Blaenavon council houses (Elgam)
1923	Open air swimming pool built
1925	Blaenavon House leased by company to Blaenavon Medical Society
1926	General Strike
	Pwll Du quarries close
1928	Eastern Valleys Subsistence scheme opens at Cwmavon

Blaenavon Time Line

1929	Milfraen Pit disaster	1968	Penuel Chapel demolished
	Death of Robert Kennard	1970	Recording survey of early Blaenavon housing set up
1934	Obsolete Forgeside plant sold for scrap		
1936	Death of King George V	1970-72	Shepherd Square, Staffordshire Row, Bunkers Row and Chapel Row demolished
	Edward VIII visits Blaenavon shortly before abdication		
1937	Film *Eastern Valley* made about subsistence scheme	1973	Sidney Gilchrist Thomas Industrial Estate opens
1937-39	New steel plant opens with aid of Nuffield Trust	1974	Conservation work begins on ironworks
1939	War declared	1976	Ironworks pass into state care
1940	Evacuees arrive in Blaenavon	1979	'Little Egypt' coal tips on Forgeside removed
1941	Blaenavon High Level Station and Brynmawr line closed to passenger traffic	1980	Big Pit closes
		1982	Church School closes
1942	Opencast mining above Pwll Du ('the Canada Tips')		Lion Street Congregational Church closes
1945	Peace	1983	Big Pit re-opens as coal museum
1949	Solid steel axle plant sold	1987	Forge Row, Cwmafon preserved
1952	Death of King George VI	1988	Ebenezer Baptist church closed
1953	Food rationing ends	1997	Torfaen County Borough Council opens Blaenavon bid for UNESCO World Heritage status
1958	Blaenavon Company Ltd wound up		
1957	Daniel Doncasters open in Blaenavon		
1959	Alexander Cordell publishes *Rape of the Fair Country*	2000	Blaenavon attains World Heritage status
1962	Blaenavon-Newport railway closes	2003	'Blaenavon booktown' opens
1963	Pwll Du inhabitants re-settled	2007	'Coalhouse' Television reality series
1966	Primitive Methodist church demolished	2008	Church school reopens as World Heritage Visitor Centre

1   The Slow Revolution: Iron making before Blaenavon

Before the Blast Furnace

In 1732 Mrs Jane Catchmay, a Monmouth woman from a family with a history of involvement in the iron industry, found herself in court. She had leased a piece of land adjacent to Monmouth's medieval town wall near the Dixton Gate with its underlying beds of iron slag from Roman or medieval ironsmelting, and therein lay the cause of her court appearance. The early bloomery process was highly inefficient, leaving so much iron in the slag that when blast furnaces were introduced in Tudor times, it became profitable for it to be re-worked. The addition of iron cinders to the mix in the blast furnace even improved the quality of the iron. Forest of Dean ore on its own produced pig iron which tended to be 'cold short' or brittle, whereas mixed with 'cinders' it made 'an excellent temper of toughness, for which the iron was preferred before any brought from foreign parts'. Another writer noted that 'these cinders ... make the prime and best iron, with much less charcoal'. Sir John Winter of Lydney, a Civil War Royalist commander and ironworks entrepreneur, told Samuel Pepys over a business lunch in August 1662 of the Forest of Dean adjacent to Monmouth where 'the timber ... and iron workes with their great antiquity and the vast heaps of cinder which they find, are now of great value, being necessary for the making of iron at this day and without which they cannot work'.[1] Sadly for Mrs Catchmay, in her desire to make a profit from the buried slag, she brought down a length of the town wall and had to pay for its repair.[2]

Bloomery slag became an item of commerce and land in Monmouth was sometimes sold with its 'cinder pit'. A dispute between the corporation, the Duke of Beaufort as lord of the manor and private individuals over the right to exploit this profitable resource led to an angry letter from the Haberdashers Company when the corporation's systematic mining for iron slag brought down the wall of the Lecturer's garden at Monmouth School, which is a Haberdasher foundation. In 1769 the Cock Alehouse in Monmouth was offered for sale with its 'iron cinder mine', and one 'cinder mine' was even found in Monmouth during rescue excavations in 2004.[3]

Iron has been worked in Gwent since pre-Roman times. The process relied on a simple chemical formula $Fe_2O_3 + 3C = 2Fe + CO + 2CO_2$. In other words. Iron oxide, heated in carbon, gave iron plus carbon monoxide and carbon dioxide. The earliest pre-Roman bowl furnaces comprised a shallow pit filled with crushed iron ore and charcoal and capped with a clay dome. Oxygen was introduced via a simple bellows and the resulting bloom of spongy iron extracted, leaving the heavier slag residue in the form of a furnace bottom. The bloom could then be hammered or forged to remove impurities, resulting in a bar of usable iron. By Roman times these had evolved into shaft furnaces, with a clay shaft or chimney, a slag pit beneath to collect the residue, or a channel to draw off the tap slag. Oxygen could now be introduced with a more efficient bellows via hollow clay tubes or tuyères.

Small bloomery sites recorded in the countryside around Trellech are probably Roman. Without excavation and scientific dating it is hard to be sure, but in Devon and Somerset excavation and survey has found a number of similar sites, scientifically dated to late Roman and Saxon times. At Glen Usk above Caerleon, Roman coins, including one of the 3rd-century AD Emperor Probus, were found near 'masses of cinders and slag'. The Usk valley above Caerleon was the site of Roman industrial activity connected with the legionary fortress. The Glen Usk slag was presumably from legionary ironworking, probably the forging of iron from rural bloomeries into bar iron for use in the fortress. Near Miskin in Glamorgan, excavation by Dr Tim Young has found a 1st-century Roman fort and a subsequent ironworking settlement, both associated with massive waste heaps of iron slag.[4]

Substantial medieval beds of iron slag are known at Monmouth, Skenfrith and Trellech.[5] There are indications that unlike the scattered rural bloomery sites of earlier times, medieval iron production was concentrated at one centre in each lordship. Industries such as pottery making and iron smelting were often confined to a specific location, to enable the steward to collect renders (taxes) and to restrict such environmentally harmful activities as the digging of clay pits, the cutting of timber for fuel and the disturbance of game.[6] The foundation charter of Monmouth Priory, issued shortly before 1086, granted three iron forges in the town with their charcoal burners, and in 1256-7 the accounts of the lordship included 'the rent of the forge' and 11 shillings from the sale of iron cinders (*de cisera vendita*).[7] In the lordship of Trellech, south of Monmouth, the rents of iron forges were similarly recorded in Inquisitions Post Mortem in 1295 and 1314 on the deaths of its de Clare lords. One group of ironworkers in Trellech in 1316 worked half the year, in autumn and winter, a tradition of seasonal alternation between industrial and agricultural work in the spring and summer which survived in Monmouthshire until the late 19th century.[8] Here, the beds of iron slag, remarked on by visitors from William Coxe onwards, were so substantial that they were known as 'Trellech treacle'.

The site of the later Blaenavon lay in the medieval lordship of Abergavenny. At Abergavenny, on the site of the Roman fort of *Gobannium* in the Usk valley, a Norman castle and priory were founded within a generation of the Norman conquest. By post medieval times this settlement had become a flourishing wool town and a centre for the distribution of trade goods to central Wales. Abergavenny's description as 'the gateway of Wales' was well deserved. Around the town were expanses of high moorland – 'Lord Abergavenny's Hills' – in medieval times used for summer grazing of cattle and for its resources of timber (the word 'collier' originally meant a charcoal burner), iron ore and coal.[9] In Abergavenny lordship, ironworking was centred around the two adjacent parishes of Llanvihangel Gobion and Llanfair Cilgedin, within sight of the Blorenge. In 1256-7 the forges and smiths of Cilgedin were contributing £17 14s 2d to the revenues of the lordship.[10]

Usually we only have the amount paid to the steward of the lordship by the ironworkers, with no further details. Occasionally, however, ironmaking formed part of the demesne of an estate and in some cases the steward's detailed accounts have survived, as at Tudeley in

Kent in 1329-59; Byrknott in Durham between 1408 and 1433, when Bishop Langley of Durham decided to try his hand at ironmaking; and at Llantrisant in Glamorgan in 1531. These give rare details of technology and working practices.

On Elizabeth de Burgh's manor at Tudeley, the *fabrica* or forge consisted of timber buildings and an *arrastrium* or smelting hearth worked by a hand-blown bellows of leather and hare skins. Thomas Springet, keeper of the works, was paid 20 shillings a year, plus 10 shillings for a robe, the normal annual gift from a feudal lord to a dependent. The master blower and his three assistants were paid 9 pence a week, plus a penny drink money. Loads of charcoal were bought in from charcoal burners and iron ore roasted. There was an output of 200 blooms of iron a year, which were passed to the smiths for working. Production was ended by the Black Death.[11]

At Byrknott there was a smelting hearth and a bloom hearth, the one for smelting the ore, the other for working the resulting 'bloom' of iron. There was also a timber forge with a turf roof, its waterwheel powered by a leat from a forge pond. The wives of the smith and foreman broke up the ore and blew the bellows.[12]

At Llantrisant in Glamorgan there is an account of work practices in the last stage of the bloomery process, before the introduction of the blast furnace. There were five furnacemen 'who keep the fire to melt the ore'; four bellowsmen 'whereof three blows at a time, and one of them stands void to refresh the others' (it was thirsty work). There were three 'collyers' (charcoal burners) and three men working in the iron ore mine – one 'hewes the mine' (cuts the ore), one cuts timber for pit props and one 'beares the ore uppe' to the surface. As at Byrknott, their wives broke up the large blocks of ore with hammers prior to smelting. This was to remain a female occupation well into the 19th century. Two 'gaddes' of iron were produced per day, each weighing a hundredweight, and were sent to Bristol.[13]

The Tyranny of Wood and Water: Charcoal Blast Furnaces in Monmouthshire

The blast furnace evolved from earlier furnace types in northern Europe, possibly in north Sweden, and spread to the Rhineland and eastern France by the 15th century. It consisted of a rectangular stone tower-like casing around a kiln interior shaped rather like an inverted bottle. They were built against a steep bank or low cliff so that the raw materials could be fed into the furnace from the higher ground to the rear (the furnace top) and the liquid iron run off at the bottom into sand beds in the floor of the cast house (the furnace yard). Unlike the earlier bloomeries, blast furnaces produced liquid iron which could be cast into pig iron or other objects, including cannon, though further refinement was needed at the forge, with its forge hammer, to produce the 'wrought' or 'merchant' iron needed for most purposes. In the earlier phases of its history, the fuel used was charcoal, but this had serious limitations and after many years of experiment it was eventually replaced by coke.

The history of the charcoal-fired blast furnace in Monmouthshire centres around three major landowning families, who controlled the reserves of woodland and minerals necessary for iron production – the Herberts of Raglan, the Hanburys of Pontypool and the Morgans of Tredegar Park. The earliest in South Wales was operated by Sir Henry Sidney at Tongwynlais in the Taff Valley north of Cardiff in 1564-8, who shipped the finished iron to his steelmaking plant at Robertsbridge in Sussex. The casting of guns was a royal monopoly, but the nearby port of Bristol offered a lucrative market for iron for ships' cannon. Edmund

Roberts, a London merchant from Hawkhurst in Kent, was suspected of using his Abercarn furnace in the Ebbw Valley above Newport for illicit casting of cannon.

These pioneer charcoal furnaces established by Elizabethan entrepreneurs in central Monmouthshire seem to have had short lives. John Challenor's Bedwellty furnace of 1597 cannot be traced after his death in 1606.[14] Richard Hanbury of Pontypool began digging ironstone on the Blorenge around 1584-5, but local commoners objected and indicted three of his workmen before a JP.[15] Hanbury acquired the Mineral and Battery Company's Monkswood furnace on former monastic land north of Usk by 1597 and Edmund Roberts' Abercarn furnace of 1576 after Roberts' death in 1579. Hanbury also operated two furnaces of his own in Pontypool. None of these are documented after his death in 1608, though the family's industrial activities continued to flourish, using a third Pontypool furnace at Trosnant.[16]

A cluster of four charcoal furnaces in the Wye Valley around Tintern and Trellech have a separate and distinctive history, as a western fringe of the Forest of Dean iron industry. The industry of the valley of the Angidy, a stream which runs into the Wye at Tintern, had however a different origin. In 1566-7 the Elizabethan Company of Mineral and Battery Works were seeking a stream unimpeded by existing corn or fulling mills to establish a wireworks. Wire was used for many things in Elizabethan England, particularly for hooks for the wool cards used to comb wool in the all-important cloth industry. They found

such a stream in the Angidy, close to the former Cistercian Abbey of Tintern and within easy reach of Bristol. The original plan was to produce brass or lateen wire using calamine (zinc ore), and German workmen skilled in the trade were brought in. They soon progressed to producing iron wire, using a blast furnace and finery established on former Tintern land at Monkswood near Usk.[17]

Raw materials were abundant in the area. The forests of the lower Wye had supported a timber trade since late Saxon times and Trellech had been a major medieval ironworking centre. The furnaces in the Tintern-Trellech area mostly date from the first half of the 17th century, associated with gentry families involved in the Civil War. In several cases substantial traces remain.

Coed Ithel, active in 1649, stands opposite Catchmay's Court at Llandogo above Tintern (Fig.1). In 1593 George Catchmay of Bigsweir expressed an interest in taking on the lease of the

Fig. 1 Coed Ithel near Tintern, a 17th-century charcoal blast furnace, probably operated by the Catchmay family

Elizabethan wireworks at Tintern and in 1635 Sir Richard Catchmay was advising Charles I on ironmaking in the Forest of Dean.[18] Sir William Catchmay and other members of the family were active Royalists, though the lawyer Christopher Catchmay was a member of the Parliamentarian County Committee. The Coed Ithel furnace was excavated by Dr R.F. Tylecote in 1964. A 1651 survey of the Manor of Porthcaseg, in which Coed Ithel stands, lists a 'mansion house'; an 'iron forge house'; a 'large Coale howse [charcoal store] built wth timber' a 'Way [weigh] house'; a 'Store house' and a 'Coalyarde' with 'one furnace to melt Iron myne wth the streames and pondes and Coalehouse to the same ... Abuttinge upon the river Wey [Wye] to the North'.[19] By 1672-6 it was in the hands of the Foley partnership of the West Midlands, producing an average of about 18 tons of iron per week. It seems to have stayed in operation until about 1717. In view of the frequent need to repair and rebuild furnaces, it may have dated, in its final form, to that period. The furnace used a high grade Forest of Dean ore, with a content of 99% haematite (Fe_2O_3) after roasting, mixed with large amounts of bloomery slag.

The Woolpitch Wood furnace at Trellech, adjacent to Pant Glas, seat of the Probert family, is undocumented. An oblique reference suggests that it may have been disused by 1649, though a furnace would be used for particular 'campaigns' of iron making and would not necessarily be in continuous use (Fig. 2).[20] Henry Probert and his son Sir George Probert were prominent Royalists, Sir George serving in Parliament at the Restoration.

The two Tintern furnaces, on land of the former Cistercian abbey, were associated with the Herberts of Raglan, Earls of Worcester. Tintern I, north of the abbey, documented between 1629 and 1651, may have been replaced post Civil War by Tintern II in the Angidy valley, first documented in 1669, the remains of which have been excavated and conserved. The Angidy valley contains a complex of furnaces, furnace ponds and associated features, but there has as yet been no full survey of landscape features associated with early charcoal furnaces in Monmouthshire of the kind carried out in Dyfed.[21]

In Glamorgan, Caerphilly furnace was built in 1680, along with two forges at Machen and a third in Tredegar Park, between Caerphilly and Newport. These were on the estates of the Morgans of Tredegar House outside Newport and were known collectively as the Tredegar ironworks, though it had no connection other than the name with the 19th-century town and ironworks of Tredegar to the north. It came to be an integrated concern, comprising the Caerphilly furnace, the Machen and Tredegar Park forges, an iron store house in Newport and the sloop *Tredegar* to convey the finished iron to Bristol. In 1732 the Tredegar complex was leased to James Pratt (1662-1747), grandfather of the Blaenavon founding partner Benjamin

Fig. 2 Woolpitch Wood charcoal furnace, Trellech, close to Pant Glas, seat of the Royalist Probert family

Pratt. James was 'for over thirty years chief agent of Tredegar estates and the Tredegar ironworks', contributing £1,500 to the capital.[22] In 1747 the partnership, trading as James Pratt and Co., included his son Samuel, but two years later Samuel had died and Thomas Morgan was settling affairs with his executors.[23] The family, including 7-year-old Benjamin, the future Blaenavon partner, returned to Stourbridge. Fifty years later, Benjamin's memorial in St Gwynllwy's church, Newport, recorded that he was 'a native of this country [county], though removed from it in early life'.[24] In 1789 the Tredegar complex was leased to the Bristol ironmasters James Harford and Co. and production ceased in about 1819.

These furnaces, fuelled with charcoal and blown with air from a bellows powered by a waterwheel, had limitations of output which prevented the large-scale production needed to meet the radically increased domestic demand for iron resulting from the industrial revolution. Furnaces could only be built singly, where streams not already occupied by corn mills or the like were available. The 'burden' or weight of ore and limestone that the charcoal could carry restricted the height of the furnaces to around 30 feet. Their water supplies were subject to summer drought or freezing winters, and though iron ore could be moved readily enough, charcoal broke up and fragmented during transport. Furnaces therefore had to be built wherever timber for charcoal burning was available and, if necessary, the ore had to be brought to the furnace from a distance, often by sea. Cumbrian ore, for example, was shipped to furnaces in North Wales, where ample timber was available.[25]

Even in Elizabethan times there had been protests from local communities at the large-scale felling of timber for iron-smelting, which interfered with established rights of common. In 1581 the tenants of the lordships of Usk, Caerleon and Trellech complained in the Court of Chancery that Philip Earl of Pembroke had, within the space of three or four years, cut down 20,000 oak and beech trees in Gwehelog, Glascoed and Wisewood outside Usk 'for the use of furnaces for the manufacture of iron erected near the said works'. These made 5 or 6 tons of iron weekly, but not enough woodland had been left for estovers (the right to collect timber for building and repairs) and pannage (the right to graze pigs and other animals in the woods), to the great detriment of the rights of commoners. Part of the trouble was that whereas established ironworks could draw on coppice wood harvested on a 20-year cycle, Pembroke and others were clear-felling for their new furnaces large areas of long established woodland, over which many local people had long-standing common rights.[26]

The Civil War increased the pressure on timber resources. Puritans who, post-war, had acquired the lands of dispossessed Royalists often 'asset stripped' the estate by felling timber for cash, and when Royalists ruined by the war regained their estates, they were often desperate to restore their fortunes by exploiting their remaining resources, riding rough-shod over the common rights of local people. Even before the war, Sir John Wintour of Lydney's depredations in the Forest of Dean had severely depleted its timber stock. As Cyril Hart has commented, 'The incessant assaults ... had much reduced the number and quality of its trees and the acreage of its coppices. Few forests had been attacked with equal intensity.'[27] The iron industry moved into areas like North Wales, where ample timber was still available, but the limitations on production led one ironmaster to speak of 'the tyranny of wood and water'. Coppicing could ensure a renewable and constant supply of timber but the shortcomings of charcoal as a fuel still limited production and there was a sharp rise in the price of timber and charcoal between 1630 and 1680.[28]

The 'tyranny of wood and water' was already being challenged in Restoration Britain, a science-minded time which saw the foundation of the Royal Society and the activities of Isaac Newton. Earlier, Edward Dudley's attempts under Charles I to smelt iron with pit-coal had several rivals.[29] Wintour, a Royalist commander, had lost his estates during the Commonwealth and been imprisoned in the Tower of London. He now needed to recoup his losses. Coke had been used as a fuel since the 16th century in industries such as glass making and lime burning and he realized that the extension of this to iron making had considerable financial potential. In the 1660s Wintour was experimenting with a new type of coking oven, for the 'charking and calcining of pit coals'. He was much involved in the iron industry and had business dealings with Samuel Pepys over contracts for the navy.

James Prodger of Wernddu near Abergavenny, another Royalist commander, was the probable owner of the Woolpitch Wood furnace. Like Wintour he was a devout Catholic, separated, like later nonconformists, from normal patterns of office holding. In 1661 he was one of the petitioners for a patent 'to melt down metals with coal instead of wood', recognising the economic potential if coke could be utilized in iron furnaces. In 1677-8 a writer on the Forest of Dean iron industry noted that the roasting of the iron ore preparatory to smelting was carried out with coal in kilns resembling lime kilns (similar calcining kilns can be seen in the furnace top area at Blaenavon).[30] Meanwhile, with the price of charcoal rising, that of pig iron falling and imports of Swedish bar iron taking over much of the domestic market, the iron industry was in the doldrums. Only around 1680-1700 did the market recover.[31]

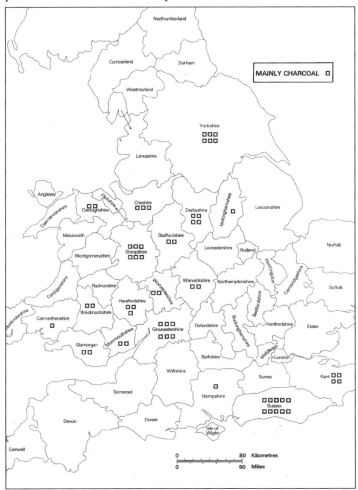

Fig. 3 Charcoal furnaces in blast 1740, on the eve of the revolution in iron making.
(Courtesy Cadw, Welsh Historic Monuments)

The Slow Revolution

After the initial breakthrough in coke smelting by Abraham Darby at Coalbrookdale in Shropshire in 1709, the process was slow to spread due to metallurgical and technical problems. The greatly increased demand for iron for agricultural and domestic uses could not for the moment speed the technological advance. Darby was involved in the foundry trade, using pig iron from his blast furnaces for the casting of large cast-iron cauldrons, known with heavy humour as 'missionary pots', where the quality of the iron was not important. Silica in the coke, however, produced iron that was brittle, whilst coal with a high sulphur content also created technical problems. Meanwhile, timber supplies had recovered from earlier over-exploitation and until mid century the costs of charcoal smelting were substantially lower than those of coke-fired furnaces. Between 1720 and 1755, 22 new charcoal furnaces were built in Britain, but in 1750 there were only three coke-fired furnaces, all in Shropshire. However, by 1760 shortage of timber was once again an issue. This was due in part to the low price of timber when supply was plentiful, which resulted in a reluctance of landowners to plant woodland. Charcoal smelting remained cheaper until 1750, but a decade later the most efficient charcoal furnaces in South Wales were £2 a ton more expensive than coke furnaces.[32]

During the following decade the new coke-fired technology spread to Maryport in Cumberland. The first coke-fired furnace in Wales was John Wilkinson's Bersham near Wrexham, followed by Carron near Stirling in Scotland and Hirwaen and Dowlais near the small Glamorgan village of Merthyr Tydfil. The number of coke furnaces almost doubled during the 1760s from the 15 that existed at the start of the decade. All were single furnaces, the blast still blown by a waterwheel and bellows. By 1775 the Caerphilly furnace had been converted to coke, but was still driven by a waterwheel. As late as 1798, James Watt found seven waterwheels at work on the furnaces at Cyfartha but only a single steam engine 'for blowing in case of scarcity of water'.[33] Where a steam engine was used, it often served merely to recycle water by pumping it back above the wheel. Only after John Wilkinson used his boring machine, originally for the accurate boring of cannon, to produce a cylinder for a steam blowing engine at his blast furnace at Willey in Shropshire in 1776, and James Watt had improved early steam engine technology, were waterwheels gradually replaced. The tyranny of water then followed that of wood into the past.

The process of conversion from charcoal to coke was a gradual one, however. For some industries, such as tinplate, charcoal was judged to give a better quality product. In 1788, 34% of Monmouthshire iron was still smelted with charcoal and as late as 1840, 300 tons of charcoal iron, probably old stock from the forges, were auctioned at Crumlin. In 1798 Coxe listed three charcoal furnaces in Monmouthshire – at Tintern Abbey, Abercarn ('not used') and Pontypool. The first two were associated with wireworks, the third with a tinplate industry – specialist trades for which charcoal iron was preferred. The seven 'pitcoal furnaces' included the three at Blaenavon and two at Nantyglo, the others, at Sirhowy and Ebbw Vale, being single furnaces. The workforce on these early furnaces was small by later standards. At Ebbw Vale in 1796 there were only 24 men, all Welsh save for nine skilled furnacemen from the English Midlands. The workers included two furnace keepers, two bridge servers, two barrow fillers, two enginemen who served the blast engine and two moulders in the cast house.[34]

Political and economic factors now favoured the growth of the coke-fired industry. From 1775 onwards the French and American wars created a wartime boom, and at the same time a partial blockade restricted iron imports from Sweden and Russia. Government borrowing drove interest rates above the ceiling set by the Usury Acts, making it more profitable for businessmen to invest directly in industry rather than in the money market. In the 1770s pioneer coke ironworks were founded at the heads of the Monmouthshire valleys, at Sirhowy and at Beaufort just over the Brecon border, by partnerships from north-west England.[35] Just as the charcoal iron industry had established itself in Cumbria and North Wales, where timber was available, so now it began to migrate to where the new fuel, coal, was plentiful.

The Making of Iron

The moorlands of the Blaenavon area were rich in the raw materials needed for iron production and had a proven record in their use. Along the northern escarpment at the heads of the valleys seams of coal and ironstone outcropped at a shallow angle and could be worked by horizontal levels and drifts rather than by vertical shafts, whilst the bituminous carbon-rich coal of the eastern part of the coalfield was particularly suited for iron smelting. Limestone for flux could be obtained from quarries on the Blorenge, whilst many streams and watercourses could run the water-powered machinery.

The raw materials were conveyed to the furnace top area above the furnaces and the coal converted to coke in long open heaps. William Needham described the scene in 1831: 'The long rows of flame produced by the burning of many hundred tons of coal, extending over a vast space of ground and flickering in the wind, the black grotesque figures of the cokers brandishing their long rakes and partially visible through the thick lurid smoke, with the roaring of the blast and the noise of the machinery [recalls] ... the infernal regions.'[36] The iron ore was broken up by women with large hammers – a long-standing tradition in the industry – and then roasted in kilns, a row of which survive in the furnace top area at Blaenavon, driving off sulphur and other impurities and increasing the iron content of the ore. The trams of ore, coke and limestone were then wheeled through the charging house above the furnace and tipped into the furnace through arches in the circular tunnel head which crowned the furnaces, using special long-handled, funnel-shaped barrows.

The structure of the furnaces can be seen in the ruined Furnace 4 at Blaenavon. They consisted of an inverted bottle shape of concentric layers of firebrick, like the skins of an onion, bound with iron bands, within an outer casing of masonry faced with large ashlar blocks. Once the furnace was fired, the column of white hot ore, coke and limestone descended through the furnace and was tapped at the base every 12 hours. Blast was introduced from a steam engine by way of a series of pipes and tapered tubes or tuyères set into blowing arches at the base of the furnace. These were sometimes water-cooled through a surrounding jacket, and rare examples of these survive in Furnace 4. The lighter slag was tapped off via a slag notch and the clay dam holding back the liquid iron breached. The central channel in the sand floor of the casting house was flanked by a series of lateral channels. This gave rise to the term pig iron, from a fanciful resemblance to a sow and her piglets. The process has now been imaginatively re-created by Cadw in a Son et Lumière display in Furnace 2. Each pig mould was stamped on the base with the name of the iron company, to both avoid theft and advertise the product. During the excavation of Furnace 4 a cast iron stamp was found for stamping the pig moulds with the inscription BLAENAVON, which is now exhibited on site.

The new steam-blown, coke-fired blast furnaces would have created a bottleneck at the forges, where the cast pig iron from the furnaces was converted to wrought or 'merchant' iron, were it not for Henry Cort's invention of the puddling furnace and rolling process, patented in 1781. This substituted coal for charcoal at the forge.[37] Pig iron was melted down in a refinery hearth to remove silica and the resulting iron then broken up for puddling in a 'reverbratory' or air furnace, using raw coal as a fuel. The molten mass was stirred or 'puddled' until the carbon was oxidized and the iron 'came to nature'. The puddled 'loops' were then 'shingled' – hammered under a large water or steam powered hammer to remove cinder and slag – and rolled between grooved rollers. At first the puddling furnaces had sand bottoms, causing much waste of iron and needing a fresh bottom for each make. The introduction of iron bottoms by Samuel Baldwin Rogers – 'Iron Bottom Rogers' – of Nantyglo greatly reduced the amount of pig needed for each ton of wrought iron and increased the speed of working.[38] Iron puddlers were skilled men, often imported from other ironmaking areas. As late as 1861, many of those at Garnddyrys forge above Blaenavon were natives of Staffordshire, Worcestershire and Shropshire. An expert puddler could produce 15 tons of wrought iron in a week, though 20% of the metal was lost during the process. The work was physically hard and dangerous, with burns from the liquid metal, chronic respiratory diseases and often, in the longer term, blindness from staring into the glaring furnaces.

The puddling process was also discovered, quite independently, by Peter Onions, a foreman at Richard Crawshay's Cyfartha. Both Crawshay and his rival Jeremiah Homfray at Penydarren adopted the new process, which became known as the 'Welsh Method' in 1787. Imports of Swedish and Russian bar and pig iron virtually ended and since the puddling process only spread to continental Europe from 1817-20 onwards, Britain enjoyed a period of huge economic advantage. In 1798 Coxe listed about a dozen charcoal forges in Monmouthshire, all singly in rural locations. They were presumably still producing bar iron for the Bristol market, but many Monmouthshire ironworks, particularly Blaenavon, were at this stage almost exclusively producing pig iron, sold on to other ironworks for refining to wrought iron.

These technical improvements in blast furnace technology, the necessary transport infrastructure of tramways, canals and docks and the availability of merchant capital were necessary before the iron industry could develop with multiple coke-fired and steam-blown furnaces. Around 1780 these conditions fused. The possibility of profitable investment attracted people seeking an outlet for their capital. Some, like the Harford Quaker ironmasters from Bristol had experience in the charcoal iron industry and in the commercial world of Bristol. Others were from a surprising range of backgrounds. Blaenavon was about to come into being.

2   BEFORE INDUSTRY

A land whose stones are iron and out of whose hills thou mayest dig brass.

Deuteronomy 8, verse 9.

The earliest visible signs of man's presence on the moorland landscape above Blaenavon are a series of stone cairns on the Blorenge presumably dating to the earlier phases of the Bronze Age. It is uncertain whether these were the work of people who lived at this altitude or on lower ground, using these uplands for summer grazing. On areas like Dartmoor, Bronze Age enclosed farmsteads of round huts survive on similar high moorland from before the time when their inhabitants were driven to lower ground by climatic change. Any such settlements on the Blaenavon landscape would probably have been destroyed by later industrial activity. Lewis Browning recorded the finding of a Middle Bronze Age palstave of about 1400-1200BC near Blaenavon, one of a scatter of similar chance finds across the county.[1]

The only Roman find from Blaenavon, a coin of the Empress Severina (274-5) dug up in a garden in Lower Glantorfaen Terrace, is probably a modern loss, but to the west, in the Taff Valley above Merthyr, there is some archaeological evidence that as early as the 6th or 7th century small farms existed in side valleys beside streams draining down from the uplands. These would have been able to exploit a range of resources from a series of ecological zones – riverside meadows, pasture on the slightly higher ground above, a belt of woodland and the open moorland for summer grazing.[2] Any evidence for such a pattern along the Afon Lwyd has been destroyed by later industrial activity. By Anglo-Norman times the area was part of the marcher lordship of Abergavenny. The resources of the upland areas were now being exploited from settlements in the Usk Valley such as Llanover, Llanfoist and Llanellen, whose medieval parishes spread out over the area of the later Blaenavon.

The medieval uplands of the lordship were used for the summer grazing of cattle, as a source of nests of sparrowhawks and hen harriers for hunting and for its natural resources of timber, iron ore and coal. In 1325 the Inquisition Post Mortem on the death of John de Hastings, Lord of Abergavenny, records a *minera carbonum* (coal mine) worth 20 shillings a year and a *minera ferri* (ironstone mine) in Bloreys and Eboith y Vaure, and in 1395 ironstone was being worked on the Blorenge. In 1446 one of the narrow roads leading up the north-east side of the Blorenge from Llanfoist was known as hewl-y-glo – 'coal road'.[3] Meanwhile in the more sheltered side valleys, free tenants of the lordship were settling in small farmsteads. There is a hint of differences between the perhaps more anglicized communities of the Usk Valley and the pastoralism and mixed farming of these uplands when, in 1295, three Welshmen were fined 'because they did not bring their cattle from the mountain' at the proper time.[4] This pattern of transhumance, with livestock being driven to upland summer pastures and back to lower lying farms to overwinter is one that is familiar in upland areas throughout western Europe. The three Welshmen were probably among those settled in the side valleys below the moorland, as opposed to the lowland villagers.

Blaenavon was not built on barren moorland, but in a landscape of small farms with patterns of woods, fields and streams which shaped the topography of the later landscape.[5] This patchwork of freehold farms was first mapped in the 18th century, but Martin Lawler's work indicates that the pattern already existed by the 14th. Population growth in the 16th century was accompanied by a system of partible inheritance, by which holdings were divided between sons. When Watkin Jenkins Howell died in 1606, his land was divided between three of his sons, with (significantly) a provision of building timber for the fourth. As the number of free tenants increased, there were new intakes of marginal land from the waste, held in customary tenure or copyhold.

The farmhouses of lowland Monmouthshire of this period were the subject of a classic study by Sir Cyril Fox and Lord Raglan.[6] Those of the upland areas are less well studied, but Lawler has shown that most of the farms existing in the Blaenavon area at the end of the 18th century can be identified in a manorial survey of 1627. A couple of late 16th-century cruck houses, with roof trusses of arched pairs of oak timbers, are known. Nant-gau-Isaf in Mynyddislyn was dated by Fox and Raglan to *circa* 1580 and Chapel Farm, Coldbrookdale, Blaina has two cruck trusses of a distinctive Monmouthshire type whose parent trees were felled, on tree ring evidence, in the summer of 1567. This is the latest example of an open hall house of medieval type recorded in Wales. Ty Godwith in Blaenavon, in the possession of William Rosser David ap John in 1585-6, with several previous owners noted, may have been a long house of similar type, though now much altered, as, from surviving photographs, was Persondy Farm, home of the coal lessee Lewis John Lewis (1701-81), demolished in the 1960s.[7]

The Hanbury family of Pontypool owned blast furnaces, forges and tinplate works around the small market town and worked the minerals of the 122,000 acres of 'Lord Abergavenny's Hills' under a series of 21-year leases. Hanbury is known to have been digging ore in Blaenavon by 1584 and in 1585-6 there is a reference to mining on Blorens (the Blorenge), Eboth Vaghan and Eboth Fawr (the valleys of the greater and little Ebbw). The extant leases form an incomplete series from 1675 to 1786, but must originally have gone back to Elizabethan times.[8]

In 1697 the polymath scientist and scholar Edward Lhwyd was collecting 'formed stones' from the limestone quarries on Llanelly Hill, Gilwern and the Blorenge above Blaenavon for his pioneer catalogue of fossils. He wrote to Sir Robert Owen that he had found 'divers sorts of fishes teeth in the limestone on top of Blorens'. At Llanelly, across the border in Breconshire, he noted an early form of opencast mining on a form of pillar and stall technique: 'Their coal works were not pits sunk like draw-wells; but great inroads made into the side of the hill so that three or four horsemen might ride in abreast. The top is supported by pillars left at certain distances.' Major John Hanbury showed him around the new water-powered rolling mills at Pontypool, 'an excellent invention of his own', for drawing hot iron (by help of a rolling engine moved by water) into as thin plates as tin. Lhwyd explained that 'with these plates he makes furnaces, pots, kettles, sauce pans etc. These he can afford [sell] at a very cheap rate (about a third part of what is usual). He sends most of his plates to London (where he has workmen), making at home only what he feels the country [i.e. local people] will take off.' In some nearby iron mines, perhaps on the Blorenge, Lhwyd 'collected some fair representations of Capillery plants'. The geology of the Blorenge afforded other minor resources. Finds of unfinished millstones suggest production for local use and one unusual stone type may have been occasionally put to use. The Black Horse fountain stood in Raglan Castle until its destruction in the Civil War, but fragments survive of a black sulphur rich limestone known locally as 'stinkstone' from the sulphurous small which fragments give off when struck. Its most probable geological source is the Blorenge.[9]

The mining of ironstone and coal on the Blorenge went back to medieval times and, apart from the series of Hanbury leases, by the late 16th century local people were engaged in mineral working, often in places that were to figure in later industrial activity. In 1586

Fig. 4 The valley of the Afon Llwyd depicted on J. Ellis' map of Monmouthshire of 1765, before Blaenavon was built

coalmining rights on the Blorenge were leased from Lord Abergavenny by William Morgan and Henry Rees. Early in the following century David Meredith 'Gentleman' and the widow of a local farmer were leasing 'the colepitts called Elgam'.[10] Pwll Du, on the northern outcrop of the Blorenge above Govilon, was being mined by members of a local nonconformist family, the Prices of Llanfoist, by 1697 and a few years later one of them, the Baptist apothecary Christopher Price, was working the Mynydd Newydd outcrop. By 1701 the name 'Blaen Avon' was in use.[11] The Price leases ended in 1733 with the death of Major Price and were replaced by shorter leases. In 1747 Morgan Morgan was leasing 'a coalwork called Nantyglo' whilst other members of his family operated a coalwork at 'Garntheroo' (Garn yr Erw between Blaenavon

13

and Brynmawr) and William John Richard opened a new mine at Varteg. By 1775 Pwll Du was in the hands of John Harris of Govilon Forge. John Lewis John of Persondy (d.1747) had been involved with Christopher Price at Mynydd Newydd and in 1775 his sons Arthur John Lewis and Lewis John Lewis were working 'Garntheroo ycha' (Upper Garn yr Erw).[12]

Along the northern outcrop of the coalfield, (the 'Heads of the Valleys') coal and iron-stone outcropped at a shallow angle, making working by horizontal levels driven into the hillside feasible. This was to have important consequences for Blaenavon, since without the considerable expense of sinking vertical shafts, people with little capital could enter the market, creating a class of sub-contractors who made up an important element in local society. Elsewhere, bell pits, shafts sunk from the surface to an underlying coal level, were used. One other method of winning coal or iron has also left its traces. Scouring was an ancient technique in use since prehistoric times. It involved constructing a makeshift dam across a mountain stream to hold back its waters. Once the autumn and winter rains had filled the resulting pond, the dam was breached, releasing a scouring flood that swept down the hillside, removing the topsoil, exposing the 'mine' (iron ore) or coal and separating the heavy nodules of ironstone from the clays and earths. The process was widespread in the Welsh valleys, as is shown by placenames incorporating the word 'race' as in Upper Race near Pontypool, Rassau at Beaufort (Rhaes-yr-glo, 'Race of the coal') or the Welsh Ysgwrfa 'a scouring place' or Ysgurio 'to scour'. One of the earliest Blaenavon coal levels was Race Work Level, presumably pre-dating the ironworks, and Thomas Deakin's map of 1819 marks the 'Old Race' above Cinder Pits, apparently out of use by that time. Peter Wakelin has studied and mapped the scars on the landscape left by this technique on the Blorenge around Pen-y-fford-goch and Forge Pond alongside the Blaenavon-Llanfoist road. These consist of the remains of dams and the long narrow scouring gullies left by this waters, part of a complex of industrial landscape comprising bell pits, coal levels and tramways stretching along the high moorland as far as Llanelli Hill, where Edward Lhwyd had noted the method of coal winning. [13]

The dates of the elements of this palimpsest are uncertain. Parts must go back to the mining activities of the Hanburys. In 1659 there were complaints that scouring by Capel Hanbury had destroyed half an acre of land: 'the miners and coalworkers of Capel Hanbury ... have encroached ... near a place called Rhas-y-fedw-fach, whereby of their said mineral and coal works and letting out the pond and sluices, the violence thereof by carrying of stones, clay sand and rubble on a long piece of customary land ... which containeth by estimation half an acre of Welsh measure.'[14] A lease of 1708 from Lord Abergavenny to Christopher Price of Llanfoist of coalworks at Mynydd Newydd and Coedcae Collin included the right 'for using, turning any brook, ryvellet, spring or any other water ... For scouring, cleaning or cleansing any said coal worke ... with liberty of making ponds, ditches, gouts, floodgates ... for the ... said works.'[15] In 1778 Edmund Jones complained that scouring had polluted the rivers and killed the fish, 'the river being often troubled with the pond waters scouring the coal works'.[16] The technique was widely used around Merthyr in the late 18th and early 19th centuries and the map of 1814 shows 'scouring works for mine' (iron ore). Wakelin has pointed out that the scouring around Forge Pond must have ended by 1817, when the pond to serve Garnddyrys was constructed, since any scouring would have silted up the pond. The technique was environmentally devastating, destroying grassland and pasture, depositing waste heaps of rubble, choking up streams and watercourses and reducing areas of moorland to a sterile desert of bare spoil. Around Merthyr this led to resentment and prolonged battles with commoners and small farmers.[17] At Blaenavon such factors may have led to its discontinuance at an early date, particularly since the area was much valued as a grouse moor by ironmasters and local gentry. In view of its devastating environmental impact, it is ironic that one of the few contemporary accounts of the process, written shortly before 1813, attributes its operation to the fairies: 'W.E. of *Hafodafel*, going a journey upon the Brecon Mountain, very early in the morning, passed by ... A Coal Race, where really there was none; there he saw many people very busy; some cutting the coal, some carrying it to fill the sacks, some rising the loads upon the horses' backs *&* this was an Agency of the Fairies upon his visive faculty.'[18]

Much of the coal and ironstone was worked not directly by the Blaenavon partner-ship, but by independent contractors or 'doggies', raising mine (iron ore) or coal on the company's land, supplying their own tools and candles. This was a system inherited from the Midlands, where it survived in Staffordshire well into the 19th century. Many such early levels were named after their contractors: Dick Keare's Slope, Aaron Brute's Level, Dodd's Slope, Frank Reid's Level or Dick Shon's Level.[19] A number of early contracts from Ebbw Vale survive in the Harford Memorandum Book, now in Gwent Archives, such as that for William Coleman:

> William Coleman, miner, agrees this day to raise 2,000 dozen of Red Vein mine [iron ore] in the level distinguished by his name at the Rassa in 33 months from the date hereof, to be paid for what be sent in monthly 14s/3d per dozen and an extra 3d per dozen [if] the which quantity is completed within the time specified – otherwise he will have no claim to it.[20]

The system was unsuitable for deeper more capitalized mines and in most places was dying out by the end of the 18th century, but was suited to Blaenavon with its many shallow drift mines. However, the efforts of small contractors to wring a profit from this fixed price system led them to seek savings elsewhere and contributed to the abuses of the truck system, whereby workers were compelled to buy overpriced goods of uncertain quality from their employers (see Chapter 5). The payment of wages in public houses was illegal, but they were sometimes owned by contractors and men could be persuaded to spend their money there on pay day, to the contractor's advantage.

Between 1760 and 1785 the remote upland village of Merthyr Tydfil, across the county border in Glamorgan, was transformed into a massive industrial complex of four ironworks – Cyfartha, Dowlais, Plymouth and Penydarren – by ironmasters from Cumbria and the West Midlands, aided by massive infusions of mercantile capital from London and Bristol and lucrative government contracts for armaments and cannon.[21] The construction of the Glamorganshire Canal in 1790-94, extended to a sea lock in 1798 and later supported by Brunel's Taff Vale Railway of 1841, ensured the prosperity not only of Merthyr, but of the future metropolis of Cardiff. The example of Merthyr showed what might be possible in Monmouthshire, and the news that the current leases from Lord Abergavenny to the Hanbury ironmasters of Pontypool was due to expire would have been of considerable interest to potential investors.

3 BRAVE NEW WORLD: HILL, HOPKINS & PRATT AT BLAENAVON

> Before the traveller quits this part of the country he will perhaps visit the famous iron
> works of Blaenavon, which constitute a principal object in the tour of Monmouthshire.
> J. Clark, *A Pocket Guide through Monmouthshire Containing an Account of*
> *Everything Worthy of the notice of strangers in that interesting county* (Chepstow 1839)

Founding Fathers: Hill and Pratt in Blaenavon and Rugeley

With the current Hanbury lease due to expire in 1786, the area, with its extensive beds of coal and ironstone, their potential already proven by earlier mining activity, was enticing for the coke-fuelled industry that had developed since mid century. Coal and ironstone outcropped on the hillsides and could be exploited by surface working, while the carbon-rich coal was particularly suitable for iron smelting. Staffordshire coal produced a soft coke which crushed under a heavy 'burden'(the weight of raw materials in the furnace), whilst South Welsh coal produced a hard coke, bearing a heavier burden, making larger blast furnaces possible. Two businessmen, Thomas Hill and Benjamin Pratt of Stourbridge in Worcestershire, began negotiations with the Marquis of Abergavenny to lease the area.

Others were also interested. In October 1787 Richard Forman, partner in several pioneer South Welsh ironworks, who had evidently been negotiating over a possible lease, wrote to Jeremiah Homfray of Penydarren, Merthyr that 'all hope of Lord Abergavenny's Royalty is at an end'. Clearly negotiations with Hill and Pratt had been successfully completed. The following month they signed an agreement to lease the area for 21 years at an annual rent of £1,300. For most of the century, the norm in South Wales had been a 99-year lease at ground rents rising from £23 per annum in 1758 (Hirwaen) to £140 8s in 1786 (Penydarren), though from about 1799 a royalty per ton of ironstone, or sometimes coal, became usual. Blaenavon's 21-year lease at £1,300 per annum was unprecedented and was to prove a burden to the company for many years. The ambitious scale of Hill and Pratt's plans needed someone with practical experience of the iron industry and they took into partnership Hill's brother-in-law, Thomas Hopkins of Rugeley. In 1789 the lease was formally signed. In the same year Jeremiah Homfray became a founding partner in the new ironworks of Ebbw Vale.[1]

The banker and ironmaster Thomas Hill I (1736-1824) of Dennis House, Amblecote (Fig. 5) – a northern suburb of Stourbridge on the borders of Worcestershire and Staffordshire – was the grandson of a scythe maker, John Hill, of Oldnall in Staffordshire.[2] Dennis House, an imposing red brick building set in 27 acres of parkland, had been built by Thomas Hill's father, Waldron Hill, and uncle, Thomas Hill, around 1769. The West Midlands had a long tradition of craft industries which had grown up since the 16th century, very different to the industrial monoculture which developed in South Wales. Along with the iron ore, coppice wood and water power needed for the iron industry, the area had other resources like the pottery clays of north Staffordshire and the fireclay of Stourbridge. The iron industry supported a host of

Fig. 5 Dennis Hall, Amblecote, built in the 1760s for Thomas Hill I. (Photograph by Harry Thornton)

minor specialist trades – swordsmiths, buckle makers, cutlers, spurriers, the needle makers of Redditch, nailers and scythe smiths. There was a hierarchy of economic groups, from the landowning families who controlled the basic resources, through the owners of blast furnaces, bottle factories or potteries to the master craftsmen and sub-contractors. Master nailers farmed out iron rods from the slitting mills to cottage workers who were paid piece-work rates for the finished nails and were usually in debt to the nailers. This elaborate symbiosis was the proto-industrial society which South Wales inherited.

The success of Blaenavon would depend on facilities to transport the iron from the works to the wharves at Newport. Isaac Pratt, a kinsman of Benjamin Pratt, was a leading promoter of canals in the West Midlands and his experience there could be put to good use by his kinsman if a canal could be built to serve Blaenavon. (The use of Old Testament names such as Isaac, Benjamin and Samuel, seems to have been a family characteristic.)

Fig. 6 Memorial to Benjamin Pratt, Newport Cathedral. (Photograph by Brian Davies)

From 1783 Isaac was involved in the sale of coal on the Stourbridge canal and until 1790 was responsible for work on the canal. In 1787 he was involved in the Dudley canal. In 1792, when arrangements for the sale of coal on the Stourbridge canal were changed, the boats and other assets were sold to Pratt. In 1791 he became one of the largest shareholders on the Worcester and Birmingham canal. Benjamin Pratt, Isaac Pratt and Thomas Hill were among the proprietors of the Stourbridge canal and James Pratt a commissioner. Benjamin Pratt's memorial in Newport Cathedral describes him not only as 'principally concerned in establishing the Iron works at Blaenafon and its vicinity', but also as 'a warm promoter of the Monmouthshire canal' (Fig. 6).[3]

The Pratt family were well rooted in Oldswinford – the older, southern part of Stourbridge – around the church and the Bluecoat school founded by the ironmaster Thomas Foley, and in the village of Chaddesley Corbet to the south. James Pratt of Chaddesley Corbet was a subscriber to a book on agriculture published in Stourbridge in 1803 and married Anna Wright in Oldswinford church ten years later. In 1817 he presented an organ to Chaddesley Corbet church and when he died in 1828, he left £678 towards a school and almshouses there. In 1836 Elizabeth Pratt left the church a further £700.[4]

Hill was a near neighbour of the Pratts, involved with Isaac Pratt in a fine lustre-ware factory in Worcester.[5] Because of its deposits of fireclay and coal, Stourbridge was famous for its glass industry, founded by Huguenot glassmakers from France who had settled in Oldswinford parish in the time of Elizabeth I. Thomas Hill's father Waldron Hill (1706-88) and uncle Thomas Hill were partners in a glass bottle factory at Coalbournbrook, Oldswinford, later run by Thomas Hill's brother, John Hill, together with a nail and scythe manufactory in Amblecote.[6] It has been remarked how 'out of marriages occasionally arose that combination of glass making with other businesses which was one of the interesting traits of the industry'.[7] The best seams of fireclay were limited in extent and the Waldron family, related to the Hills by marriage and, from 1760, their business partners, were among the main families controlling the fireclay pits.[8] Stourbridge also had a long tradition of ironmaking.

Thomas Hill's Stourbridge bank, called Hill, Waldron and Co., existed by 1788.[9] He was also a partner in another bank, Hill, Bates and Robins, which provided much of the capital for Blaenavon, on the security of Hill's Staffordshire estates. This was taken over by the Birmingham and Midland Banking Company in 1851. Abergavenny Old Bank (Hill and Hopkins, later Hill, Wheeley and Morgan) would have dealt with the local transactions needed by the Blaenavon partners.

Like the other Blaenavon partners, Hill was a devout Anglican and supporter of education. Apart from building St Peter's church at Blaenavon, in 1813 he founded a church and parsonage at Lye Waste east of Stourbridge, the present parish church of Christ Church, Lye. Lye, in the 19th century, was described as 'a rude irregular village, with a population of a very peculiar description'. It was however the source of the all-important Stourbridge fireclay, though the seam reached as far as Amblecote, where Hill had his glass works. Hill also built a school there with money left for that purpose by his uncle and namesake, and in his will left it £130. Inside the church a stained glass window of 1885 commemorates Thomas Hill and his grandson, Henry Thomas Hill, vicar of Lye and prebendary of Hereford Cathedral. In 1815 Hill also part-funded a National (i.e. Anglican) School at Amblecote.[10]

Thomas Hopkins of 'Cankwood' (Cannock Chase) Forge outside Rugeley in Staffordshire, the third partner, had married Hill's sister, Sarah in February 1761. He was then proprietor of an ironworks, Thomas Hopkins and Co., with forges, a rolling mill and slitting mill at Rugeley. In the 1770s he and John Hopkins of Rugeley were partners with the Kendalls in a complex of ironworks and tin mills in Staffordshire, Shropshire, Cheshire and Cardigan. He died in October 1793 and in his will expressed the wish that if he died at Cankwood, he should be carried to his grave by his workmen. This hints at the different working conditions and organization in the craft-based industries of the West Midlands and the South Welsh industrial monoculture that led to a different relationship between masters and men. He left his capital, including his share of Blaenavon, to his son Samuel Hopkins. Samuel's sister Sarah was left £3,000, an annuity of £100 a year whilst single and arrangements were made for her marriage settlement. She was also to have the pianoforte and part of the family library.[11]

After the signing of the lease, work on the new ironworks got underway, the cost of its construction being £40,000. The site had been purchased from Lewis Robert Lewis, a yeoman farmer who had been involved in the digging of ironstone and its transport to the Hanbury furnace in Pontypool. Past the site ran an old road called in 1672 Hewle Gwas Dewy (Heol Gwas Dewi – road of the servant David), also known as Heol Garegog, now represented by the line of King Street and Queen Street. This was probably the main route

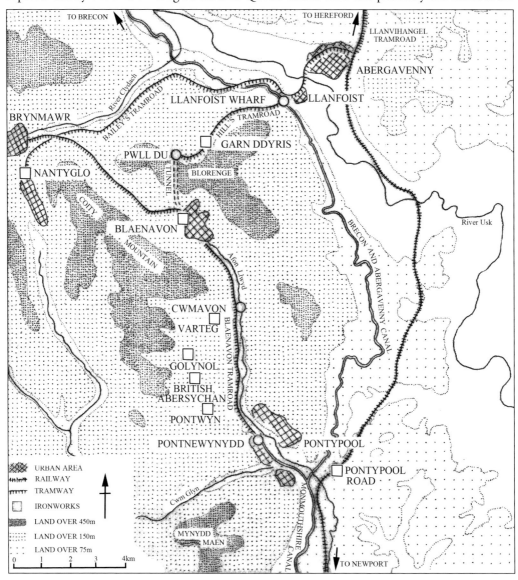

Fig. 7 Blaenavon and its transport connections. (Courtesy Cadw, Welsh Historic Monuments)

out of Blaenavon until the building of the North Street tramway.[12] Benjamin Pratt became resident managing partner, but his connection with Blaenavon was to be brief. On 24 May 1794, whilst travelling from Stourbridge to Blaenavon, he stopped for dinner at the Angel Hotel in Abergavenny. What followed was described by the *Gentleman's Magazine*:

> Died Suddenly at the Angel Inn, Abergavenny, on his road to Blaenavon, Samuel Pratt Esq of Astley near Stourbridge Co. Worcs. and one of the proprietors of the ironworks at Blaenavon, Co. Monmouth. He had just dined in company with a friend at the above inn, and rose from his chair to ring for the waiter, when, on sitting down again, he found himself giddy and exclaimed 'I die, but I die an honest man' and instantly expired.[13]

If the *Gentleman's Magazine* got his name wrong, perhaps by confusion with Samuel Hopkins, his cenotaph in St Gwynllyw's church, now Newport Cathedral, adds to the muddle. It describes him as of 'Great Whitty' (Great Witley) in Worcestershire and as buried at 'Chadley' (presumably Chaddesley Corbet). It praises him as 'principally concerned in establishing the ironworks at Blaenafon and its vicinity', and as a 'warm promoter of the Monmouthshire Canal'. By his will he left his share in Blaenavon to Thomas Hill, in trust for his widow, Jane Pratt and their son.[14]

The Monmouthshire Canal was completed in 1796, extending from Newport to Pontnewynydd north of Pontypool, with a branch canal to Crumlin in the Ebbw Valley. Blaenavon was the most easterly in the chain of ironworks which in time it came to serve. From Pontnewyndd a tramroad to Blaenavon also served a chain of other ironworks in the Afon valley, at Varteg, Golynos, Pentwyn and Abersychan. From the head of the Crumlin branch of the canal a tramroad served Ebbw Vale, its neighbour the Victoria ironworks, Nantyglo, Coalbrookvale, Blaina and Cwmcelin. Further west, at the head of the Sirhowy Valley, were Sirhowy, Tredegar and Beaufort.

The Sub-Leases – Nantyglo and Varteg

The 12,000 acres of the Blaenavon lease were so extensive that, in order to help cover the heavy ground rent payable to Lord Abergavenny, part of the area was sub-let to the Bristol Quaker ironmasters Harford, Partridge and Co., who had been expanding into the Monmouthshire iron industry. In 1789 they had leased the Caerphilly furnace and its forges from the Morgans of Tredegar Park and in 1791-6 acquired Ebbw Vale ironworks. Thomas Hill therefore wrote to James Harford proposing a partnership for the building of two blast furnaces on the Blaenavon holding. Benjamin Pratt and John Partridge rode out to agree the siting and chose a place with established coal workings in the Ebbw valley west of Blaenavon at Nantyglo ('Valley of coal'). On 30 April 1792 a formal partnership was agreed, with Hill to contribute a maximum of £10,000 towards the cost. In October 1794 the furnaces were ready to blow in, but the cost had been more than anticipated and Hill refused to increase his contribution.

The following year the Harfords used the new Nantyglo ironworks, with their blast furnaces, forges, workers' housing and a steam engine, to work off the stock of iron ore, at the conclusion of which the iron miners were dismissed. Hill then sent his agent Joseph

Harrison to claim half the resultant pig iron, which he felt he was due under his agreement with the Harfords. They demurred and the lawyers were called in. When William Coxe visited in 1799 and was taken around by Richard Harford, the furnaces were derelict and 'hastening to decay'. The Harfords subsequently withdrew from this unhappy enterprise and in 1802 Nantyglo was being worked by a partnership comprising Hill, Joseph Harrison and John Griffiths, the innkeeper of the Crown at Blaenavon, to supply pig iron to Penydarren. In 1811 the works were acquired by Joseph and Crawshay Bailey.[15]

An important market for Blaenavon's pig iron was the Stour Valley in Worcestershire, close to the homes and businesses of its West Midlands partners, where its many forges were using more pig iron than the local iron furnaces could produce. By the 1780s Merthyr and Hirwaen were providing the Stour Valley ironmaster John Knight with pig iron, and were joined in this trade by Blaenavon between 1791 and 1804. This might help to explain the otherwise puzzling absence of any evidence for an early forge at Blaenavon to convert its pig iron into the more profitable and saleable wrought bar iron. Blaenavon was not alone in producing only pig iron. According to Evan Powell, Tredegar only began its puddling furnaces in 1807, before which it too presumably produced only pig iron.[16] Thus parts of the Welsh iron industry were being used not as an integrated ironmaking concern, producing the finished bar iron, but simply as a source of pig iron as raw material for works elsewhere.

Knight subsequently decided to cut out the middleman and produce his own pig iron in South Wales, and in 1802 he leased land at Varteg Hill south of Blaenavon from Thomas Hill for £2,600 per annum, plus £750 for each furnace constructed. Presumably this arrangement was more profitable for Hill than the sale of his pig iron in the West Midlands, and helped him to cover the heavy ground rent to Lord Abergavenny.

Varteg's single furnace began shipping iron on the Monmouthshire Canal in 1803. By 1807 there was an associated forge in the Afon Llwyd Valley at Cwmavon below Varteg, on the line of the Blaenavon tramroad, where water power was available. The ironworks along the western side of the valley such as Varteg suffered from a shortage of limestone, though other raw materials for ironmaking were abundant. For this reason an incline was built from close to the Varteg furnace on the high ground to the valley floor below, in order to access limestone deposits across the valley.[17] In 1810 Knight sold Varteg in order to concentrate on his forges in the Stour Valley. Nine years later the works were in the hands of Fawcett, Whitehouse and Co. In 1821 they were purchased by West Bromwich iron founder Archibald Kenrick, who specialized in household iron fittings and a range of tinned cast iron hollow ware. Archibald's son and namesake became a director at Varteg, but the family's main interests were in Birmingham (where the firm still exists) and a younger son of Archibald junior, George Smith Kenrick, was sent to manage the Welsh enterprise. By 1839 there were five blast furnaces there, outproducing Blaenavon. However, by 1843 it had been inactive for some time and was up for sale; the Kenrick family had evidently decided to concentrate on their main business in Birmingham. This cost the Blaenavon Company £2,600 a year in lost rent.[18]

Samuel Hopkins

Fig. 8 The tombslab of Sarah Bissell, Thomas Hopkins' widowed sister, in St Peter's churchyard.
The West Midlands tradition of cast iron tomb slabs, made in the works, was kept up in Blaenavon.
(Photograph by Simon Hardy)

On the death of Benjamin Pratt, Samuel Hopkins took over as resident partner and began building the present Blaenavon House, 'a comfortable and elegant mansion at the northern extremity of this beautiful vale.'[19] His niece, Sarah Bissell, Thomas Hopkins' widowed sister, moved to Blaenavon to live with him. When she died there in November 1809, at the age of 84, she was buried at St Peter's church in traditional West Midlands style, beneath a cast iron grave cover made in the works (Fig. 20).[20]

In 1798 Samuel Hopkins received a visitor. Revd William Coxe, a traveller, writer and historian, visited Blaenavon, 'a new and interesting object in the tour of Monmouthshire' three times in 1798-9, twice with his friend the landowner Sir Richard Colt Hoare of Stourhead in Wiltshire. They were engaged on Coxe's *Historical Tour in Monmouthshire* (1801), written by Coxe and illustrated by Colt Hoare.

'At some distance,' wrote Coxe 'the works have the appearance of a small town, surrounded with heaps of ore, coal, and limestone, and enlivened with all the bustle and activity of an opulent and increasing establishment. The view of the buildings, which are constructed in the excavations of the rocks, is extremely picturesque, and heightened by the volumes of black smoke emitted by the furnaces. While my friend Sir Richard Hoare was engaged in sketching a view of this singular scene ... I employed myself in examining the mines and works.' This view would have been very similar to that from the large window which once existed in the company office in Stack Square, and this may have been Colt Hoare's vantage point.[21]

James Cockshutt, a Yorkshire-born ironmaster, formerly Richard Crawshay's partner at Cyfartha, conducted Coxe around the works and explained recent developments in the industry. A hundredweight of ore produced 44 pounds of pig iron, and coal was so plentiful that large amounts of surplus house coal was sent to Abergavenny, Pontypool and Usk. There were 350 men employed in the works and with their dependents and others, the population of Blaenavon was over a thousand. Colt Hoare's drawing gives an invaluable

Fig. 9 Colt Hoare's drawing of the ironworks, shown within a decade of its foundation, from William Coxe's An Historical Tour in Monmouthshire *(1801)*

picture of Blaenavon within a decade of its foundation (Fig. 9). A steep slope had been cut back to form a vertical rockface against which the furnaces were built. They could thus be charged from the higher ground to the rear – the 'furnace top' – and tapped in the lower 'furnace yard' below. The three tapering rectangular furnace stacks are shown, each with a gabled charging house on the higher ground to the rear and a 'tunnel head' on top, where the raw materials were fed into the furnace. In front are three cast houses, two with louvres for ventilation, where the molten iron was run into channels in the sand floor of the 'pig bed'. Between the furnaces is the engine house, its chimneys emitting smoke. The engine is one of the earliest blowing engines on record, but its maker is unknown.[22]

The incidental features of this lively scene repay study. On the right are two of the 'numerous mules, asses and horses, employed in carrying the lime, coal etc' that Colt Hoare noted around the works. They are crossing a low bridge or arched entrance to a level, on the site of the later balance tower. From here, an elevated wooden walkway on piers, on which a man is watching a woman with a load on her head, crosses the furnace yard to a hopper at the far end. This would have conveyed raw materials (probably sand for the casting floors) across the furnace yard. Some horizontal ladder-like features on the front of the furnaces may be scaffolding for repair and maintenance of the masonry. A low rectangular structure with a chimney, next to the gable end of Stack Square, has a collection of iron pigs at one end. This may be a cupola furnace, where small castings could be made, like the later example on site. On the horizon are more mules, a section of tramway and a haulage device for a level or incline.

Coxe also described the 'Ten Arches' behind the furnace yard, where a viaduct with a pentise roof had been thrown across a deep dingle to give access to a mine. The viaduct was

Fig. 10 Underneath the arches: Colt Hoare's drawing of the viaduct near the furnace yard, with its arches blocked for housing

built against a vertical rockface and, to alleviate a shortage of housing, its arches had been blocked up to provide dwellings. The scene was, for Coxe, both picturesque and novel:

> Numerous workmen continually pass and re-pass, and low cars [i.e. trams], laden with coal or iron ore, roll along with their broad and grooved wheels. These objects, losing themselves under the roof of the bridge, again emerging and then disappearing in the subterraneous passages of the rock, form a singular and animated picture, not unlike the moving figures in a camera obscura.

Colt Hoare also made a drawing of the viaduct, showing the blocked arches with doors and windows inserted and chimneys above the pentise roof (Fig. 10).[23]

Coxe also described another novelty – a railway, or 'rail-road', one of which he saw under construction and which he had to explain consisted of 'iron rails, lain lengthwise, and fastened or cramped by means of cross bars [sleepers]'. The ground having been levelled and metalled, the sleepers and cast iron rails, four feet in length, three inches thick and one and a half broad, were laid down. Their ends were alternately concave and convex so that they dovetailed into each other and were fastened at the ends to the sleepers by two wooden pegs. The sleepers were originally of cast iron but fractured easily and were now of wood, which was cheaper and needed less maintenance. Under the ends of the sleepers were wooden blocks or 'under sleepers'. The iron rails 'form a ridge above the surface, over which the wheels of the cars glide by means of iron grooved rims three inches and a half broad ... The road, sometimes conveyed in a straight line, sometimes winding round the sides of precipices, is a picturesque object, and the cars, filled with coals or iron, and sliding along occasionally without horses, impress the traveller, who is unaccustomed to such spectacles, with pleasing astonishment.' [24] The overall cost of such rail roads was rarely less than £1,000 a mile.

The form of the first phase of the railroad from the Tyla limestone quarries on the Blorenge has been reconstructed from archaeological evidence in situ. It consisted of simple bar rails fixed to stone blocks, with intermediate cast iron 'chairs' supporting each rail at mid-point for greater stability. Soon after Coxe's visit this was replaced by a tramroad (i.e. with flanged rather than bar rails) of the kind designed by the engineer Benjamin Outram. The cast iron sleepers noted by Coxe were probably the distinctive 'horned sills' in use c.1794-1802, which comprised a central bar whose terminals had three upward projections to hold the ends of the rails.[25]

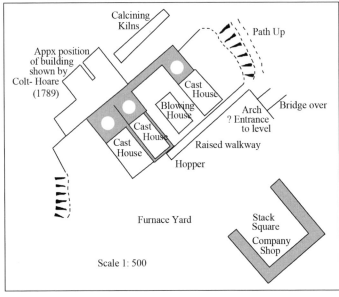

Fig. 11 Plan of the ironworks c.1800

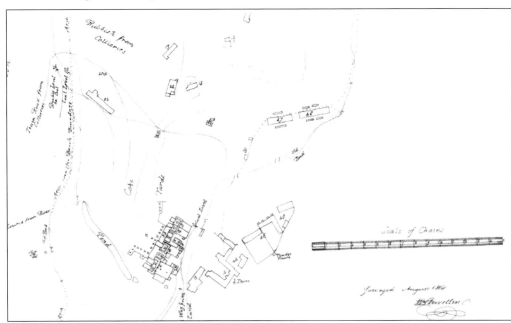

Fig. 12 Plan of the ironworks in August 1814 by William Llewellin.
(Courtesy of Gwent Archives)

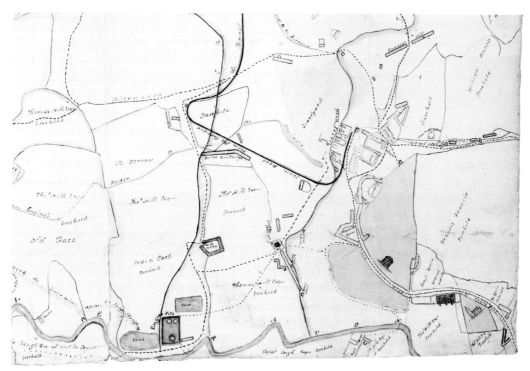

Fig. 13 Thomas Deakin's 1819 map of Blaenavon. (Courtesy of Gwent Archives)

Connections with Staffordshire were kept up. In May 1805 the vicar of Rugeley, Revd Charles Inge, and a solicitor, John Hickin, toured the works with a Mr Rose of Varteg and dined at the Big House with Samuel Hopkins before visiting Cardiff and Llandaff.[26]

By 1812 Blaenavon was one of the big three of the South Wales iron industry, along with the Merthyr giants of Dowlais (which had five furnaces as at Blaenavon) and Cyfartha (which had six).[27] The expansion of Blaenavon began soon after Coxe's visit, when the company acquired a Boulton and Watt beam engine, the drawings for which, dated 1800, survive. This was to supplement their earlier blowing engine.[28] Two additional furnaces, nos.4 and 5, of which impressive remains survive, were then built and came into production about 1805-6. As a result, Blaenavon iron shipped on the Monmouthshire Canal increased from 6,000 tons in 1807 to 12,000 tons in 1810. Thomas Deakin's map (Fig. 13) of 1819 shows the five furnaces and two engine houses and a source of 1816 claimed that £250,000 had been spent 'in the erection of furnaces, forming [coal] levels, building houses and endowing a church' since the works started.[29] Just at the time when Deakin was producing his map the works was acquiring a second beam engine to replace that of 1789. The new engine, made in the Neath Abbey ironworks, was housed in a new engine house, with a hipped roof, set in front of Shop Square (the later Stack Square) at a slightly lower level. Deakin's map shows both the two older blowing houses and the new engine house.[30]

Labouring Men

As the new ironworks began to take shape, young men found their way there in quest of work. Thomas Browning from the Forest of Dean came to Blaenavon in 1788 and helped to build Furnace no.1. His son William married a farmer's daughter from Myddislwyn and became the progenitor of a notable and still extant Blaenavon family, including the historian Lewis Browning. It was a Welsh-speaking family, since the children, as was normal, took the mother's tongue. One can identify a number of similar families in the 1841 census. Richard Keare, 'not born in the county', who gave his name to the coal level Dick Keare's Slope, was in Blaenavon by 1806, but his wife Anne Keare was 'born in the county'.

Aaron Brute (1763-1818) came from a dynasty of versatile country builders and monumental masons, whose wall monuments, sometimes brightly painted, are an attractive feature of churches in the Monmouthshire-Breconshire borders. He came to Blaenavon to work as a jobbing stonemason and branched out as a sub-contractor with his own coal level appropriately named Brute's Level. He later built a row of houses with a pub, The Lamb, on the end next to his level and an iron bridge of 1812-8, recently restored, across the river to link up with a tramway. This was only a short distance from a stone bridge, replacing a ford on the road from Blaenavon to Varteg, built in 1713 by his ancestor, John Brute of Llanbedr at a cost of 5 guineas. Aaron Brute had a reputation as a Calvinistic Methodist debater and his son Moses Brute became a noted Baptist preacher. Later residents understandably preferred Lamb Row to Brute's Row, but the old name was still remembered (Fig. 14).[31]

In 1798 a 22-year-old Shropshire collier arrived in Blaenavon seeking work. Thomas Deakin (1776-1851) was an intelligent and able man, a Wesleyan Methodist with a taste for reading, writing and surveying (Fig. 15). He had begun work underground aged 7, and at 9 was drawing coal trucks with the notorious 'belt and chain', a belt around his middle attached to a chain (see Fig. 46). Samuel Hopkins made him mineral agent, and he is said to have played a role in introducing into South Wales the long wall mining of his native Shropshire, where the whole coalface was moved forward in a single operation, whilst the

Fig. 14 Brute's Row, built by the mason Aaron Brute before 1818 (centre). The Lamb Inn on one end has since been demolished, but his coal level is nearby and his iron bridge survives and has recently been restored.

roof of the mine was supported behind the working area. This had been in use since the 18th century in Shropshire, as opposed to the older 'pillar and stall' technique of South Wales. In the latter coal was worked in a series of 'stalls' at right angles to the main heading, separated by substantial 'pillars' of uncut coal. The pillars were afterwards cut away, causing the roof to fall. In 1849 Deakin wrote an article in the *Mining Journal,* one of a number he contributed, in which he recommended long wall working for its greater safety; he might have added the fact of its less prodigal waste of coal. However, the technique was not generally introduced into South Wales until the later 1850s, after Deakin's death. In 1826 Deakin invested some of his money in building a long since demolished row of houses – Deakin's Row – in King Street, on the model of the standard Blaenavon Company house. He was often called on for help by men with problems in matters of law and order, particularly before the arrival of Police Sergeant Hodder. His son, Thomas Hedges Deakin, was later the mineral agent at Varteg colliery, whilst a grandson, George Deakin, was a well known retail chemist, musician and choirmaster.[32]

Fig. 15 Thomas Deakin (1776-1851).
A sketch by his daughter Elizabeth Davies, from her birthday book

Fourteen years before his death, Deakin wrote his own epitaph, which can still be read on his tombstone in St Peter's churchyard (Fig. 16):

Beneath the Rocks I used to toil for bread
Beneath this rock I rest my weary head
When rocks and mountains shall into ruin fall
On Resurrection's rock I rest my soul'

Fig. 16 Thomas Deakin's cast iron tombslab in St Peter's churchyard

Blaenavon was still a rough frontier society, however, and not all Shropshire immigrants did as well as Thomas Deakin. George Kenrick remarked on conflict, sometimes violent, between local people and the new English arrivals. Within a few weeks in the spring of 1820, two Shropshire men, Thomas Ferriday and Francis Butt, were buried in St Peter's churchyard 'in consequence of fighting'.[33]

Early Housing

The provision of housing for this new workforce soon became a priority. By the time of Dadford's map of 1792, Office Square, later Stack Square and now part of the Cadw guardianship site above the furnace yard, and two rows of back to back housing at Bunker's Row on the hillslope above, already existed, with two other rows of housing. By 1806 they had been joined by Shepherd Square lower down near the church. In Office Square features like the low-centred brick arches over door and window openings are a common West Midlands feature, foreign to earlier traditions of vernacular building in Monmouthshire (Fig. 17). Stack Square also housed the company shop. When the new blowing engine house was built in 1860, a large chimneystack was erected in the middle of the square, giving it the name Stack Square. The masonry of its base is still visible, though the stack itself was pulled down in 1912 with the help of two steam engines, attached to it by hawsers (Figs 18 & 19).

North Street, which runs down from the ironworks to the church, is on the line of the tramroad from the furnace yard to the head of the Monmouthshire Canal, its broad curves making a convenient gradient for the horse-drawn trams. In North Street was the Old Crown Inn, familiarly known as the Drum and Monkey and now Messrs Caddick's workshop. The town stocks were nearby, outside Engine Row (part of Stack Square), as in an Elizabethan village. When the new police station and lock up was added in 1839 in

Fig. 17 Life in Stack Square about 1840.
The details of the community are taken from the 1841 census:

Emmanuel Hartshorn, 37 - Coker	Timothy Macarthy, 25 - Filler	Jonathan Rogers, 40 - Labourer	John Mathews, 31 - Moulder
Margret Hartshorn, 32;	Mary Macarthy, 25	Martha Rogers, 37	Margret Mathews, 32
Elizabeth Hartshorn, 4	Timothy Macarthy, 9	Thomas Rogers, 15	Anne Mathews, 14
Mary Anne Hartshorn, 18 months	Thomas Macarthy, 7	Elizabeth Rogers, 12	Herbert Mathews, 10
Ellan, Williams, 15 - Servant	Daniel Macarthy, 11 months	William Rogers, 10	John Mathews, 5
	Jeremiah Macarthy, 20 - Labourer	Richard Rogers, 5	Elizabeth Mathews, 2
	Hannah Macarthy, 19	John Rogers, 3	Joshua Mathews, 2
		David Rogers, 2	William Mathews, 7 months
			Mark Rowley, 23 - Labourer

(Illustration by Gareth Darbyshire and Howard Mason)

North Street, it stood opposite the Crown, on the slope below the ironworks. The Crown was more than a mere beerhouse. The landlord, John Griffiths, was a substantial figure, a business partner of Samuel Hopkins and sponsor, with the vicar James Jenkins and the landowner Frances James, of the 'Blaenavon Second Society', a benefit society 'of tradesmen and others' which met at the inn.[34] Later, the company shop was moved here from Stack Square, with the inn retained as a sort of back bar.

Some of the early housing may have been designed for particular classes of workers, in proximity to their workplaces. Stack Square, built between 1789 and 1791, originally

Fig. 18 (left) Stack Square cottages before restoration

Fig. 19 Stack Square after restoration. The base of the central stack is the foreground, furnaces 4 and 5 of 1805-6 and the water balance tower of 1837-9 are in the background. (Photograph by Simon Hardy)

31

comprised two rows of four comparatively good quality houses of varying size: Engine Row to the south and an upper block on the north. With a linking range to the east, these were set around a square or courtyard. The east range has been much altered, but detailed analysis by Jeremy Lowe whilst it was being conserved showed that it originally comprised three equal sized sections, each roofed in three bays, separated by stairs set between cross-partitions. The northern block was probably the company offices which gave the original name to Office Square. The central section had a cellar, later filled in, and may have housed the company shop. The southern part of the range, of three storeys, seems originally to have contained domestic accommodation. This might have been the residence of Samuel Hopkins before the construction of Blaenavon House, which was in course of building during Coxe's visit. The range was converted to housing in the 1860s.[35]

The two side ranges, with houses of differing size, were for the key workmen and managers brought from the West Midlands when the works were built. These were men like Joseph Hampton, described at his death in 1832 as 'for nearly thirty years "superintendent" of Blaenafon and Garndyrys ironworks', who may have had links to a firm of Stourbridge nail makers or the nine skilled furnacemen from the Midlands imported by Harford at the setting up of Ebbw Vale.[36] North Street and Shepherd Square near the church housed furnacemen, whilst Stable Yard, Stable Row and Upper Stable Houses accommodated the

grooms and ostlers who looked after the many horses and mules that Coxe and Colt Hoare noted around the works. The census of 1841 showed an ostler and a haulier still in Stable Row, though most of the row now housed colliers and their families. Coaltar Row housed the cokers and coal setters.[37]

Staffordshire Row, a starkly imposing two-storey split level housing block, stood along one side of North Street (Fig. 20). Entry to one home was at ground-floor level from the street, and to the other at first-floor level from the rear, the site having been cut back into the slope. This must have housed many of the West Midlands immigrants. Bunker's Row, or Bunker's Hill above the ironworks, near the present Rifleman's Arms, comprised two rows of back to back housing, flanking the road to Abergavenny (Fig. 21). Each house

Fig. 20 Staffordshire Row in the 1960s.
(Courtesy of John Owen)

Fig. 21 Bunker's Row photographed in the late 1960s or early 1970s.
(Photograph by Jeremy Lowe)

comprised a single room on the ground floor, with a loft serving as a single bedroom above. Later the pairs of back to back houses were converted into single dwellings. The line of houses along the hillside may have suggested to a local wit the lines of American Colonial infantry at the Battle of Bunker's Hill in June 1775 during the American War of Independence. These, Quick Building and River Row housed colliers and miners. River Row stood not far from Cinder Pit, where many of its inhabitants worked, and they suffered severely in the 1838 disaster (see p.53), when at least four River Row men and 15-year-old Mary Hale drowned.[38]

None of this housing had any form of sanitation and outside visitors commented on the contrast between the heaps of filth everywhere and the clean and neat interiors of the cottages. In 1853 the Health Inspector, writing of Brynmawr, noted the shocking lack of sanitation, but added, 'Within the houses, as is usual in these districts, the rooms are swept, the floors whited and the furniture and kitchen utensils kept bright and clean.' [39]

Sarah Hopkins and the Free School

Samuel Hopkins died on June 1815, in the week which saw Napoleon's empire end in the evening light at Waterloo. Hopkins was accorded a funeral at St Peter's church which was remembered for many years. The year before, he had established a small school in Bunker's Row and hired the wife of a workman as a teacher. Another school followed in Little Quick Buildings, run by a Mrs Jeremiah, the children paying 2d a week. From the wording of the inscription on the school founded by his sister, Samuel Hopkins may have been contemplating a larger foundation.

*Fig. 22 Sarah Hopkins' school,
the oldest ironworks school in Wales,
is now a visitor centre
and museum.*

*Fig. 23 The now badly weathered
Latin inscription of 1816 that records
Sarah Hopkins' foundation of the
school is retained inside the building.
It can be seen in its original position
above the left-hand window in Figure
22 (taken in the 1960s). It records
that she built the school in memory of
her brother and for his 'Blaenavonites'
(*Glenavonienses suis).

Samuel's sister Sarah (1768-1844) now established a church school next to St Peter's in her brother's memory. This was a National School, so named from the 'National Society for Promoting the Education of the Poor in the principles of the Established Church'. Built in what might be described as a minimalist Gothic style and flanked by houses for the schoolmaster and schoolmistress, it opened in April 1816 for 150 boys and 180 girls, each sex housed in a single large room (Figs 22 & 23). Sarah Hopkins gave the school a £3,000 endowment, which still survives as the Hopkins and Hill Charitable Trust. She paid regular visits to Blaenavon and to the school until 1841, distributing prizes of clothing and footwear. Unusually the rules included a provision that 'the children be stimulated by reward rather than by punishment and that the money appropriated by the patroness be applied in rewarding acts of merit and encouraging emulation'. In 1849 an adjacent infants school was added and in 1860 a boys' school in an added block, after which the original building became a girls' school.

Lewis Browning first attended Mrs Jeremiah's school, but later the National School, where he was 'quite a favourite with the old lady' (Sarah Hopkins). He tells us that he was among those receiving prizes in the form of clothing.[40] On the exterior of the school Sarah placed a lengthy Latin inscription:

> Ut / ex ore/ parvulorum/laudes domini/ perpetuas evocaret/ Nec non ut fratris desideratissimi / optimaque de se promerentis/ benevolentiae in Glenavonienses suos/ Aliqua ex parte vel mortui satisfaceret/ hunc ludum literarium / suis sumptibus aedificandum curavit SARA HOPKINS /Anno Domini MDCCCXVI

> That she might elicit the perpetual praise of God from the mouths of Children and that she might in some measure even when he is dead carry into effect the benevolent intentions of her deeply lamented and most deserving brother towards his Glenavonians [*Glenavonienses*], Sarah Hopkins at her own expense caused this school to be erected and founded in the year of our Lord 1816.

Possibly translations were displayed on a board inside, for Lewis Browning gives Welsh and English versions. This, the oldest ironworks school in Wales, closed in 1982, but was re-opened as the Blaenavon World Heritage Centre by Rhodri Morgan, First Minister of Wales, in March 2008.

Even though Lewis Browning's family were Methodists, he had to attend St Peter's church on Sunday mornings whilst at the National School. In time this led to friction between Anglicans and Nonconformists and in 1857 a 'British' (Nonconformist) school was opened. A Catholic school followed in 1870, adjacent to St Felix's church in King Street, and one for Wesleyan children the following year. Under the Education Act of 1870 elementary schools were taken over by local School Boards, and then in 1902 Board Schools became the responsibility of local authorities.

Sarah Hopkins' school at Blaenavon was only part of her work for Anglican charities and education. In Rugeley in Staffordshire, where she lived from 1808 until her death in 1844, she founded an almshouse for four poor women, and built a residence for the schoolmistress of the National School for Girls (now the Rugeley Church of England Primary School for Girls). She also built a school in Cannock Chase, near the site of her father's ironworks and forge. In her will she left £1,000 to Rugeley church, the accumulated funds from which were used to build an enlarged chancel in 1906. The charity was only finally wound up early in 2013. Someone who remembered her from their childhood described her as 'very like Queen Elizabeth, according to my notion of what the great Queen was like. Miss Hopkins was rather awful [?awesome] to children but a thoroughly good woman, a kind neighbour and a benefactor to the parish. But she liked people to know their own station and be very respectful to their "betters".' One wonders if she knew 19th-century Rugeley's most famous inhabitant, the poisoner Dr William Palmer.[41]

Thomas Hill II and Garnddyrys

On the death of Samuel Hopkins in 1815, Thomas Hill II, who had been living at Broome House in Broome, south of Stourbridge, moved to Blaenavon to manage the ironworks. His father was now sole owner, save Thomas Hill II's quarter share left him by Samuel Hopkins. Thomas Hill II was a widower, his wife Anne having died in September 1804 at the age of 35. She was buried at Broome, where a marble memorial by Thomas Flaxman shows her gowned and bare footed, holding a book.[42]

Hill's daughter, Ellen, wrote from her new home to her friend Emma Hodgetts at Kinver in Staffordshire:

> The House is surrounded with mountains, with a great number of white cottages upon them. The women wear little black beaver caps, exactly like men's caps, with mob caps under them, which I admire, though it gives them a rather singular appearance. ... The little geraniums which you gave me are looking very well at present, and I hope they will take root. There are a great many more plants here than I expected to have seen ... better than what we have in the greenhouse at Prestwood.[43]

Soon after Thomas Hill's arrival in Blaenavon, a major storm blew up in what became, in many ways, a conflict between long established local landowners and the new industrialists from outside. The medieval marcher lordship of Abergavenny, as it had existed until the time of Henry VIII, comprised 28 parishes and 18 manors. Among them was the parish of Llanover, with the small sub-manor of Parc Lettice, a variant of the name Laetitia, from the wife of its 14th-century lord, Hywel ap Einion Sais. Though within the lordship of Abergavenny, Parc Lettice had never been in Norman hands, but remained under the family of its Welsh lords until the 18th century. Hywel ap Einion had gained his by-name Sais – 'Englishman' – by his residence at the English court and service under Edward III at the battles of Crécy and Poitiers. A descendant, Richard ap William, was the subject of a praise poem by the late 16th-century bard Dafydd Benwyn. The estate then passed by marriage to Lewis Morgan of Ruperra and to Sir Charles Kemeys of Cefn Mably, who sold it John Burgh, the agent of the Duke of Beaufort. Through a series of marriages and inheritances it came into the hands of two Breconshire men, Thomas Harcourt Powell and Osborne Yeates, shortly after 1782.[44]

The boundaries of the parishes adjacent to 'Lord Abergavenny's Hills' were complex and poorly defined. In 1794 the lords of the manor of Llanover sought counsel's opinion on whether the workers in the new ironworks might become chargeable to the parish should the ironworks fail (no record of the counsel's opinion has been found), and in 1808-10 there was legal action against Hill and Hopkins. Powell and Yeates now came to believe that they had beneficial rights over large areas of the wastes. In 1816 they began a legal action for ejectment, claiming all waste lands in the parish of Llanover, including the site of the ironworks, citing boundary stones on the hills and claiming that they had exercised acts of ownership by appointing manorial officials and permitting use of the natural resources. Powell and Yeates versus Hopkins and Hill was heard before Mr Justice Richards and a special jury at Monmouth Assizes in August 1816. Mr Taunton, counsel for Powell and Yeates, claimed that the parish and manor of Llanover shared the same boundaries and cited acts of ownership and perambulations of the boundaries spread over 50 years.

Lord Abergavenny had briefed the Solicitor General, who showed that the Barony of Abergavenny went back to William the Conqueror and that its early lords had granted land to their followers. He also showed that the minerals on the land in question had been leased by Lord Abergavenny to the Hanburys of Pontypool in a series of leases since Elizabethan times. Mr Illingworth from the Tower of London (then the depository for State Archives) documented these claims from the Records. In a final peroration to the jury, the Solicitor General claimed that the plaintiffs had 'slept quiet in their little manor in the valley and seen for the last five and twenty years his clients raise the most magnificent works; people a barren mountain; found and endow a church and erect in short a City, as a monument of the Commercial Grandeur and Industry of the British Nation'. The jury supported his arguments.[45]

When the news reached Blaenavon in the early hours, wild celebrations began. A tall standing stone on the hill above Bunker's Hill was pointed out to visitors years later as having been erected, crowned with a blazing tar barrel, to celebrate the victory. The Revd James Jenkins recorded the case in highly partisan detail in his church register, with a note that there had been no service in St Peter's that Sunday, as he had been unable to return from Monmouth. On 24 August Thomas Hill's daughter Ellen wrote to her friend Miss Hodgetts in Staffordshire to tell her how, in the early hours the town had been woken by the ringing of church bells and the firing of cannon and how on her father's return from the trial at Monmouth, the colliers met him beyond Abergavenny and wanted to take the horse out of the shafts and draw him through the town, though he forbade it.[46]

By 1816 the wartime boom had ended. The return of discharged soldiers, the ending of armaments orders and a fall in home demand led to severe unemployment. This coincided with a rise in food prices due to climactic downturn and the resultant failure of the wheat crop and associated scarcity of barley meal and oatmeal. Furnaces were blown out as ironmasters tried to maintain prices by cutting production. There was also a lengthy strike and in June, informers at Blaenavon were told to look for evidence of co-operation between strikers across the coalfield, though they found none. That autumn a gang of 700 men arrived in Blaenavon. They had been touring the ironfield bringing men out on strike and stopping the furnaces. They told Thomas Hill that they needed food, that their wages were insufficient (food prices, particularly of bread, had risen steeply) and that they wanted to return to their native parishes. Significantly, they told Thomas Hill that they were ready to return to work if they could be paid weekly, instead of the monthly 'long pay' and could buy goods where they wished rather than in the company shop. Hill gave them bread and cheese and offered beer, but the leaders said it was better if the men remained sober.[47] By the following year, the worst was over, though there was another slump in 1819 (the year of Peterloo) and widespread panic among the governing classes as protests at social conditions morphed into demands for political reform. Even without this, Thomas Hill may have realised that economic conditions meant that Blaenavon had to change or die.

Blaenavon relied on the expensive and inefficient Monmouthshire Canal for the transport of its iron on the 20-mile journey to the docks at Newport. The quantity of iron and coal conveyed by the South Welsh canal system was by now stretching its capacity to the limits. Until 1830 Newport enjoyed an advantage over its rival, Cardiff, since coal shipped east of the Holms – Flatholm and Steepholm – was exempt from duty. In 1840 Newport still shipped three times the amount of coal that passed through Cardiff, but the opening of the Marquess of Bute's West Dock at Cardiff in 1839 and the completion of the Taff Vale Railway from Cardiff to Merthyr in 1841 freed Merthyr from dependence on the Glamorgan Canal and gave Cardiff a commanding advantage which led to the city's greatness. Newport by contrast lagged behind, whilst the proprietors of the Monmouthshire Canal resisted any attempts to obtain a Parliamentary Railway Act which might challenge their monopoly. In 1842 the industrialist R.J. Blewitt of Llantarnam Abbey, Member of Parliament for Monmouth Boroughs, explained the canal's shortcomings to the House of Commons. Transport charges were 2.25 pence per ton mile compared with a halfpenny per mile on the Glamorgan Canal, and that was before taking the new railway into account. The poor state of the Blaenavon company's tramroads was such that coal carried on them was shaken up and reduced in value. In addition, traffic on the Monmouthshire Canal suffered delays caused by drought or freezing weather and the canal was closed for a fortnight each year for repairs.[48]

Thomas Hill II duly conceived an ambitious plan to free Blaenavon from the stranglehold of the Monmouthshire Canal. A tramway over the Blorenge 'mountain', north-east of Blaenavon, would be carried through a tunnel utilizing an existing horizontal coal level and down a series of incline planes to wharves and a warehouse on the cheaper Brecon and Abergavenny Canal, which had reached Llanfoist in 1812. Although this linked to the Monmouthshire Canal, a clause inserted in the Brecon and Abergavenny Canal Act meant that goods carried on it could continue to Newport at the cheaper rate. Also, a railway could be built from Llanfoist to convey Blaenavon coal to Hereford. Hereford consumed

Fig. 24 Hill's Tramroad is still a prominent landscape feature. Its route, seen here from Garnddyrys, curves around the hillslope (left) and continues as a terrace along the hillside on the other side of the valley, heading to Pwll Du and the tunnel to Blaenavon. (Photograph by Simon Hardy)

Fig. 25 The site of the forges at Garnddyrys is marked by spectacular waste heaps of eroded slag. (Photograph by Simon Hardy)

20,000 tons of coal annually, brought on barges up the Wye from the Forest of Dean. As early as 1810 there had been proposals for a tramway from Llanwenarth on the canal above Abergavenny and a Bill was laid before Parliament in the following year by the Grosmont Railway Company. Its earthworks can be seen as a landscape feature beside its successor, the modern Abergavenny-Hereford railway, but attempts to extend the line to Hereford were opposed by the bargees of Hereford, who feared for their lucrative monopoly and broke up meetings to plan the extension.[49] In 1802, the Monmouthshire Canal Company had appreciated the threat that the Brecon and Abergavenny Canal proposed to their monopoly position and inserted a clause into their Parliamentary Bill requiring Blaenavon and other ironworks to convey their goods exclusively on the Monmouthshire Canal. There was strong opposition to this and a Parliamentary petition was organized against it. Eventually Sir Charles Morgan of Tredegar House and the proprietors of the Monmouthshire Canal agreed to drop the offending clause.[50]

Thomas Hill's tramroad over the Blorenge, 5.5kms in length, was a two-foot gauge plateway with cast iron sills and flanged plates. It utilised an earlier horizontal coal level as the start of a 2km tunnel, the longest tramroad tunnel ever built in Britain, through the high ground above the ironworks to Pwll Du on top of the Blorenge. From here, the tramroad curved around the slopes of the Blorenge on a terrace that is still a striking landscape feature (Fig. 24) to new forges and puddling furnaces at Garnddyrys. There were two shorter tunnels, built by the 'cut and cover' technique, the 40m Blorenge tunnel and the Garnddyrys tunnel.[51]

In 1817 Garnddyrys forge opened in an isolated spot high on the Blorenge, the land having been bought from William Price for £7. It had puddling furnaces to convert the pig iron from the blast furnaces into more profitable wrought bar iron, a forge and rolling mills, workers' housing and two reservoirs to supply the works. Garnddyrys, marked by a spectacular dump of red-brown slag (Fig. 25), lies on sloping ground below the present

B4246, built as a toll road by the company in 1825, with toll houses at Garnddyrys and outside Abergavenny. At the southern end, where Hill's tramroad entered the site, was a weighing machine, where pig iron and other raw materials arriving could be checked and weighed. The waterwheels on the site needed large amounts of water and there were two reservoirs, now dried out, but still visible features. The large Upper Pond, linked to the Lower Pond by a culvert, has a dressed stone retaining wall with a series of added buttresses. In time, the water supply from the reservoirs proved insufficient and by 1828 Forge Pond (now called Keepers Pond after a nearby gamekeeper's house) was added as a feeder.

The main works complex lay on a terrace below the Upper Reservoir on the western slopes. The 1833 sale catalogue included two steam engines, one of some size. At the southern end of the complex was the site of the manager's house, where excavation in 1973 revealed a cellar. This may also have housed the company shop. Beyond, earthworks mark the sites of the forges and puddling furnaces and at the northern end three ranges of houses around a courtyard, as in Stack Square. Garnddyrys housed over 30 families and contained two pubs, a school and a chapel. Most of the men were iron puddlers or specialised iron workers in the forges, but there were also managers for the forge and the mill, a grocer, who managed the company shop, a bricklayer, a carpenter and five widows. The Garnddyrys tunnel, below the works, carried through traffic along Hill's tramroad.

A second community grew up at Pwll Du, around the twin entrances to the mouth of the tunnel through the Blorenge. Most of its workers were quarrymen in Pwll Du and at

Fig. 26 Llanfoist wharf. A series of incline planes led down from Hill's tramroad on the Blorenge down to the wharf on the Brecon and Abergavenny Canal. (Photograph by Simon Hardy)

Tyla to the north, supplying limestone for the Blaenavon blast furnaces, but it was a self-contained community, with a school, Baptist and Methodist chapels, two pubs, a company shop and two long rows of housing for its 60 households.

By May 1818, Hill was building a bridge and embankment over the canal at Llanfoist to link with the railway. In December 1819 Revd James Jenkins recorded the burial of Sarah Wood, the wife of a bricklayer: 'This is the first funeral from Garnddurus' he noted. In the same year, 'Garnddyrys works' and 'Garnddyrys weighing machine' (near the later Keepers Cottage) were noted on Thomas Deakin's map.[52] In 1822-4 land was purchased for the series of four incline planes running down the slope of the Blorenge from Garnddyrys to Llanfoist wharf on the Brecon and Abergavenny Canal (Fig. 26).

Thomas Hill also sank one of the first deep coal pits in Blaenavon, as opposed to the earlier horizontal levels (Fig. 27). The twin shafts of the future Cinder Pits appear on Thomas Deakin's map of 1819, annotated 'Intended engine pits for the deep work'. The company could now enjoy profitable coal sales from Llanfoist wharf, though between 1844 and 1851 the *Mining Journal* repeatedly claimed that Blaenavon was being forced into coal sales in desperation at its unprofitable iron business. However, in view of the busy trade on the canal this may have been only partly true.[53]

Thomas Hill I died in 1824 at the age of 87, having outlived his initial Blaenavon partners by many years. He was buried in Oldswinford, where memorials to him and his wife are to be found inside the church. His death may have freed up capital for his son. In August 1825 the plan for a railway to Hereford was revived by Thomas Hill II and Hereford business interests, with meetings held in Hereford Guildhall. It was planned to build a 12-mile-long railway from Monmouth Cap to Wye Bridge, Hereford at a cost of

Fig. 27 Hill's Pit – the winding engine chimney of 1844

£25,000, of which Hill would contribute £1,000. In May 1826 the Bill received royal assent and in September 1829 the new railway was open for traffic with the arrival of the first 15 trams of Blaenavon coal in Hereford. Sadly, by that time Thomas Hill II was dead.[54]

4 HOPE DEFERRED: BLAENAVON 1827 TO 1870

Thomas Hill II died suddenly on 29 November 1827 at the age of 59, leaving a son, Thomas Hill III, and three daughters. Educated at Eton and Brasenose College Oxford, the third Thomas Hill was that proverbial figure in industrial history, the third generation businessman. The first generation is the founder of the firm, the second, represented at Blaenavon by Thomas Hill II, is often the most enterprising and successful, brought up in the business and building on the work of its founder. By now, the family has established itself and made its money. The heir is sent to public school and Oxford, where, among his peers, he has no wish to be thought to be 'in trade', or worse still, in industry. The result is predictable. Thomas Hill III was later remembered as 'a typical country squire, complete with a pack of hounds'.[1] Soon after his father's death, Thomas and his uncle Waldron Hill went into partnership at Blaenavon with Charles Wheeley and William Morgan of Abergavenny Old Bank, trading as Hill and Wheeley. The Wheeleys, with local interests in brewing, iron making and banking, were a Staffordshire family who had taken over the Hill family glassmaking business at Dennis near Stourbridge.[2]

Blaenavon had long been losing its share of the market. In 1806 it was second in production only to Cyfartha, but by 1823 had been overtaken by the other Merthyr giant Dowlais, as well as by Ebbw Vale and Nantyglo (Fig. 28). By 1830 it was eighth in the production league of South Welsh ironworks, now also behind Tredegar and the other two Merthyr works, Plymouth and Penydarren. Charles Wheeley died in 1832. The loss of his business partner may have persuaded Thomas Hill that it was time to sell up, for the following year he attempted to sell the ironworks, but failed to find a buyer.[3] Instead he struggled on with the badly undercapitalised business during an exceptionally turbulent period. Trade depression and wage cuts led to strikes, with men being sent to prison or hard labour for 'neglecting the work' of their employers. In 1831 some men joined the Friendly Society of Coal Mining, an early trade union, which had been introduced from northern England and had branches at Blaenavon, Varteg and Abersychan, though this proved short-lived. Three years later Robert Owen's Grand National Consolidated Trade Union established itself in the Pontypool area. Hill, in common with other local employers, sought to have his workers sign an undertaking not to join the Union or the Scotch Cattle; in the first half of the 1830s, Monmouthshire became known as the 'black domain' of the Scotch Cattle (the origin of the name is unclear), as desperate men banded together under a 'Bull' for night time raids to intimidate non-strikers and unpopular shopkeepers.[4] The men at Varteg and Blaenavon refused and a lock out followed. In July 1834 Hill blew out (shut down) the Blaenavon

Fig. 28 Nantyglo ironwork: 'The immense ironworks of Nantyglo seem to the distant spectator as if the whole surrounding country was on fire', Henry Gastineau in Wales Illustrated *(1830).*

furnaces and a detachment of the 12th Lancers were called to the town. Eventually, the men capitulated and signed the agreement.[5]

Thomas Hill probably became even more anxious to sell up, and in 1836 succeeded in selling the works to a London-based Joint Stock Company for £220,000, whereupon he retired to a country seat at Rudhall near Ross-on-Wye, though he retained a seat on the Board of the new company and was influential in its affairs for some years. That December he represented the new company at a meeting of ironmasters in the King's Head, Newport, when it was agreed to cut production in an attempt to shore up prices. Over 20 furnaces were to be blown out across South Wales, including one at Blaenavon.[6]

The Blaenavon Iron and Coal Company 1836-1864

In May 1836, The Blaenavon Iron and Coal Company was launched. As the *Monmouthshire Merlin* told its readers:

> Great changes are to occur at Blaenavon as the Iron and Coal Company go public and become a Joint Stock Company under the direction of James Ashwell and his eight co-directors. Capital of £400,000 is to be raised through the sale of shares of £50 each. So the Hill family, owners for forty years, are making way for new blood and perhaps they believe for more go-ahead and expert leaders, though Thomas Hill is still on the board of directors.[7]

The prospectus of the new company spoke of the high quality of Blaenavon iron, with a production of 18,000 tons of pig iron a year and 100 tons of bar and cable iron a week, and optimistically offered investors an annual dividend of 10%. By September of the following year £195,000 had been raised.[8]

The resident Managing Director was James Ashwell, the ambitious 37-year-old son of a Nottingham ironmaster and coal owner. Ashwell (1799-1881), educated at Edinburgh University, had worked in ironworks in Derbyshire and Scotland before being asked to prepare a report on Blaenavon for the new company and was then appointed to his post. The eight other directors included a London financier William Unwin Sims; Thomas Hill III; John Masterman, who held a joint account at the Bank of England with Sims, representing the company's bankers; Francis Warden of the East India Company, and Robert William Kennard of the bankers Heywood, Kennard and Co. The Kennard family were to be central to the story of Blaenavon for several generations. Apart from Thomas Hill and Kennard, who had interests at Falkirk in Scotland, only Ashwell had practical experience of the iron industry.[9]

As a young man, Ashwell had been apprenticed to Bryan Donkin, a Victorian engineer in the same league as Brunel or Telford, though he left no monumental buildings to preserve his memory. Instead his *forté* was the invention of machinery for everyday industrial processes, including the manufacture of tin cans for the preservation of food (his pioneer company survives as Crosse and Blackwell), machine-made paper and coloured postage stamps. Donkin was the first vice-president of the Institution of Civil Engineers, the president being Thomas Telford. The Institution was founded by Ashwell's fellow apprentice and friend Henry Robinson Palmer, Ashwell being a founder member.[10]

Fig. 29 Furnace top area – the calcining kilns for roasting iron ore.
(Photograph by Simon Hardy)

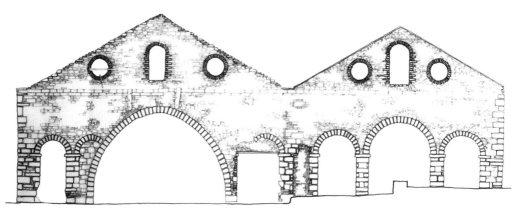

Fig. 30 The façades of the foundry (left) and of the cast house of Number 2 Furnace. Reminiscent of Roman architecture, they are probably as rebuilt by James Ashwell. The large arch in the foundry façade was cut through in 1860 when the large flywheel for the new blast engine was cast here. (Drawing by Neil Daniels, courtesy of Cadw, Welsh Historic Monuments)

Fig. 31 The Cupola furnace in front of the foundry, used to make small iron castings

The new company faced a heavy financial burden. Under a lease of 1806 from Lord Abergavenny it had to find a ground rent of £5,200 a year for up to nine blast furnaces, with an additional £500 for each additional furnace. Its total annual rent bill was £6,500, against which it received £2,075 annual rent from the Baileys for Nantyglo and £2,600 for Varteg. In 1837 it had an unsold stock of iron of 1,100 tons and only three furnaces in blast owing to a resolution of Welsh ironmasters to limit output in an effort to shore up prices. By the following August, £280,000 in share capital had been raised, later to rise to £400,000, but much had been absorbed in covering the purchase price. To provide working capital, the works were mortgaged to Thomas Hill I's old Stourbridge Bank, now Bates and Robins, for £70,000.

William Unwin Sims (1797-1839), the Company Chairman, was a London businessman, a partner in Jacob, Sims and Company, West India

Fig. 32 Furnaces 4 and 5, with furnace 2 and the cast house and foundry to the left. (Photograph by Simon Hardy)

Merchants and in the London iron merchants Neville, Sims and Williams. As chairman of the Great Western Railway, present at the meeting which coined the historic name from the earlier 'Bristol and London Railroad', he conducted the Duke of Wellington around the newly opened predecessor to Paddington Station. The Iron Duke distrusted railways, which he feared might encourage the lower orders to travel.[11] It was hoped that Sims could give the company access to lucrative railway contracts.

From 1828 onwards the South Wales iron industry had relied increasingly on the railway industry's demand for wrought iron rails and the various fittings that went with them. Laurence Ince has published a list (admittedly incomplete) of British railway companies supplied with rails from South Wales. Nantyglo, Beaufort, British and Ebbw Vale are well represented, but Blaenavon is conspicuously absent. Indeed, the company's 1836 prospectus spoke only of pig, bar and cable iron. The surviving correspondence from the Dowlais ironworks shows both the dependence of the South Wales industry on railway orders during the period of radical worldwide expansion of the rail network, from America to Russia, and the business infrastructure needed to obtain and execute such orders, which Blaenavon then lacked. A tragic event then served to curtail any opportunities for lucrative railway contracts that Sims's chairmanship might have created. In November 1839 Sims committed suicide. His lengthy *Times* obituary, unusual for an early Victorian businessman, reflected Sims' status in the City of London, but was also intended to reassure investors that his suicide was due to depression over the sudden madness of a sister and overwork, and was not for financial reasons.[12]

The new chairman was Robert Kennard M.P., a wealthy Scottish ironmaster, whose Falkirk ironworks were his main concern at this time. He was the son of a London banker, John Kennard, involved in railway finance and the City of London, where he was associated with the Rothschilds.[13] His family were to be active at Blaenavon for the next three generations.

Ashwell's strategy depended on the building of a new ironworks across the valley from the old works, with six blast furnaces, puddling furnaces and rolling mills. These would be on freehold land, free of the heavy ground rents payable to Lord Abergavenny, and once built the company could abandon the Garnddyrys forges with their unwieldy complex of tramways and tunnels. His first priority, however, was to modernize the existing works, and at the company's annual general meeting in April 1839 he was able to report good progress.

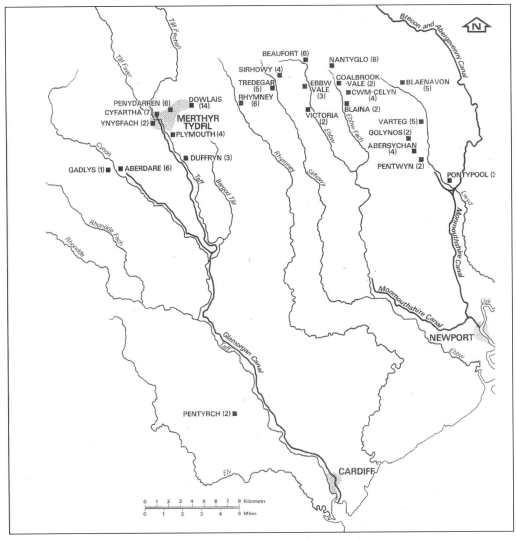

Fig. 33 Working iron furnaces in south-east Wales in 1839.
(Courtesy of Cadw, Welsh Historic Monuments)

Fig. 34 James Ashwell's Water Balance Lift, known as 'the guillotine', in the furnace yard

Fig. 35 The Balance lift in 1911, with the wheel still in situ. Massive blast pipes cross the furnace yard in the foreground.

The blast furnaces were being remodelled and the Water Balance Tower, which would carry pig iron from the furnace yard to the furnace top and the tramroad to Garnddyrys, still such a striking feature of the site, was being built (Figs. 34 & 35). This was popularly known as 'the guillotine': when Thomas Waters, a Staffordshire labourer, was killed in an accident at the lift in February 1840, the burial register recorded that he had been 'killed at the lift or guillotine'.

Whilst much coal and ironstone was won from horizontal levels, as mining progressed, vertical mine shafts were needed and winding engines became necessary. A particular South Welsh development, using the abundant water supplies of the area, was the water balance lift, an hydraulic counterpoise mechanism. Two lift cages, each with a large water tank below it, were attached by chains to a wheel supported on horizontal beams and two A frames. Water from a pond or reservoir was used to fill one water tank at the surface, which then sank, drawing up the other cage. At the pit bottom, the water in the tank was drained off and the process reversed. Balance pits first appear at the end of the 1820s and the oval shaft of the first phase of what is now the Big Pit, which dates from the 1830s and is still used to take visitors underground, is characteristic of balance pits. It is not known if Thomas Hill III introduced balance pits to Blaenavon, but James Ashwell certainly favoured them. His balance tower in the furnace yard is of this type, as is a lift

Fig. 36 Cwmbryrgwm Water Balance, Abersychan (now destroyed). Similar counterpoise machines for winding were used at many smaller mines in 19th-century South Wales

at the Tumble on Hill's tramroad, raising limestone from a quarry. One example survived until recently at British Ironworks near Abersychan, another, originally from Rogers Pit, Rhymney has been re-erected as a museum exhibit at Big Pit. They remained in use for much of the century, particularly in smaller and less technically advanced mines (Fig. 36). They were in use in Crawshay Bailey's pits at Nantyglo and Beaufort until the 1870s, though by that time they were coming to be regarded as historical curiosities. Johnson's and Dyne Steel's new Blaenavon pits of the 1840s had steam winding engines.[14]

Fig. 37 Chapel Row, of 1839, part of James Ashwell's building programme. A terrace in classical style, with a large Wesleyan Methodist chapel in the centre and a larger house at each end. The row, which came to be loomed over by a waste tip, was demolished in 1971.
(Photograph by Jeremy Lowe)

At the company's AGM of April 1839 it was noted that the price of iron was rising and that the company's shares now stood at £43.15. The following year, Ashwell was able to report that the old works were now in a state of high efficiency and a start had been made on the new furnaces across the river. Iron prices and wages were high and the truck shops had made a record profit (for the latter see Chapter 5). The meeting authorised a debenture issue of £150,000 to fund the new work. All seemed set fair.

By now, however, the share price was falling and stood at £35. Shareholders, led perhaps by Thomas Hill III, were critical of Ashwell's expenditure, which could be seen as an implicit criticism of Hill's own neglect of the works. In May, Ashwell was forced to defend his ambitious programme before a hostile meeting of shareholders. He listed the repairs and improvements: the furnaces and cast houses at the old works had been repaired; one Old Side blast furnace had been taken down and rebuilt, with its back wall, charging house and steam engine; the balance tower and its feeder pond had been constructed, together with a new blast engine and boiler, smiths shop and stables; three new pairs of coal pits had been sunk, with two engine houses; and 500 workers houses had been built or reconditioned. These last may have been part of the concern at the cost, since Ashwell's houses, demolished in the 1970s, were architecturally ambitious by contemporary standards, and included a terrace at Chapel Row with a large Methodist chapel as a centrepiece (Fig. 37).[15]

Fig. 38 An artist's impression of Blaenavon in the later 19th century. Staffordshire Row is bottom left with the cast houses beyond. Beyond them are the furnaces with Ashwell's water balance tower to their right. Right again is Stack Square with its stack tower. In the foreground is the truckshop and the Drum and Monkey pub.
(Illustration by Francis Keen)

*Fig. 39 British Ironworks, Abersychan. A speculative venture of the 1820s,
it was not a commercial success, and was eventually taken over by the Ebbw Vale Company*

The meeting was so acrimonious that in place of the usual longhand account in the company minute book, a newspaper cutting reporting the meeting was pasted in. Ashwell resigned as Managing Director in 1841, the result, according to his obituary (of 40 years later) of 'an accession of property'. He received a 'handsome testimonial', but his obituary then goes on to say, somewhat baldly, that he 'later worked on continental railways'. It may be that Kennard, who was involved in railway construction in France and elsewhere, may have employed him, for Ashwell was living in Dieppe in 1859.[16]

The experience of the Monmouthshire iron industry with Joint Stock Companies had not been a happy one. The repeal in 1825 of the 'Bubble Act' introduced after the speculative mania of the South Sea Bubble in the early 18th century and a temporary boom in iron prices led to a wave of new ventures, not all of which stayed the course. The British Iron Company of 1826 that established the British Ironworks at Abersychan was part of a combine in Glamorgan, North Wales and Staffordshire owned by the Taylor family. They had experience of non-ferrous metalworking, but not of the iron industry. At Abersychan they were crippled by a poor choice of site, a ruinous ground rent of £2,400 a year and a heavy royalty on each ton of pig iron (Fig. 39). After a history of mismanagement they collapsed in 1843 and their successor, the New British Iron Company, collapsed in 1851, when they were bought up by Ebbw Vale at the knock down price of £98,400.[17]

The Monmouthshire Iron and Coal Company of 1836, a group of railway directors and Somerset landowners headed by Sir Thomas Lethbridge, planned to bring Cornish and Devon iron ore, in exchange for coal, to their Victoria Ironworks at Ebbw Vale, named in honour of the new Queen.[18] Four furnaces went into blast on New Years Day 1837, but were hit by the economic depression of the 'hungry forties'. They failed in 1845 with debts of £800,000, including £16,000 to the Monmouthshire and Glamorgan Bank, who were forced to take over the works. This proved too heavy a burden for the Bank, which failed in 1851.[19] The Joint Stock Companies, founded in boom times, often lacked the capital to survive the ensuing slump. With few directors experienced in the iron trade, as latecomers they were often in geologically inferior areas. Had it not been for Ashwell's improvements, however unpopular they were with the more conservative shareholders, Blaenavon might have gone the same way.

The Cinder Pit Disaster
The last days of November 1838 saw heavy snow fall, followed by two days of incessant heavy rain. By the 28th, the Afon Llwyd, swollen with meltwater, was some feet above its normal level. When a fallen tree blocked a bridge over the river close to Persondy Farm, the waters burst over an embankment and poured down a horse drift into the workings. The miners and colliers 'to the extent of many hundreds' were quickly evacuated, but Cinder Pit, in the valley bottom, was inundated with the loss of eleven men, two girls – Mary Hale and Elizabeth Havard – and two boys, aged 10 and 12. One of the men, 60-year-old Thomas Thomas, had gone back to fetch his lantern; another, David Evans, refused to leave his 10-year-old son William, and both were drowned; whilst a third man put another boy, not related to him, on his shoulders and carried him above the water for a considerable distance until the flood caught up with them. Pumps were set to work day and night to drain the mine and eventually the bodies were recovered and buried in St Peter's church-yard. River Row, close to the mine, was hard hit, at least six of the victims being from there. Elizabeth Havard's parents, John and Mary Havard, lived at 9, Lower New Rank, next door to Lewis Browning. This was a doubly unlucky household, for their lodger, John Ellis, a Staffordshire man, was killed underground by a fall of stone.

Cinder Pit (sometimes referred to as Cinder Pits as it had a double shaft) was one of the first deep pits in Blaenavon. Thomas Deakin's map of 1819 notes the shafts as 'Intended engine pits for the deep work'. They may have been abandoned after the disaster, for in 1865 they were re-opened, 'having been long abandoned as worthless'. They finally closed in 1895.[20]

Blaenavon and the Hungry Forties
In the spring of 1839, a Liverpool iron merchant, Joseph Johnson, toured South Wales to gather information for a paper he was preparing to deliver to the Liverpool Polytechnic Society. He noted that Blaenavon was one of the best and most valuable mineral proper-ties in the county, known for the strength and excellence of its iron, though when James Ashwell took over in 1836 the works were 'in a most dilapidated state', having been previ-ously neglected. It was, he wrote, being greatly enlarged. Five furnaces were in blast, blown by cold air, Ashwell's six new furnaces were building, and new forges and rolling mills were planned. Half the weekly make of 400 tons of pig was refined as bar iron, with some cable iron and the remainder sold for tinplate and foundry work. He thought that the profitable bar iron and new forges promised well for the future of the company.[21]

At the time of Ashwell's resignation in 1841, the new furnaces on the freehold land across the river were only built to the boshes (the lower tapering portion of a blast furnace, situated immediately above the air-inlet tuyères) and though work on them continued into 1842, they were left incomplete as the hard times of the 'hungry forties' set in, when industries suffered revived competition following a period of peace after the ending of the Napoleonic wars, harsh new poor laws were being introduced and food prices were kept high due to protective corn laws. (For how this affected the people of Blaenavon see Chapter 5.) Ashwell however had left the old works 'in a condition of great efficiency' and little work was needed for some years, save the rebuilding of the interior of one furnace in 1844.[22]

The manager appointed in Ashwell's place was Harry Scrivenor (1770-1862). His *Comprehensive History of the Iron Trade,* first published in 1841 by 'Harry Scrivenor, Blaenavon', is a remarkable production, tracing ironmaking from Biblical and classical times to 'the Present Period' and in all parts of Europe and America. It merited reprinting as an 'industrial classic' in 1967. Scrivenor did not have a seat on the board, marking a step in the transition from managing partner to salaried professional manager.

The famine years of the early 1840s were unhappy ones for Blaenavon's workers and for the iron industry itself. 'Bad as times were for the poor, they were equally so for the capitalist' Scrivenor told an Oddfellows dinner at Blaenavon in 1842.[23]

By 1844 the worst was over, but the speculative boom and bust rollercoaster continued. The 'railway mania' of 1844-7 saw the rail mileage of Britain rise from 2,000 to 6,000, with railway construction in France and Belgium following suit. Ashwell's modernisation works now allowed the company to produce the tracks and ironwork required by the railways, and under its new chairman, R.W. Kennard, the director of several railway companies, it was well-placed to exploit this boom. Wages rose by 17%. The company directors celebrated their prosperity with a gift of £100 to the infants school.

In 1847 Blaenavon's communications were improved when a new turnpike road was constructed from Pontypool via Abersychan and Varteg, but in the same year the latest boom collapsed. By the following April £78 million had been wiped off the shares of the leading railways and the Blaenavon Company was faced with bad debts of £8,000 amid 'mercantile disasters almost unparalleled'. A committee – comprising Thomas Hill, Robert Wheeley, son of the partner of 1827-32 and a banker, Philip Jones, representing the interests of a major shareholder, the Herberts (formerly Jones) of Llanarth – was appointed to visit the works and recommend economies in all departments. Harry Scrivenor was replaced as manager by Richard Johnson, brother-in-law of William Crawshay of Cyfartha.

Innovations: Thomas Brown and Thomas Dyne Steel

In 1842 the Harford ironmasters, owners of Ebbw Vale, which had earlier absorbed Sirhowy, went bankrupt following the failure of their Bristol bank due to heavy losses on un-repaid American loans. In the ensuing auction of the works, Crawshay Bailey was outbid by Josiah Guest and Thomas Brown. Had Bailey been successful, Ebbw Vale might have followed a very different trajectory, as Bailey became known for his lack of investment (see p.57). By 1844 it was in the hands of Abraham Darby and his very able manager Thomas Brown.

With Darby's capital and Brown's technical skills Ebbw Vale began a period of confident expansion. It was able to buy up several victims of the boom and bust years of the 1830s and '40s, acquiring its bankrupt neighbour Victoria Ironworks in 1849 and expanding into the Pontypool valley below Blaenavon, buying British Ironworks at Abersychan in 1852 and Pentwyn in 1857.

Brown was the son of a Worcestershire ironworker who had migrated to Cyfartha in 1786 and in 1803 made the mechanisms of Trevithick's locomotive. His son established a laboratory at Ebbw Vale and appointed a works chemist, a post later copied at other ironworks. Concerned that Britain was falling behind Germany in scientific education, he used an existing Mutual Improvement Society, founded to establish a library and hold lectures, as the basis for the remarkable Ebbw Vale Literary and Scientific Institution, on the model of English Mechanics Institutes. Housed in 1852 in a purpose-built building funded by the Ebbw Vale Company, this had laboratories, a fine library that included several manuscript histories of Ebbw Vale produced for eisteddfod competitions, and, from the 1890s, it ran courses in such subjects as chemistry, draftsmanship and geometry, together with a wide range of social and educational activities.[24] In 1854-5 George Parry successfully made steel using the American Martiers process, a predecessor of Bessemer steel.[25]

One controversial invention had been Nielson's hot blast process, invented in 1828. This led to great economy of fuel, reducing the coal required per ton of pig iron from 8 tons to 3 or less, and further economies were possible with closed top furnaces and waste heat boilers. One of Brown's innovations was to seal off the top of blast furnaces with a cap and cone, collecting the inflammable waste gases at the furnace top, piping them to ground level and recycling them through waste heat boilers, saving considerably on fuel and enabling hot blast working without hot blast stoves. This was a process devised by the works chemist George Parry at Ebbw Vale in 1850, though there was the usual conservative resistance to innovation and it was slow to spread. Hot blast pig was disapproved of by conservative ironmasters and was long thought inferior, but by the end of the 1830s it was produced in many South Welsh ironworks. Tredegar introduced hot blast in 1835, Varteg had only one cold blast furnace out of five and at Pontypool Capel Hanbury Leigh used hot blast for his foundry pig, whilst retaining cold blast iron for his tinplate works. By 1839 a sixth of South Welsh iron was produced by hot blast, but the amount increased by mid century due to competition with 'Cheap Scotch pig' produced by hot blast. Where plentiful fuel was available, there was less incentive to use the new patent process. Abersychan remained faithful to cold blast until 1848, and it was not until 1853 that the Blaenavon directors decided to put one furnace on hot blast to compete with the cheap hot blast pig iron from Scotland. Cold blast iron continued to be produced on the Old Side furnaces until the 1870s.[26]

Another area of expense were the sandstone hearthstones in the furnace bottoms. As early as 1831 William Needham had noted that 'hearths and boshes are generally of large pieces of a coarse grit or plum-pudding stone, carefully jointed with fireclay. Recently however some hearths have been constructed of firebrick, which is a great saving in expense.' Since ordinary firebricks floated loose in the heat of the furnace, special interlocking hourglass shaped bricks were designed.

In 1848, Thomas Dyne Steel (1822-98) was appointed, at the age of 26, as the new assistant manager and engineer of Blaenavon. He had been born in Abergavenny to a local medical family and his father William Steel, an Abergavenny surgeon, had been a close friend of Samuel Hopkins, a neighbour in Neville Street, Abergavenny and a beneficiary under his will. Another member of the family, surgeon to the 23rd Dragoons, had died 'of fatigue and privation in the discharge of his duty to the sick and wounded during and after the Battle of Waterloo.'[27] Dyne Steel spent his school holidays at Blaenavon House and around the works before being apprenticed to the engineer J.H. Randall.

Johnson and Steel set about replacing the horse-drawn tramways, with their cast iron tramplates, with 'locomotive roads' of wrought iron, and wooden sleepers. As a result, Blaenavon was able to enter the lucrative market for wrought iron rails. Steel designed the first steam locomotive to be built for the works at Newport and transported it, by canal and horse drawn tramway to Blaenavon. By the time the company had two locomotives, *Blaenavon* and *Garn-yero* (Garn yr Erw, literally 'hill of the acre' is a district of Blaenavon), they saved the keep of 16 horses and £3,000 a year. In 1844 two new deep collieries were built at Hill's Pit and Garn yr Erw, linked by tramroads and an incline to the main tramroad near Upper New Rank on the present B4248 (Fig. 40). At Hill's Pit, the square chimney for the winding engine stands like a monument, surrounded by tips and traces of the associated buildings, whilst at the incline top the brake for the counterbalance wheel has been excavated in a stone-lined pit (Fig. 27). Whilst Ashwell made widespread use of water balances in coalpits, in the hydraulic lift in the furnace yard and on Hill's tramroad, Johnson and Dyne Steel used steam-powered winding engines in their new pits and else-where. So far as Blaenavon was concerned, water balances became obsolete.[28] In 1850 Dyne Steel also built a pair of inclines, which still bear his name, to bring limestone from the Tyla quarries on the north-east face of the Blorenge over the hill to the ironworks, bypassing the busy Pwll Du tunnel. Traces of the steam winding house and an adjacent cottage are still visible on the summit of the ridge. Despite these improvements, working conditions in the shallow Blaenavon drift mines were often haphazard. Dyne Steel wrote:

Fig. 40 Upper New Rank, built by the Blaenavon Company about 1825. Each house originally had a sitting room, kitchen and back bedroom on the ground floor, with an open sleeping area above. The company built over 200 houses of this type. (Photograph by Jeremy Lowe)

The underground operations at this period were of a somewhat primitive description, but gas explosions were rare. Colliers with scorched faces and hands were frequently to be met. The deficiency of air caused the gas to burn, not explode. When visitors went underground, gas was frequently fired for their delectation. It simply flashed about the roof of the headings w[it]h blue ribbon like flames.[29]

One other innovation brought in by Johnson and Steel was the replacement of the wasteful coking in open heaps with coke ovens. Previously, the long heaps of smouldering coal with thick smoke and fumes and the black figures of the cokers with their long rakes in the flat area above the furnaces inevitably reminded visitors of the infernal regions. Thomas Brown had replaced the open heaps at Ebbw Vale with Cox's patent coke ovens, and in 1849-50 the open heaps at Blaenavon were replaced by coke ovens at a cost of £1,400. These used previously useless soft coal, at a saving of 5d per ton of pig iron or £470 a year. Crawshay Bailey, as in other respects, failed to keep up with changes in the industry and Nantyglo and Beaufort continued to use open heaps until they closed in the 1870s.[30]

In 1845, after considerable public pressure, the Monmouthshire Canal Company agreed to apply to Parliament for an Act giving them power to build a railway from Newport to Pontypool, to convert its horse-drawn tramways for locomotives and to reduce its charges. After some delay, the line from Newport to Pontypool eventually opened in 1852. Two years after the Newport-Pontypool railway was built, it was extended and on 2 October 1854 the first train ran from Newport to Blaenavon; by 1866 six trains daily ran between Newport and Blaenavon. Kennard could now think about completing the ironworks on the freehold land across the river from the old works and abandoning the inconvenient mountaintop forges at Garnddyrys, with their tramways and tunnels. The outbreak of the Crimean War in the spring of 1854 offered a wartime boom, not only for armaments, but as a result of many large iron steam ships being commissioned. Francis Warden was replaced on the Board of Directors by Captain Frederick Warden R.N., commander of the 74-gun warship *HMS Ajax*.[31] Dyne Steel, meanwhile, had left the company in 1853 on appointment to an engineering post in Newport.

The following April the directors faced warfare of a different kind. A group of shareholders forced through a resolution for the appointment of a committee of shareholders to make 'a full enquiry into the affairs of the company'. This produced a report critical of Kennard, Masterman (a banker and one of the company directors) and Johnson, who were accused of failing to consult the shareholders and of wasting the company's assets on unfruitful and expensive schemes when faced with heavy debts. They had invested £15,000 in the Hereford and Abergavenny Railway, spent £71,000 since 1839 on unfinished new works and allowed the Varteg ironworks to fall into ruin at the expiry of the lease, though the rent was still paid to Lord Abergavenny. The new forge and mill were unauthorised by the board and against the wishes of Thomas Hill (who seems to have been influential in the whole affair). The company had assets, they concluded, of £331,000, but debts of £147,000 and were owed bad debts of nearly £10,000.[32] The dissidents had shot their bolt, however, and at the next Annual Meeting a proposal to appoint a board of 'persons practically acquainted with the manufacture of iron and with iron, coal and mine works' was defeated.

'Old Things are Giving Place to New': Modernization 1860-1864

By 1856, the renewal of the lease of 1806 from Lord Abergavenny was looming and a £50,000 mortgage would fall due in the following year. By spring 1857 it was clear that the annual rental under the new lease would be £3,500 a year and a meeting was called to consider putting the company up for sale. A few years earlier the *Merlin* had commented that 'The company never had ... a large working capital; in fact we might say that it never had a working capital at all. And if it had not been for the confidence of the directors in affording means and particularly the banker [Masterman] ... the company would be in a sad condition in respect of capital.'[33] Kennard gave a personal covenant to cover the mortgage, but begged the shareholders to release him from the burden as soon as possible. The alternative was to modernise the works so as to make sale at a reasonable price possible, and this seems to have been Kennard's strategy, for an ambitious programme of modernisation was put in hand, the capital for which presumably came from Kennard's other enterprises.

Its progress was followed nationally by the *Mining Journal* and locally by the *Monmouthshire Merlin* and *Pontypool Free Press*. The *Merlin* announced 'There is a new era at Blaenavon, old things are passing away and giving place to new.'[34] A new forge, giving the name of Forgeside to the new works across the river, opened in 1859 and a mill in 1860, with a pair of horizontal engines by James Watt and Co., able to work a rail mill or a heavy bar and plate mill. In February 1860 the old company offices next to Stack Square, latterly in use as a reading room and library, were demolished to make way for a new engine house with a Boulton and Watt engine, whose parts were made in Blaenavon. In June this new blast engine was 'taken from the [casting] sand in the foundry'. It may have been at this time, to accommodate the moving of large castings, that the wide arch was cut through the façade of the foundry. In July, Messrs. Caddick were building a new blast furnace on the site of the boiler of an old blast engine. (This is the circular furnace 6 visible on site, the most complete surviving example of its type.) A new engine house with a semi-circular corrugated iron roof was built beside the old 1819 blast engine house and massive cast iron pipes were carried across the furnace yard on iron pillars, some of which remain, as do the excavated remains of the engine house. That Christmas the new blast engine started work, wreathed with holly.[35] A waste heat boiler was built next to the old side furnaces to utilize their heated gases, so reducing fuel consumption. Early in 1862 the new tyre mill, producing the patent weldless tyres for railway carriages of the major French engineering firm of Petin, Guadet et Cie, came into operation and six months later the new rolling mills began work. In the old works, the Boulton and Watt steam engine, in service since the beginning of the century, was replaced. Blaenavon's weldless tyres won a prize in the Great Exhibition of that year and the Red Lion organized a club for a visit to London to see the exhibition.[36]

In October 1869 the *Mining Journal* summed up the plant of the Old and New Works. On the Old Side the six blast furnaces were still blown with cold air and open-topped, though with some collection of waste gases. The three Forgeside furnaces were more up to date, with closed cap and bell tops and blown by hot blast. There were 72 coke ovens, the same number of puddling furnaces; 3 steam hammers; 25 balling furnaces and 5 rolling mills, plus the patent tyre mill. The works produced 850 tons of iron a week, over 70% of which was used for rails or other railway equipment.[37]

The company was still making heavy losses, however, and Kennard was still saddled with his personal guarantee of the mortgage. At 64, he felt he had carried the burden for long enough; at least the new assets made sale at a reasonable price possible. He therefore opened negotiations with a financier, Francis Waring, who agreed to buy the company. On 24 May 1864, at a special meeting, R.W. Kennard proposed from the chair the winding up of the company. He still held a controlling interest, he and his sons holding 3,900 of the 7,612 shares, with Waring holding 1,900. It would seem that R.W. Kennard, no longer resident in Blaenavon, wished to concentrate on his extensive interest in the Falkirk ironworks in Scotland, leaving his son, Thomas William Kennard (1825-93), looking after the family's other business interests in South Wales. In 1853 Thomas had established the Crumlin Viaduct Works which built the iconic Crumlin viaduct in 1853-7, linking the Newport, Hereford and Abergavenny Railway with the Taff Vale Railway at Quaker's Yard. It used castings from Falkirk and wrought iron from Blaenavon. The Viaduct Works later diversified into other engineering work, with a world-wide reputation as builders of iron bridges, including Blackfriars Bridge in London. Thomas built Crumlin Hall, which became the family residence. When his brother Henry Martyn Kennard accidentally shot Carlo, a cherished gundog, on the opening day of the grouse season in 1864, Henry erected a cast iron monument on the site of the accident on Mynydd Varteg, on which he described himself as 'H.M. Kennard, Crumlin Hall'. With R.W. Kennard's departure, the running of the ironworks was now in the hands of salaried managers like Edward Pritchard Martin.[38]

In February 1868 the *Monmouthshire Merlin* recalled how some 30 years before, the company had begun building new works on the Coity (Forgeside) side of the valley and how the bases of three large furnaces and part of an engine house had been completed before work stopped, 'and the thousands of pounds expended on them were lost to the company for upwards of a quarter of a century'. The furnaces had now been completed and the first had just been turned on by Edward Kennard, another of R.W. Kennard's sons. Nine heavy cannon were fired to celebrate the event, which attracted large crowds. In October 1866 a large driving wheel for the rolling mill was cast in one piece in the foundry in the old works.[39] Soon, all would be operating and by 1870 the three new Forgeside furnaces and the five across the river in the old works were all in blast.

Local Mine and Imported Haematite

As mentioned earlier, ironmasters had been attracted to Blaenavon by the abundance and cheapness of native iron ore and coal, raw materials making up between 75% and 85% of the cost of ironmaking. Whilst coal remained plentiful, by the later 1850s surface deposits of ironstone were exhausted and the cost of mining was increasing. Welsh ironworks were coming to rely on imported haematite from northern Spain, Somerset, the Forest of Dean or north east England.[40] Some imported ore was also of considerably higher quality; Cumbrian haematite, for example, had a metal content of 60%, compared with the 30-35% of local ironstone.

There was nothing new in the importation of iron ore to an ironworks. In the 18th century Cumbrian ore had been moved by sea to areas like North Wales, where abundant wood for charcoal burning could be found, for whilst ore travelled well, charcoal did not.

As the use of charcoal as a fuel source was replaced by coal, the destination of Cumbrian ore changed. The Dowlais Company letterbooks contain, from Napoleonic times onwards, much on the shipment of ore to Cardiff from Cumbrian ports like Ravenglass and Whitehaven. By the 1770s ore was being shipped into Newport. With increased metal-lurgical knowledge, ironmasters learnt how to use a mix of ores – haematite, local ore and cinders – to produce iron for particular uses such as railway rails.[41]

In 1856 Thomas Powell, a major figure in the Welsh coal industry and one of its largest exporters of coal, noted that it was possible to buy Somerset or Cumbrian ore cheaper than locally produced 'mine', whilst William Menelaus of Dowlais said of the latter, 'it is every year becoming more difficult to get' and noted that 'if we confined ourselves to Welsh ore ... .the works would be shut up'. Merthyr had an advantage over the Monmouthshire works, for the Taff Vale Railway and Glamorganshire Canal provided an efficient supply route for imported haematite from Cardiff Docks direct to Cyfartha and Dowlais. By this time, Monmouthshire ironworks like Ebbw Vale, Rhymney and Golynos were importing Northamptonshire ore by rail. Ebbw Vale under Thomas Brown owned the Brendon Hill Mining Company in Somerset, along with its West Somerset mineral railway, though this was not a financial success.[42] With the new railway from Newport able to carry Spanish haematite direct to the new Forgeside works, the old forges at Garnddyrys closed about 1860, though Garnddyrys and Pwll Du survived as isolated mountaintop communities until after the Second World War.

Blaenavon Expands – the New Town

With the 'Hungry Forties' behind them, the people of Blaenavon entered a more settled mid Victorian period in a town that had outgrown the old industrial housing around North Street. A major figure in this expansion was John Griffiths Williams, a brewer and entre-preneur, who arrived in Blaenavon around 1830. Originally a shopkeeper and draper, he opened the first brewery in the town and built the Red Lion Inn, which gave its name to Lion Street, installing his son-in-law as landlord. In the 1840s he gave Blaenavon a new centre when he laid out and developed Broad Street and built a covered market to replace the old open air market near the ironworks. He is also credited with building the Coliseum, a large gabled theatre or assembly hall, later a cinema, in Lion Street, demolished in the mid 1980s. Its name may have been a joke from its location, though there was also a Coliseum cinema in Lion Street, Abergavenny. In 1865 he described himself as 'draper, brewer [and] proprietor of gas and water works'. By 1875 this had become 'brewer, proprietor of the Market Place and Town Hall and the Cambrian brewery'. He is also said to have established a short-lived pottery near the present Pottery Inn on Llanover Road.

By the early 1860s the town was becoming larger and more complex and the Local Government Board decided that the streets should be named and the names painted up as 'the place has become more intricate in the last twelve months'. In May 1862 the opening of the new Town Hall was marked by a 'grand concert' with the Blaenavon Choral Society under their conductor, the chemist George Deakin, performing works by Handel and with the Rifle Corps in full dress uniform (see below). Many new houses were being built, mostly by local builders, but in 1867 the Blaenavon Mutual Building Society, a co-operative venture, built 20 'Club Houses' in Queen Street. Williams also founded the Blaenavon Gas Company to provide a gasworks for the town (called by the *Pontypool Free Press* 'Mr Williams's gasometer'), the chandeliers of the new Town Hall of 1862 being lit by gas. When, in 1872 a rival company, the Blaenavon Gas and Water Co., was set up, Williams assembled his workmen and tried to tear up their newly laid gas pipes. By 1874 the streets of Blaenavon, despite opposition from some ratepayers, were lit by gas.[40]

The Rifle Volunteers

In 1859 the activities of Napoleon III and a wave of anti-British phobia in the French press led to fears of war with France and a French invasion. Forts, subsequently known as Palmerston's Follies, equipped with heavy Armstrong guns were erected along the south coast and on the islands of the Bristol Channel. There were concerns that Britain's small professional army was inadequate to cope with those of continental powers and a volunteer rifle movement developed. This was aided by the poem *Riflemen Form!* This, published anonymously, was actually by Martin Tupper, but Alfred Tennyson was much annoyed when popular opinion ascribed it to him:

> There is a sound of thunder afar,
> Storm in the South that darkens the day!
> Storm of battle and thunder of war!
> Well if it do not roll our way.
> Storm, Storm, Riflemen form!
> Ready, be ready against the storm!
> Riflemen, Riflemen, Riflemen form!

Monmouthshire had never really had a county regiment and the units recruiting in it often reflected the divisions between its two halves, rural and industrial. The Royal Monmouthshire Royal Engineers is a Monmouth-based unit, the senior militia regiment of the British army, associated in the past with the Dukes of Beaufort and still retaining memories of the county's Catholic recusant past. In the 19th century it was sometimes popularly called, from its many Catholics, 'The Royal Monmouthshire Militia (The Pope's Own)'. The Monmouthshire Light Infantry, the 43rd Regiment of Foot, which had served with distinction in the Peninsular Wars under Moore and Wellington became, under the Cardwell army reorganization scheme of 1881, the First Battalion, the Oxfordshire and Buckinghamshire Light Infantry ('The Ox and Bucks').

In September 1859 companies of Rifle Volunteers were formed at Chepstow and Pontypool and others soon followed at Abersychan and Ebbw Vale. The following month a rifle company was formed at Blaenavon. This was very much a works affair, with R.J.P. Steel (possibly an uncle of Thomas Dyne Steel) as Captain, Fred Plum, the General Manager, as Colour Sergeant and four sergeants, including Joseph Eley, landlord of the Market Tavern. There was some debate over uniform. A proposal by Lady Llanover to dress the volunteers as Italian Berseglieri, with cock feathers in their hats, was abandoned after being tried out on the Abersychan company, who were judged deficient in Italian panache. Eventually the

Fig. 41 The Rifleman's Arms and Rifle Green commemorate the Rifle Volunteers of 1859, predecessors of the Monmouthshire Regiment. (Photograph by Simon Hardy)

rifle uniform of dark green with black facings was adopted, changing to scarlet in 1874. In January 1861 the rifles for the Blaenavon Company finally arrived. When David Davies, a rifle volunteer, died he was accorded a full military funeral, with a band playing the funeral march and a firing party under the command of Captain Steel.[41]

Under the Cardwell Reforms of 1881, the 24th Regiment, the Second Warwickshires, became the South Wales Borderers, recruiting in the industrial areas of Monmouthshire and Glamorgan, with their Headquarters at Brecon. Shortly afterwards the Monmouthshire Rifle Volunteer Corps became battalions of the South Wales Borderers. The Blaenavon Rifle Volunteers became part of the 3rd Volunteer Battalion, South Wales Borderers, which from 1892 until 1911 was commanded by Colonel Joseph Bradney, the historian of Monmouthshire. In 1907-8 under the Haldane reforms, which created the Territorial Army, the 3rd Battalion became the 2nd Battalion of the Monmouthshire Regiment, exchanging scarlet for khaki. Blaenavon became the Headquarters of E Company, 2nd Battalion the Monmouthshire Regiment.[42] If the whole episode of the Rifle Volunteers has irresistible echoes of Dad's Army, it is worth recalling that this was the origin of a regiment which fought with distinction in both World Wars.[43]

Eisteddfodau and Election Riots

1868, the year in which Thomas Hill III died in retirement at Rudhall in Herefordshire, saw two contrasting events showing very different faces of the town. In July there was a Grand Eisteddfod, presided over by Edward Kennard, with a marquee housing three to four thousand people and special trains to bring in visitors. Eisteddfodau were popular cultural events in 19th-century South Wales. In Monmouthshire a major inspiration was the Cymreigyddion y Fenni (Welsh Society of Abergavenny), founded in 1833 by such establishment figures as Lady Charlotte Guest, translator and compiler of the *Mabinogion*, whose husband was the proprietor of Dowlais ironworks; Lady Llanover (Augusta Hall), wife of the M.P. and industrialist Sir Benjamin Hall ('Big Ben'); Sir Charles Morgan of Tredegar House; and Baron and Baroness Bunsen. The whole enterprise, in its emphasis on the creation of a Welsh identity, recalls Sir Walter Scott's creation or re-creation of a Scottish identity in the same period. The 1838 Abergavenny Eisteddfod was a particularly splendid event, attended by the nobility and gentry of the county and with a grand procession of robed bards led by Taliesin Williams, son of Iolo Morganwg, the Glamorganshire stonemason scholar who was the inventor of much 19th-century Welsh tradition, including the bards of the National Eisteddfod.

The Blaenavon Eisteddfod of 1868 was a less grand event, very much a company affair. There were prizes for essays, poetry, singing, recitation and choirs (the last won by the Blaenavon choir). An Ebbw Vale poet won a prize of £1 for verses on the Blaenavon ironworks and the poet Gwilym Gwent was installed as a chaired bard (a winning entrant at an eisteddfod) by Mrs Paton, wife of the general manager.[47]

Disraeli's Second Reform Act of 1867 gave the vote for the first time to urban workmen in the boroughs and large towns, but in 'country' seats like Monmouthshire, the franchise was restricted to freeholders with land or houses over £2 in rental value (the 'forty shilling freeholders'). Monmouthshire, excluding the boroughs, was a two member constituency, each seat held by the Conservatives. There had hardly been a contested election for the seats in living memory, but in the 1868 General Election they were challenged by a Liberal, Colonel Henry Clifford, a local landowner.

The new working class voters expected great things from the new franchise. Evan Powell wrote many years later of the 'memorable and historical election of 1868'. At Blaenavon, where the number of voters had merely risen from 162 to 240, an election campaign was a novelty and Clifford's meetings had been attended by an 'immense concourse' with flags and banners, harking back to the days of the Chartists. The Baptist minister Daniel Morgan addressed the election meetings in Welsh and one banner read 'Eir Gwlad, Eir Hiaith, a'n Crefydd' – 'Our country, language and religion'. Kennard had notices posted around the town stating that voters were free to vote as they wished, but the elections coincided with a period of deep economic depression and earlier in the year a 15% wage cut for colliers had resulted in a long strike ending in failure for the miners. Resentment possibly still lingered. Robert Kennard had just stood down as Conservative M.P. for Newport on the Isle of Wight and his son H.M. Kennard had seconded the nomination paper for Octavius Morgan, one of the Conservative candidates for the county seats.[48]

The contest was hard fought. This was the last election before the introduction of the secret ballot and at Nantyglo the intimidating Crawshay Bailey (Fig. 42), who had stood down as the Conservative M.P. for the boroughs seat, and two of his agents were present at the voting. As was normal at the time, results were spread over some time (in this case a week) and the result in the county seat was eagerly awaited. The voters in the industrial areas supported Clifford, but the rural vote went to the Conservatives Octavius Morgan and Paulett Somerset, members of the two major landowning families in the county, who were duly elected. The Liberals did however win the Monmouth Boroughs seat, where Crawshay

Bailey had stood down to be replaced as Conservative candidate by his fellow ironmaster, Samuel Homfray.

There was bitter disappointment in the industrial areas when it was heard that the two Conservatives had been returned for the county seats. It seemed that nothing had changed and there were riots in industrial towns throughout the county. At Newport a peaceful bystander, the wife of a tailor, was killed by a bayonet thrust as soldiers cleared the crowds. At Tredegar a boy was killed, houses and shops attacked and troops called in. At Blaenavon, at 5 o'clock, as the pubs closed, a large crowd of young men gathered and attacked the shops of tradesmen who had supported the 'Blues'. The grocer's shop of James

Fig. 42 Crawshay Bailey (centre)

Ellis was broken into, sacks of flour emptied into the street and sides of bacon carried off. Joseph Lewis, a shoemaker, also suffered, much of his stock being thrown into the street or carried off. The Red Lion hotel, the Conservative election headquarters, was a particular target. It belonged to the entrepreneur John Griffiths Williams and had recently been re-opened after extensive renovation, with Williams' son-in-law Morris as landlord. Outside, Thomas Wells, one of those later arrested, was reported to have stood in front of the crowd, shouting 'Come on you buggers, I've got the strongest army'. According to Lewis Browning, the police held back, unable or unwilling to intervene, and the crowd smashed the windows and threw the furniture into the street for an election night bonfire, with the hotel's piano on top. Bottles of wines and spirits were looted and barrels of beer emptied into the gutters. One unfortunate rioter fell from an upper window and broke his neck (Fig. 43). Later the landlord put in a claim to the authorities for £1,672 in respect of the damage. Outside the Prince of Wales down the street, the landlord, John Vincent, an ex-policeman, held the rioters at bay with a shotgun, though this did not save his windows, whilst Thomas Jones, the quick-witted publican of the White Horse, rapidly switched his blue banner for a red. At 9pm a detachment of the Royal Welsh Fusiliers arrived from Newport by train and Thomas Kennard read the Riot Act by the light of a candle.

Order was restored and some 50 prisoners were to appear at the police court, 38 of them from Blaenavon, including three women accused of the possession of stolen property. By their surnames, many were English immigrants, no doubt the young single lodgers whom the Varteg ironmaster George Kenrick had regarded as the most troublesome element of the population. Those charged were remanded to Usk prison and the following Tuesday brought to Pontypool Town Hall handcuffed to a long chain and guarded by soldiers from

Fig. 43 The Lion Hotel, sacked in the 1868 election riot. One looter was killed when he fell from an upstairs window. (Photograph by Simon Hardy)

the Royal Welsh Fusiliers. At Monmouth Assizes, Thomas Aldridge, a 22-year-old labourer, was given 12 months hard labour for breaking into shops armed with a hatchet. Other rioters were given six months apiece.[48]

Nationally, the election was a triumph for the Liberals, resulting in Gladstone's first period as Prime Minister, with 21 Welsh seats won.

Election riots in themselves were not a novelty and those of 1868 were in some ways a throwback to earlier times. In the 18th century, when candidates plied voters with much drink, such events were commonplace. The open voting system made it possible for ironmasters to mobilise their workmen in favour of their chosen candidate. If neighbouring ironmasters supported rival candidates, violence could result. In 1837 the Harfords of Ebbw Vale and Sirhowy supported a Whig candidate, whilst Samuel Homfray of Tredegar favoured a Tory (his brother-in-law Charles Morgan of Tredegar House). When the Sirhowy men entered Tredegar in support of 'their' candidate (though none of them had the vote) fighting broke out. In 1852 Crawshay Bailey was Conservative candidate for Monmouth Boroughs, but Thomas Brown of Ebbw Vale was a Liberal supporter and 200 Ebbw Vale workmen descended on Newport, wrecking many inns sporting the blue Tory colours. Bailey dispatched a similar force of Nantyglo men to Newport, who paraded the streets shouting 'Blue for ever, sweet Nantyglo'.

Whilst the immediate cause of the riot in Blaenavon in 1868 was the local election result, it would have been fuelled by the effects of alcohol on a crowd predominantly of young men in their 20s. Riots are often directed against some element seen as intrusive or alien to that society, often on racial or religious grounds. Small shopkeepers, able to give or withhold credit and sometimes keen to show themselves as socially superior to their neighbours, are often also singled out. In the present case, an election campaign was a novel and unfamiliar experience, previous elections being uncontested, and the 'Blues' and their supporters may have been seen as outsiders, alien to the local community.[49] Though the rioting at Blaenavon was serious enough, the horrified reactions may have owed something to the new mid Victorian respectability.[50]

5 FORGING A COMMUNITY: THE PEOPLE OF BLAENAVON 1840 TO 1870

I would not send my children to work as I did fifty years ago. I would sooner send them to the West Indies for slaves.

Thomas Deakin, Mineral Agent, Blaenavon 1842

Masters and Men: Education and control

In the first quarter of the 19th century, the population of Monmouthshire grew faster than that of any other county in Britain, doubling between 1800 and 1810 and increasing by 70% in each of the two following decades.[1] By 1840 the rate of growth had slackened off, but it was still a frontier society, like the rapidly growing cities of the modern 'third world', with many young single migrant workers, a high birth rate and high infant mortality. Of a population of 5,000 at Blaenavon, almost 1,500 were lodgers – nearly all young single men – and the same number were children under the age of 15. According to the survey carried out in 1840 by the Varteg ironmaster George Kenrick, 60% of the population of Blaenavon were Welsh, just under 40% English and 1% Irish, though with the Welsh he does not distinguish (as he does in the text) between the 'aborigines' of Monmouthshire and immigrants from other parts of Wales.[2]

Speculative investment during railway booms led to instability in the iron industry which in turn was a major cause of social unrest on the ironfield. In December 1836 the ironmasters met and agreed to cut output and blow out furnaces in an effort to maintain prices. This led to wage cuts and in the following month eight Blaenavon colliers were prosecuted for leaving work without notice. One, Henry Morgan, was given three months' hard labour for using threats and intimidation to persuade the Blaenavon colliers to quit work.[3]

Three years later, the Chartist attack on Newport shocked the authorities and the middle classes. A virtual army had been raised within 20 miles of a major town without anyone in authority being aware of it. Something had to be done, whether out of philanthropy or common prudence, and as a result the Government developed a sudden interest in social conditions and education. Much the same thing happened five years later after a bitter strike in the Durham coalfield led to a renewed interest in education.[4]

As the result of the unrest, a 25-year-old barrister and civil servant, H. Seymour Tremenheere, educated at Winchester and New College, Oxford and the first government Inspector of Schools, was sent to South Wales 'to enquire into the state of education generally in that part of the country'.[5] He consulted George Kenrick, whom he may have known through the London Statistical Society. Kenrick had contributed a statistical and social study of Blaenavon and Varteg 'in the district recently disturbed' to the Society's journal in January 1840, within a few months of the Newport rising, and the following May developed this in a lecture to the Pontypool Mechanics Institute, later published as a book.[6] Kenrick, from a family of Birmingham Dissenters, was a widower, his wife Elizabeth having died in 1838 at the age of 26. His grandfather had set up a works library and savings bank for his West Bromwich workers and he established two schools at Varteg, one for boys and one for girls, partly funded by the company, partly by a levy. The Varteg Hill colliery schools long survived. In 1840 a church Sunday School was started in Blaenavon.

Kenrick's survey of Varteg, Blaenavon and Pontypool sought to prove that drink and lack of social control, rather than poverty, were the main causes of unrest and he hoped that his work might improve the image of the 'disturbed districts'. He gave details of housing, wage rates and social conditions. He considered young single lodgers the most turbulent section of the population and noted disapprovingly that they earned good wages and could therefore afford to patronise beershops. A typical Whig of the period, his ideals were philanthropic, but with strong concerns for social control and defence of property rights. When 30 Varteg colliers and miners joined a trade union, he sacked them, informed his other workmen that if they joined they would also be dismissed, and consulted with other ironmasters to ensure that 'the evil should be crushed in the bud'. A keen teetotaler, he opened three 'coffee taverns' at Varteg and saw sobriety as central to an ordered society. In a revealing aside he claimed that 'sobriety and twenty four shillings a week are more valuable to a working man ... than drunkeness and sixty shillings a week'.[7]

This reflected the common view among early 19th-century employers that workmen should be kept short of ready cash to keep them out of the alehouse. At the very time when coal owners in Monmouthshire were restricting output in order to shore up prices, causing much suffering in the process, Seymour Tremenheere was complaining that the Miners Association, an early trade union, was 'a threat to the cheapness of coal and iron, the very foundation of our national advantage as a manufacturing people'. Whilst he noted with satisfaction that there were now many more 'prudent and well conducted colliers and colliers' families', he regretted that high wages often led to 'sensuality and extravagance'. This was one reason for the 'long pay', when men were paid monthly not weekly (see also p.81).

In 1840 the Whig reformer James Kay Shuttleworth wrote to Sir Thomas Phillips, who the previous November had stood in the breach against the Chartists at the Westgate Hotel when the miners and ironworkers of the Monmouthshire valleys had marched on Newport in an armed insurrection whose precise aims are still a matter for debate. Shuttleworth stressed the need for working class education in South Wales. He cited three reasons for this – the dangers of 'disorganized doctrines' (like those of the Chartists) to businessmen with 'so much at stake'; the prevention of 'self destruction' by drink caused by 'high wages' among what he called 'an uncivilized population'; and the paternal duty of property owners to those under them. The paradox was that Phillips, despite his role at the Westgate, was no reactionary, but an advocate of the education of the poor, the founder of a school, an opponent of truck shops and later the defender of the Welsh people against the libels of the 'Treason of the Blue Books'. This government enquiry, using hostile evidence, much of it from Anglican clergy, who represented a frustrated minority faith in much of Wales, produced a report libelling the culture, education and morals of the Welsh people and markedly hostile to the Welsh language. These Whiggish views, in their official blue paper covers, bore a marked family resemblance to those of Shuttleworth.[8]

In 1840 Lord Ashley secured a Royal Commission on the employment of children in coal mines. Inspectors were sent to interview workers and obtain information and the resulting report led to an Act of 1842 prohibiting women and boys under ten from working underground, banning the paying out of wages in public houses, fixing a minimum age of 15 for winding enginemen and making provision for an Inspector of Mines with powers to enter collieries at all times. In the following year Tremenheere was appointed the first Mines Inspector. In 1850 the Coal Mines Act established a Mining Inspectorate, largely staffed by people with mining experience. (Tremenheere, though a knowledgeable geologist, never ventured underground.)

In the run up to the census of 1841, rumours, heard by both Tremenheere and Kenrick, spread through South Wales that the census was part of a government plan to count working class children in order to be able to collect together one in ten or all those aged under 3 and ship them to Australia, or to impose some draconian form of birth control.[9] This nightmare conflation of Malthus and the Massacre of the Innocents may have begun as a sour joke, but is a telling comment on social attitudes in the wake of the Newport Rising.

Hard Times for the Poor: The Hungry Forties
The Chartist rising of 1839 took place at the beginning of the period that became known as The Hungry Forties, a time of economic recession and high food prices. In 1841 itinerant gangs of workers spread strikes through much of the ironfield, but the worst distress, as always, was in the sale coal pits around Bedwellty and Blackwood. Of the two branches of the coal industry, the sale coal pits, which produced coal for domestic consumption, were more exposed to the immediate effects of market forces than the ironworks collieries, where the effect of any slump took longer to percolate through. A cartel of Newport coal shippers tried to arrest the fall in coal prices by limiting the amounts brought to the wharves and it wasn't long before starving colliers and their families around Bedwellty stole the tops of potato plants in the fields, not daring to take the potatoes themselves. As previously quoted, the Blaenavon manager Harry Scrivenor told an Oddfellows dinner at the Old Crown Inn in Blaenavon that 'Bad as times were for the poor, they were equally so for the capitalists'.[10] In a sense he was right, for the Blaenavon Company's £50 shares sank to a value of £2 each. Even after conditions had improved in 1844 and people spoke of the 'late hard times', they had only climbed painfully back to £11. In 1843 the Blaenavon Company made a loss of £13,000.

Part of the problem for the iron industry was that Scottish ironmasters were flooding the market with hot blast pig iron ('Cheap Scotch pig'; see also p.55), where the air blast to the furnace was pre-heated. This reduced the amount of fuel needed per ton of iron from 8 tons of coal (converted to coke), to 5.25 tons. In December 1842 *The Times* complained

The Trial, Lamentation,

and Farewell, of the Unfortunate

JOHN FROST,

Who his now taken his Trial before The Right Honourable N. C, Tindal, Knight, the Honourable Sir J, Parke, Knight, and the Honourable Sir J. Williams, Knight, and C. Bateman, Sheriff. Monmouth, For High Treason, and Sedition,

The Court opened on Tuesday and the Day was spent in selecting the jury, and the court adjourned at half-past five o'clock till nine o'clock the following morning. On Wednesday the court opened and the Clerk of the Arraigns Read the indictment against Frost, who pleaded not guilty, and he said it was now their duty to proceed and find the truth of that plea.—After opening the case for the prosecution and given a long address to the Jury, the Council for Frost Objected to the present mode, stating that the prisoner had not had the list of witnesses and jury delivered ten days previous, according to the Act.—Which took up much time and the court Adjourned. On Thursday the court opened and commenced examining the Witnesses againt Frost, which continued on Thursday, Friday, and Saturday, and the Sentence deferred, and the legality of the Trial, for the decision of the Twelve Judges. It is expected to be transportation.

Come all you tender Christians,
  That dwell both far and near,
Unto my Lamentation,
  I pray you lend an ear.
With grief and woe I am oppressed,
  Sorrow absorbs my mind,
My aching heart beats in my breast,
  My sighs invades the wind.

Oh, in Newport Town I once did dwell,
  In harmony and peace,
Where with my wife and children dear,
  All blessings did increase,
Until treachery and rebellion,
  My spirits did inflame,
Caused me from virtue's paths to stray,
  And bring myself to shame,

Its for the crime of treason
  For which I am to blame
Come listen for one moment
  While I relate the same,
On the fourth day of November last,
  It was the fatal day,
The bare remembrance of the same,
  It fills me with dismay

With pikes and swords and pistols,
  We most of us armed were
When we got to the Westgate Inn,
  Some one fired at the Mayor,

It was a shocking sight to see,
  The blood run from the wounds,
But what was much more malancholy,
  Was the dead bodies on the ground.

I quickly apprehended was,
  Examined then with speed,
And to await the assizes,
  To Monmouth was conveyed,
There to await our trials,
  All at the bar to stand,
And to appear before the Judges,
  To hear their dread command.

Before the sentence on me is past,
  The judges to me do say,
You must now prepare to meet your doom
  Without the least delay,
That others may take warning
  By your unpleasant fate,
And shun the crime that you have done,
  Before it is too late,

Farewell my wife and children dear
  I bid you all farewell
What pain I feel on your account
  No human tongue can tell
May God be your protector
  while in this world you stay
And may I meet you with sins forgiven,
  Upon the Judgment day,

W. BEAR, PRINTER, SWANSEA

Fig. 44 *Through much of the 19th century, itinerant ballad singers visited Blaenavon, selling their broadsheet ballads. They were a major source of news, rather like modern tabloid newspapers. Murders and executions were popular topics and this account of the Newport Rising of 1839 copies these, though Frost was reprieved. (Courtesy Gwent Archives)*

that this caused 'fearful severity on the mining interests of Staffordshire and South Wales', leading to wage reductions and social unrest. It continued, 'Neither Chartist nor Corn Law agitator would have been listened to ... had not distress ... made the workmen ripe for disturbance.'[11]

Tradespeople also suffered. When bailiffs tried to seize the goods of Samuel Deakin at Blaenavon they were met by several hundred men and women carrying placards, the men with their faces blackened. This echoed the Rebecca Riots in west Wales against toll charges on roads, and indeed the *Merlin* proclaimed that Rebecca had come to Monmouthshire. A number of people were arrested, including three women, one of them Esther Cairns, a respectable married woman, later a prominent Primitive Methodist.[12] Similar events sparked riots in Pontypool.

Social tensions fell the following year as conditions improved. In December 1843, the *Merlin* had made no mention of Christmas, but a year later it noted a Christmas market and fair at Blaenavon and under the heading 'The Poor' announced that 'the kindly spirit of Charles Dickens was abroad' (*A Christmas Carol* was published in 1843).[13]

Fig. 45 The Lock Up or Police Station in North Street, built when Sergeant Hodder (locally Constable Order) took up his duties in 1838. It was later discovered that the iron used in the grates was stolen from the works.

Until 1847 there was then a period of relative prosperity, but the bursting of the bubble of 'railway mania' and a wave of financial failures that summer led to panic and wage cuts. In the summer of 1848 Blaenavon endured a three month strike.[14]

Law and Sergeant Hodder

Until the appointment of Blaenavon's first policeman, John Hodder. in 1838, law enforcement consisted of a pair of stocks outside Engine Row in Stack Square and a pair of unpaid parish constables, Thomas Ledbetter, a furnace manager and John Williams, a colliery foreman. This arrangement was more suited to an Elizabethan village than an industrial boom town. Hodder was a sergeant with the locally organized Trevethin force, there being no county police force until 1855.[15]

Professional criminals were rare. Some years before Hodder's arrival, Joseph Giles Annelly, a former assistant in the company shop at Varteg, was something of a specialist thief. In April 1832 he burgled the Blaenavon company shop in Office Square, taking a quantity of silk handkerchiefs. At Usk sessions he was given 12 months hard labour. Shortly after his release the Blaenavon shop was robbed again. In April 1834 tiles were taken off the roof at the back of the Varteg company shop and various goods stolen, including a quantity of silk. Annelly was arrested, tried at Monmouth Assizes and sentenced to transportation for life. In March 1835 he was one of 320 convicts who sailed for New South Wales on the *Marquis of Huntly*. Four years later the drapers shop of John Griffiths Williams, later responsible for the development of mid-Victorian Blaenavon, was broken into, but the two burglars were seized.[16]

Most of Hodder's work however was taken up with routine assaults and drunkenness or thefts of geese, sheep and scrap metal. When a quantity of iron was stolen in August 1840 it transpired that some of it had been used for the fire grates in the police station. He may also have been involved in November 1839 when three privates of the 45th Regiment, who had deserted a few days after the Newport Rising, turned up in Blaenavon seeking work and were arrested.[17]

'We Work Like Little Horses' – Women and Children at Work

In 1831 William Needham described the workforce at an ironworks with five furnaces, probably Blaenavon. There were just over 1,100 men employed, compared with 84 women. At Varteg, there were 74 working women out of a labour force of just under 1,500, loading and unloading trams of ironstone and coal, stacking up iron in the forges and making bricks.[18] Forty of the Blaenavon women were described as (ironstone) miners, probably workers on the 'patches', a primitive and dangerous form of opencast mining. Thirty-nine women were working in the furnaces and five at the forge and mill. Needham's list of furnace trades includes the making of firebricks to line the furnaces, and it may have been in this work that some of the women were employed. Most, however, were girls wheeling the trams of ironstone that had been loaded at the pit mouth to the furnace top, or breaking up the ore on the furnace top, as described later by the Cambridge barrister turned social investigator A.J. Munby. The *Morning Chronicle* reporter saw such girls at Merthyr: 'On a day of heavy rain and high wind, I saw them at work ... with the rain literally running off their coal bedecked petticoats over their boots, in black streams, to the ground.'[19]

In 1841 the Children's Employment Commissioners Robert Hugh Franks and Rhys William Jones toured South Wales interviewing workers. At Blaenavon they interviewed, in Welsh, 14-year-old Mary Daniel and 15-year-old Margaret Thomas. They spoke of filling the 'mine' (iron ore) from the bank of ore into the trams for 12 hours a day. They had time off for breakfast and dinner, and as they lived nearby were able to go home for meals. Margaret had previously worked underground in the coal levels, pushing trams.[20] This was much harder, she said; the levels were wet and she was sometimes in water 'half leg deep'. She mentioned that there had been a number of girls as young as her in the levels. Both girls went to Sunday School, though neither could read.

They told the Commissioners that they would rather work at the mine than go into service. Domestic service was widely said to be unpopular and Dyne Steel claimed to know of country girls who came to Blaenavon to visit friends, but stayed on, taking jobs underground rather than return to domestic service.[21] Work discipline tended to be more strict in service and there was less personal freedom. Charlotte Chiles had worked in Lord Kensington's house near Carmarthen, but preferred drawing and landing coal at Graig colliery in Merthyr for 40 shillings a month to working as a kitchen maid for 60 to 70 shillings a year, with keep. She had more to spend on clothes and more liberty. The work was hard, but she had her health and strength.[22]

Widows and orphans needed to find some way to support themselves, and one such was Mary Deacon, who was interviewed by the Children's Employment Commission. An orphan aged 16, she was the daughter of a man from 'Wesley' (?Westbury on Severn) in Gloucestershire, who now lodged with the Tovey family in Upper New Rank. She described how she and her 15-year-old friend Mary Tanner sat 'four or five girls together in a house or lodge at the pit mouth with a fire in it, waiting to receive the wagons out of the iron ore mine, and return the empty wagons'.[23]

Many women worked in the years before marriage, when still living with their parents, since early marriage was seen as improvident and leading to poverty. Some girls did marry early, however. In Upper New Rank in 1841 there were three 15-year-old mothers with infants. They may have 'got caught' as the saying was, but a young collier in his early 20s was at the peak of his earning power, wages had been high in the years before the census and the disincentive to marriage less. Certainly Kenrick believed that one result of the relatively high wages of 1839-40 was that young girls 'left Sunday School' at 15 or so to get married. Women normally, however, married in their early 20s and of 23 women in their 20s living in Upper and Lower New Rank in 1841, 70% were married, six were still in paid work (three in 'mine work', three in service) whilst Martha Alsop may have been reluctant to leave her mother to cope unaided with a household of five working men.[24]

In the following year, 1842, it became illegal for women to work underground with the passing of the Mines and Collieries Act. In the deep mines, female labour was of little use and its removal met with little opposition. There had been no women in the Durham and Northumberland mines for 60 years, nor in local deep mines like John Russell's Risca steamcoal colliery, the sale coal pits of the Blackwood area or the new deep pits of the Rhondda. In the ironworks collieries, with their warrens of levels and drifts worked in an elaborate sub-contract system, things were different and the Act was virtually ignored for some years at Blaenavon and elsewhere in South Wales. In 1850 Tremenheere noted that women were still working underground at Blaenavon, Clydach, Nantyglo, Beaufort and Blaina and a writer in 1858 referred darkly to the 'unfeminine occupation' of girls working on the tips 'or, as we fear is sometimes the case, underground'.[25] At Crawshay Bailey's Beaufort, a young woman, Ann Davies, was killed underground as late as August 1866.[26]

It was true that many of the horrors that had shocked the Victorian conscience were absent in South Wales. There were no women coal bearers like those in eastern Scotland and the notorious belt and chain was rare, though not unknown, being used in parts of Monmouthshire with narrow coal seams. Fourteen-year-old Elias Jones drew coal trams in this way at Risca. 'It is very hard work indeed', he told the Children's Employment

Fig. 46 'We work like little horses.' This method does not seem to have been used in Blaenavon, but sadly 14-year-old Elias Jones at Risca was not speaking metaphorically, but literally.

Commissioners, 'it is too hard for such lads as we, for we work like little horses' (Fig. 46). Sadly, he was speaking literally, not metaphorically. At some ironworks, women filled trams with coal or iron ore and pulled the trams to an unloading point with a leather girdle around their waist, a work method memories of which were still recalled, presumably from their grandparents, by old people at Beaufort in 1929.[27] Usually, people worked in small, often family, groups in the levels and stallwork.

In 1849 the manager and the newly appointed mineral agent at Blaenavon launched a campaign against women workers underground, an event not unconnected with the impending visit of a government inspector. Two years earlier, 30 female underground workers had been sacked at Rhymney ironworks after pressure from the inspector. The Blaenavon mineral agent, Robert Smith, was a County Durham man, where work practices differed and he may have regarded the employment of women underground as an outdated (as well as illegal) practice. Morris and Williams have noted how mining engineers and managers from northern England were instrumental in improving mining techniques in South Wales.[28] At Blaenavon the reason given out for the banning of female underground workers was that 'immorality had become so general and flagrant' that something had to be done. Nothing was said of the company condoning illegal practices for seven years. 'Immorality' often meant no more than immodesty (by Victorian standards) of dress and such was probably the case here. Similar complaints were often made about such occupations as cockle gathering or salt boiling, where the normal modest covering of the Victorian female was impossible but prying middle class male eyes were rare.[29]

After due warning, a search was made of the rabbit warren of mines and levels and some 70 women and girls turned out, including some 20 aged no more than 11 or 12. Some girls were found alternative work, but Smith admitted that a number of orphan girls had been thrown on parish relief and that some men had left for other ironworks, where they could still take their wives and daughters underground. The affair caused a great stir at Blaenavon and the under manager Dyne Steel was attacked and mobbed by angry women outside the company offices.[30] (In 1843 the *Mining Journal* described an 'old miner' elsewhere, with a large family, all girls. It noted that if the girls were thrown out of work, the whole family would become inmates of the workhouse, since he could not support them unaided.)

Not all mineral extraction at Blaenavon was underground. Patch mining was a primitive and often dangerous form of opencast mining due to the frequent falls of earth and stone from the loose sides of the excavation. Reports of fatal accidents were common and it seems to have been a job of last resort for English immigrants and women who could find no other employment. At Ebbw Vale the patches survived until 1875. In 1860 a 16-year-old girl, Elizabeth Jones, was killed on the Blaenavon patches, and in 1857 an Englishman and the widow of a miner left with six children were killed on the patches at Rhymney. When Ann Davies was killed underground at Nantyglo in 1866, the company tried to explain away this illegal situation by claiming that she normally worked on the patches, but had sought temporary employment underground because of bad weather. At Blaenavon, areas of patching are shown on William Llewelyn's map of 1814 (Fig. 12) and traces can be seen around the brow of hill above Garnyrerw near the Brynmawr Road, in an area known as 'The Patches', and between Elgam Avenue and Keepers Pond.[31]

In September 1865, Blaenavon received its strangest Victorian visitor. Arthur J. Munby (1828-1911) was a poet, diarist and barrister, educated at Trinity College, Cambridge, where his papers now are.[32] His working life was spent in the offices of the Ecclesiastical Commissioners, but he had a life-long interest in working-class women, particularly those engaged in hard manual labour. He had a long relationship, ending in marriage, with a maid of all work, Hannah Cullwick, and collected hundreds of photographs of female mine workers and other working women. He had a genuine concern for working-class education, being much involved with the Working Men's College, and always vehemently denied that his interest in working woman had any sexual element.

He came to Blaenavon on 22 September 1865.[33] 'The whole of the upper end of the Blaenavon valley is filled with the coal pits, coke ovens, iron blast-furnaces and brickworks of the Blaenavon company', he wrote. He first visited the brickworks where the women worked three to a kiln, with a shoveller and a 'gaffer' over them. The 'well grown, healthy lasses', aged from 15 to 21, 'wore coarse ragged smocks – "pinnies" they call them – belted at the waist and strong laced boots and kerchiefs tied round head and neck. Some had on hoodbonnets, some wideawakes or mushroom straw hats, with a ribbon or bunch of hawthorn berries stuck therein. The smocks reach to just below the knee and under them some of the girls wore short cotton trousers and some woollen stockings only.' The women also operated the pug mill, where the clay and other raw materials were ground and mixed. This could be dangerous work and in the autumn of 1860, two young women, Sarah Pritchard and Martha Booth were crushed to death within the space of a few months when their clothes caught in the machinery.[34]

At the coke ovens above the furnaces women were digging and sifting coke or emptying trams of coke or ironstone into the ovens. 'There were no mere girls here, the work being too hard', Munby wrote. Most were working inside wooden sheds, breaking up lumps of ironstone. 'The girls smash them up' with large hammers, 'bringing [them] down with manly skill and force ... fine strong girls they were; bare-armed and sinewy, with kerchiefs only on their heads ... They break stones thus from 6 a.m. to 6 p.m. every day, only ceasing for breakfast and dinner for 6 shillings to 7 shillings a week ... Most of the stonebreakers were of a yellowish grey colour, like the stone; but one lass with stout bare arms, who was breaking Northumbrian ore was red like a red Indian; her face, which was comely and her limbs all glowing with ruddy sweat.' At Nantyglo, Munby found over a hundred women similarly employed breaking ironstone. It would have been interesting to have heard the girls' comments on Mr Munby.[35]

Child Labour

'With his solitary candle, cramped with cold, wet and not half fed, the poor child, deprived of light and air, passes his silent day,' recorded the Childrens' Employment Commission.[36] In March 1841, the Commission took evidence from Thomas Deakin and the colliery manager, John Samuels. They asked about the 'door boys' – the small children (there was only one door girl at Blaenavon) who opened and shut the underground ventilation doors. They were paid 10 or 12 shillings a month for a 12-hour day, from 6 a.m. to 6 p.m. and 'do not burn a light, but are in the dark, excepting when the trams come out, when they see by the driver's candle'.

In the furnace top area William Lloyd, the furnace manager, had about 37 children working, the youngest a boy of 7. Boys of between 8 and 12 helped the fillers load barrows of iron ore, coke and limestone and push them to the furnaces. One of the fillers, Timothy Macarthy from County Cork, lived in Stack Square. He and his two sons, Timothy and Thomas, worked for 12 hours a day pushing the 'dandies' to the top of the furnace, with night work every other week. He claimed that Timothy was 14 and Thomas 10, though the ages given, presumably by the boys' mother, in the 1841 census show that they were actually 9 and 7. Thomas, he said, was really too young to work, but because of his large family, with six children in Blaenavon and another in Ireland, he was forced to employ him, since otherwise he would need to employ another boy and the whole family would suffer. Unlike at Varteg, there were few Irish in Blaenavon (as noted above) – 86 in total, according to Kenrick, including the Macarthys. As late as 1943 a Beaufort man remembered how he had been hidden in a mine stall as a child during a visit by the Mines Inspector enforcing the ban on the employment of children under 10 underground.[37]

In the flat area behind the furnaces were the coke ovens. Here, some 14 girls aged between 10 and 16 worked. They were paid, not by the company but by the cokers, between 6 and 9 shillings a week. Some six boys aged from 10 to 14 worked around the cast houses in the furnace yard 'and sometimes get burned, but not very bad', said Mr Lloyd.[38]

The accounts by Munby and the Children's Employment Commission of girls and children at work can be supplemented by other sources which describe small children working with their parents in the cast houses, refineries and rolling mills, or boys in charge of trains of horse-drawn wagons. Sadly, these are all too often newspaper accounts of inquests on accident victims.

Below ground at Blaenavon, children started work at 8 or 9. A 9-year-old boy, Thomas Goodall, was killed by a roof fall at Blaenavon in 1836 and an 8-year-old boy and his father were drowned in the 1838 Cinder Pit disaster, along with two girls, Elizabeth Havard aged 9 and Mary Hale, aged 15.[39] Parents took their children underground even earlier, at 6 or 7, for the sake of being allocated an extra tram of coal to fill, so increasing their pay, but they were not formally employed at that age. John Samuel thought that children should begin work underground at 10, but Thomas Deakin 'did not wish to see young children underground before ... 11 or 12. At that age, for the males, if they are to be brought up to mining, it is time for them to begin.' He himself had worked underground in Shropshire aged 9, drawing trams of coal with the notorious belt and chain. 'I would not allow my children to work as I did fifty years ago,' he said, 'I would sooner send them to the West Indies for slaves.'[40]

On the Tramp: Labour Mobility and Emigration

It was common for a young man to wish to see something of the world and to go 'on the tramp' for a year or so, working in various places before settling down, rather like the modern gap year. It was said that 'no man knows his own ability, or what he is worth, until he has worked in more towns than one'.[41] Lewis Browning, the Blaenavon collier and historian, went 'on the tramp' for a while as a young man, after a quarrel with his boss, and found it a formative experience. His grandfather, a Methodist from the Forest of Dean, tramped to Blaenavon as a young man, when the first furnaces were being built. Lewis, as a child at the church school, had gone to church each Sunday despite his family's Methodist tradition. On the tramp, he went to church at Llantwit Fardre in Glamorgan, but was shocked when the parson abandoned the service because of the poor turn out and treated the congregation to gin and water in a beerhouse. Back home, he joined Penuel Chapel and remained a Calvinistic Methodist for the rest of his days.[42]

This was in many respects a highly mobile society. In 1818 rumours of an advance in wages in Staffordshire and Shropshire triggered a large scale exodus of workmen from Tredegar and Nantyglo. Most of the original workforce of Blaenavon had come from the English West Midlands or from the subsistence hill farming economy of south-west Wales. Slightly later there was an influx from forest edge areas in Gloucestershire and Herefordshire.

Labour migration was not an invention of the Industrial Revolution. Agricultural work was, by its very nature, seasonal. Gangs of harvesters from west Wales had been a common sight in the English West Midlands throughout the 18th century, though towards its close they were being replaced by even more numerous and cheaper harvesters from western Ireland. Some may have diverted to the new industrial areas. Kenrick noted how many Cardiganshire men, proverbial for their thrift, returned home each winter with £15 or £20 savings from a summer on the ironfield. According to Browning, they were employed to mow the hay on the company farm, a task at which they were considered expert.[43] Of 16 men from Pembrokeshire and Carmarthenshire whose birth dates are known from the 1851 census (the first to give places of birth), all of the former and six of the latter were born between 1771 and 1797 and would have been in their early 20s between 1795 and 1820. Even in the 1890s a government commission could note of Monmouthshire farm labourers: 'With respect to many of them, it is difficult to determine whether they may be styled wood-cutters and quarrymen, coming to the land for hoeing, harvesting and sundry piece work, or whether they are in the main agricultural labourers, going to the woods, quarries and mines in the winter months.'[44]

The proportion of English immigrants at Blaenavon, at 40%, was easily the highest in the ironfield. By mid century, the main areas of recruitment were from neighbouring Herefordshire, Gloucestershire and Somerset. A number of Herefordshire families arrived in the 1840s, judging from their birthplaces and those of their children in the 1851 census. These were mainly craftsmen, including blacksmiths, carpenters and a baker. Few were colliers or ironworkers. They may have been concentrated in certain areas of the town, for in 1861, of the 23 families in River Row, 18 were from those three English counties, the remainder from other parts of England. In Pwll Du by contrast, at the same date, 25 of the 41 families were from Monmouthshire and adjacent parts of Brecon, six from elsewhere in Wales and ten from adjacent parts of England.

People also left Blaenavon. From the 1830s there were regular emigrant sailings from Newport to Philadelphia and New York in ships like the *Nestor*, *Bordidina*, *Herald*, *Franklin*, *Louise* and *Mary Ann*, and in April 1837 the *Monmouthshire Merlin* reported that over 50 families of colliers and miners had left Abersychan, Blaenavon and Varteg for 'the land of promise' in expectation of higher wages. These sailings were organized by 'recruiting agents' in Abersychan and Nantyglo. In hard times, emigration to Australia and America was on a large scale. Emigration was particularly heavy in the early 1860s. In 1860, 39 families left by the 11.30 train en route to Australia. Five years later a group of 30 Blaenavon people left via Liverpool for America. The same year John Rees of Blaenavon announced himself as 'printer, stationer, tea dealer, postmaster [and] emigration and insurance agent'.

By 1865 mining families from Blaenavon were emigrating to the Newcastle coal mines

Fig. 47 Mary Ann Caddick, daughter of a Blaenavon iron puddler who migrated to Hughesovska (Donetsk) in the Ukraine. Mary married another Blaenavon man, Thomas Caddick, in Odessa.

in New South Wales. Typically one member of the family would leave for the promised land and would then encourage and help others to follow. Shadracke Morgan, for example, went to Newcastle but then sent money home for the rest of the family, including his father, Abednego Morgan and two brothers, to follow him, though the process took some years.[45]

The skills of Blaenavon colliers and steelworkers were in demand in many places. In 1870 John Hughes, son of the chief engineer at Cyfartha, left for the Ukraine with a fleet of ships containing around a hundred Welsh colliers and ironworkers to set up an industrial complex with eight blast furnaces at Hughesovska (now Donetsk) which as late as 1913 was producing three-quarters of Russian iron. During the strikes of the early 1870s the *Pontypool Free Press* noted 'several of the puddlers have left to go to Russia'. George Caddick, a nut and bolt maker from Blaenavon left for there in the 1880s. His son Thomas married Mary Ann Taylor, daughter of a Blaenavon iron puddler at Odessa. In 1897 they were joined by Josiah Thomas, a blower in the Blaenavon bessemer shop. Mary Ann Caddick (née Taylor) later returned to Blaenavon (Fig. 47). Fittingly, her story is told in her own words and with her photograph in the display in the World Heritage visitor centre.[46]

From Cradle to Coffin – The Company Shops

The map of 1814 and Thomas Deakin's map of 1819 have the caption for Stack Square: 'Houses and shop'. It was often necessary for a company to provide a shop for its workforce in such a remote spot, just as it would be on a modern oil rig. In the 1790s a series of poor harvests led to a dearth of corn which in areas like Merthyr would have rapidly led to famine, resulting in the ironmasters organizing emergency shipments of flour on a substantial scale. When the Dowlais company opened a shop in 1799 they claimed that it was a benefit to their workmen. Much of the food sold was bought in Bristol – cheese from the southern English dairying counties, together with flour and potatoes. In the hard years after Waterloo, grain shortage due to the weather, poor harvests and a rising population led to food riots. There were even attempts to make bread from potatoes, as Byron noted. Bacon, mutton and some potatoes were produced locally and the Blaenavon company, like other iron companies, had its own farms, with flocks of sheep and a shepherd. A group of eight pillow mounds on Coity Mountain above Forgeside, marked as 'rabbit warren' on early editions of the Ordnance Survey, show that in its early days the company was also breeding rabbits for food. When Harris and Co., lessees of the company shops at Garnddyrys and Pwll Du, went bankrupt in 1863, the inventory of their stock, which included American cheese, flour, tea, butter, bacon, clothes and footware, gives an insight into the scale of their operations, as does the surviving plan of the North Street truckshop.[47]

Until about 1820 company shops do not seem to have been regarded as unduly oppressive, but their abuse created the notorious truck shop system which some said provided

Fig. 48 The Crown Inn in North Street was later the company truck shop, with the Drum and Monkey as a back bar. It is now Caddick's workshop.

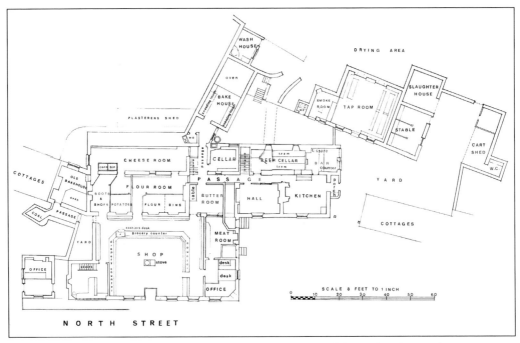

WASH HOUSE

DRYING AREA

oven

BAKE HOUSE

SMOKE ROOM

TAP ROOM

SLAUGHTER HOUSE

STABLE

PLASTERERS SHED

CART SHED

w.c.

CHEESE ROOM

CELLAR

BEER CELLAR

corn bin

B A R counter

COTTAGES

OLD BAKEHOUSE

BOOTS & SHOES

POTATOES

FLOUR ROOM

BUTTER ROOM

HALL

KITCHEN

YARD

FLOUR BINS

COTTAGES

oven

COAL

PASSAGE

cashiers desk

grocery counter

MEAT ROOM

YARD

SHOP

stove

desk

OFFICE

desk

OFFICE

SCALE 8 FEET TO 1 INCH

N O R T H   S T R E E T

Fig. 49 The plan of the company truck shop shows the scale of the undertaking. The tap room to the rear was the famous Drum and Monkey. The shop itself resembled an old fashioned grocers, with counters around the edge. Tracing of original plan in possession of Messrs. Caddick. (Courtesy of Cadw, Welsh Historic Monuments)

a man with his cradle and his coffin and half starved him between. The first Blaenavon company shop was in Office (later Stack) Square, in the area of the present shop. Later it moved down North Street, to the site of the former Crown Hotel, now Caddick's workshop (Figs. 48 & 49). There were also company shops in the hilltop settlements of Garnddyrys and Pwll Du. The profits from the shops appeared in the company's annual accounts, alongside those from iron and coal, but their management could prove troublesome. In a migrant society, many left with their shop debts unpaid, and when men were laid off the shops could be hit by bad debts. In 1843, during the Hungry Forties, the shareholders were told 'The management of the shops has always been a subject of anxiety ... [particularly] ... during a period like the present from the extreme difficulty of recovering the debts due [from] the men prior to their discharge whenever such a measure becomes necessary.' Employers sometimes justified the truck system as enabling them to retain a more stable workforce by tying men to their employment, but this could be a double-edged weapon. On occasion the company tried to lease the shops out to private contractors. In 1853 they temporarily ceased trading. In 1861 the Garnddyrys and Pwll Du shops were leased out to John Harris and Co., but proved unprofitable and after several attempts to relinquish the lease, Harris and Co. went bankrupt in 1863. The company was forced to resume control. In 1871 they were leased out at £1,000 a year and continued trading until at least 1877.

Truck had technically been illegal since 1817, the law stating that men should be paid in 'good and lawful money' or 'current coin of the realm', but as the practice still persisted the law was reiterated in anti-truck legislation in 1831. Many larger, more established employers regarded the system as encouraging social unrest and as giving their competitors an unfair advantage. A well-informed army officer, Colonel Lowe of the 11th Regiment, blamed it for the Merthyr Rising of 1831 and it was said to be a cause of the Newport Rising of 1839. Lord Bute inserted a clause in a renewal of the Dowlais lease forbidding Truck and William Crawshay II of Cyfartha wrote to a local newspaper that he totally disapproved of Truck and would 'while he lived, pay my men for hard work in hard money and money only', even though Truck gave his competitors a 10% advantage over him. The ironmaster M.P. Benjamin Hall ('Big Ben') introduced an anti Truck Bill in the Commons and Sir Thomas Phillips, knighted for his role at the Westgate Hotel, Newport, in November 1839 paid his men in cash and would not allow a truck shop at his collieries in the Sirhowy valley.[48]

The worst abuses of the system were by cash-strapped small companies and sub-contractors under pressure to wring a profit from their contracts or by larger companies facing a cash crisis in times of recession. In 1823 the coal owner J.H. Moggeridge of Blackwood wrote to the Home Office that Truck was more prevalent in the sale coal collieries around Newport than at any time since 1816. This, he said, was mainly among the small independent sale coal collieries – the major iron and coal masters having stuck to an earlier agreement to end the practice. According to Moggeridge, prices at truck shops were between 20% and 40% above the market rate.[49] The 1842 Act was partly successful in curbing truck shops but in the depression of 1849-53, when iron companies were desperate to shore up their profits, many shops re-opened, including those at Abersychan and Nantyglo, and 12 of the 17 major iron companies operated truck shops.[50]

The 1847 report on the state of the population in the mining districts noted that 'the payment of wages in public houses is much encouraged by the habit of employing contractors to raise the coal and ironstone'. The mason Aaron Brute had a coal level, with next to it a row of houses he had built, with a pub, the Lamb, on the end of the row.[51] It had been illegal since 1842 to pay workmen in public houses, but the bar takings would have been a convenient source of cash for payment and it would have been a strong-minded man who refused to have a drink after work on pay day. At Nantyglo in the 1840s, workmen were paid in groups with notes on Crawshay Bailey's private bank. They then adjourned to the nearby Bush Hotel, where the landlord charged half a crown (2 shillings and 6 pence) commission on each £5 note changed (a rate of 2.5%).[52]

The shortage of small change in turn led to 'long pay' (see p.68). At Blaenavon in 1871, colliers were paid fortnightly, ironworkers monthly. Between were fortnightly 'draws' at which men could claim advances of cash. However, if they did not use the company shop, they were not allowed to use the 'draw', and the Truck Commission heard evidence that the cashier would issue promissory notes rather than cash to workmen suspected of intent to 'slope', i.e. shop privately.[53] In 1873, Charles Nutt, working in Dodd's Slope, was subject to stoppages for the works' doctor, rent and coal, and needing to draw cash advances of around £2 to £3 10 shillings each month, was left with a balance of little more than £1 or once a mere 3 shillings 9 pence in his pay packet.[54] The 'long draw' led to considerable inconvenience, particularly to housewives. When the Secretary of the Truck Commission visited Abersychan on Sunday, 27 November 1870, a 'draw day', he found that a queue of women and children had started before 2 a.m. and that by the time the shop opened at 5.30, between 50 and 60 women were queueing, some having to wait hours before being served, indicating how dependent upon the truck shops they were.[55]

The Blaenavon company claimed that the men were under no compulsion to use the shops, but Edwin Jones of 1 Engine Row told how he had ignored the shop and bought from private traders, but the shop cashier reported him to his 'gaffer' John Lloyd, who questioned him about this. He claimed that there was much dissatisfaction with the company shop, since private traders in the town sold higher quality goods at lower prices. The Commission also heard that at Ebbw Vale (where private shops were not allowed on the company estate), Sirhowy and Abersychan an ingenious dodge was employed to circumvent the law. The shop was divided into goods counters and cash counters. The goods were ordered at the one and paid out of the individual's Truck account at the other. If men took the cash they were noted in the book as having 'sloped'. Though Ebbw Vale had a good reputation for welfare, medical care and education, Abraham Darby, in the manner of Kenrick 30 years before, defended the system as preventing drunkenness on pay day and claimed that it created a more stable workforce, since if men were able to save cash, they would be freer to move to other employment. Here, the company shops were retained until 1872. Elsewhere in South Wales Truck was dying out. It had been abandoned at Tredegar by a new manager in 1853, along with the contract system, men now being paid direct by the company, and was abandoned at Blaina in 1864 following a court case. The publicity generated by the Commission report helped to end it elsewhere, as contemporary commentators noted, though the last Monmouthshire Truck Shop, at Rhymney, did not close until 1885.

Paid in Tokens?

Among the items once sold by Cadw to visitors to the ironworks were modern replicas of brass tokens issued by the Blaenavon Company for sums ranging from 3d to 7d and current between about 1860 and 1880. However, men were not quite 'paid in tokens' as popular myth claims. A number of ironworks in Monmouthshire and elsewhere struck their own token coinage, but these were different in character from the Blaenavon 'dibs' and much earlier. The root of the problem lay in a chronic shortage of small change due to the inertia and indifference of the government and the Bank of England, who ceased striking copper coins in 1775. (Even earlier, from 1740 on, this led to a rash of 'evasive' [fake] halfpennies. Matthew Boulton found that two-thirds of the money paid at tollgates was 'evasive'.) Many of the earlier tokens bear dates between 1800 and 1816. It was not until 1817 that the Bank of England was re-organized and only in the following January were 'evasive' coins declared illegal.[56] These earlier tokens were

Fig. 50 Blaenavon shop token

Fig. 51 Carmarthen ironworks halfpenny token, showing the tapping of a blast furnace like the Blaenavon examples. Note the casting channels in the floor of the pig bed.

usually well struck and designed. A number have representations of blast furnaces, forge hammers or other industrial machinery on the reverse, a useful source for industrial historians. This 'money of necessity' was sometimes controversial. When Samuel Homfray had tokens minted by Boulton and Watt to pay his Penydarren workmen in 1800, there was an outcry that went far beyond Merthyr. The ironmaster John Wilkinson issued large numbers of copper pennies bearing his portrait and the inscription 'John Wilkinson, Ironmaster', mostly struck by Matthew Boulton, laying him open to satire: 'In Greece and Rome your men of parts/ Renowned in arms or famed in arts/ On glorious coins and medals shone/ To make their deeds and persons known' – a precedent which, the poem claimed, inspired Wilkinson to 'stamp his brazen face in copper'.[57]

The Blaenavon company tokens were different and later, closer to the 'pub tokens' which many pubs, including several in Blaenavon, struck around this time (Figs. 50 & 51). In 1871 the government Truck Commissioners explained that behind the company shop was a bar (the Drum and Monkey). The shop manager supplied the men with written 'checks', which could only be taken to the bar, change being given in small coins stamped 'Blaenavon Company Shop' valued at 4d, 6d or 7d, which could only be exchanged for drinks. Thomas Parry, a draper in the company shop, tried to explain away the tokens by claiming that they were given to workmen by their 'gaffers' in return for extra work done or as a form of bonus payment, which could be exchanged for beer at the Drum and Monkey, but this was plainly contradicted by other evidence.

Lewis Browning: A Collier Historian
Lewis Browning (Fig. 52), author of *A Short History of Blaenavon*, was a working collier, the grandson of a man who had come to Blaenavon from the Forest of Dean seeking work when the first furnaces were being built. Lewis was the fourth of eight children of William Browning and his wife Margaret, born at Bunker's Hill on 24 July 1828. The family were Calvinistic Methodists, his elder brother Thomas leading the singing at Penuel Chapel, which he

Fig. 52 Lewis Browning, the miner-historian, from his Blaenavon, A Short Historical Sketch

gave up when English was introduced, not being equal to the language. A sister, Elizabeth, emigrated to Australia in 1857 with a group of local people, through a 'recruiting agent' at the canal head at Pontnewynydd.

As a boy, Lewis attended the church school. He was a bright pupil and 'something of a favourite' with Sarah Hopkins, winning some of the prizes of clothing which she gave to the pupils. His schooling entailed attending St Peter's church and in his words he had been 'a churchman from a boy', had been confirmed as an Anglican, sang in the church choir and was a Sunday School teacher and communicant. However, when he was 27 he went 'on the tramp' after a dispute with his master. Back home, he returned to the family tradition of Calvinistic Methodism.

In 1906 Lewis Browning described the perils of a miner's life. 'Twice, water from old workings carried me. Several times I was rendered unconscious by explosions, once badly burnt. Buried underneath a fall a few times, with broken bones and mangled flesh. Once, the carriage in the pit broke the slides ... and the chain came down on the carriage. If the cage had given way ... We should have been hurled to the bottom, but the engineer and the bankman knew that something was wrong and soon pulled up the slackened chain, but the cage could neither be pulled up or let down, so we had to break the sides with mandrills and guide the cage into the slides as it was pulled up. We were two men, the remainder being boys, and our danger was very great for a time.'[58]

6   PUBS, PARADES AND POPULAR CULTURE

Lewis Browning has a story of a Blaenavon man who set out to see Abergavenny Races. Having walked to the top of the Blorenge he looked at the wide panorama spread out before him and turned back home, saying he had not realized the world was so large. The story is clearly *ben trovato* and apocryphal, and many Blaenavon people had family members in America, Australia or at Hughesovska in the Ukraine, but the story does underline the geographical isolation of Blaenavon. This perhaps helps to explain the rich cultural life of choirs, brass bands, eistedfoddau and poetry. It was essentially a home-grown culture, a culture that revolved around the two polar opposites of the chapel and the pub. One visiting Roman Catholic lady remarked that in Blaenavon, the one was as numerous as the other.

An evocative photograph shows the landlord of the Royal Exchange pub in James Street seated in a rocking chair in the yard of the pub, glass in hand, on a warm summer afternoon a few years before the Great War. His wife stands behind, along with a group of favoured customers in a variety of head gear (Fig. 54).

Fig. 54 The landlord of the Royal Exchange pub in James Street, with his wife and a group of customers on a summer afternoon shortly before the Great War.

The Old Crown Hotel in North Street was, in its early days, at the upper end of a hierarchy of public houses and beerhouses that provided the framework of much of the social life of Blaenavon. Its landlord, John Griffiths, was a substantial figure, with business interests quite apart from his role as innkeeper. It was common for an iron company to build an inn, both as a profitable investment and to accommodate visitors. At Coalbrookvale, in addition to the 'ironworks, collieries and shop' the company owned the Royal Oak, though they would have been surprised had they known that their publican was the future Chartist leader Zephaniah Williams. In its later manifestation as the Drum and Monkey, the Old Crown was, to judge by Lewis Browning's comments, less select. Its position seems to have been taken over by John Griffith Williams's Red Lion in the new centre of town.

The Beer Act of 1830, designed to counter the social evils of gin, allowed any householder who paid poor rates to open a beerhouse subject to a licence fee and a certificate of good character. The result was a proliferation of pubs, which came to be seen by some as a social evil in their own right. In the 1840s the Whig reformer James Kay Shuttleworth condemned public houses not only for what he pompously called 'the abuse of spiritous and fermented liquors', but as a local hub of working-class economic and political organization where working people met 'for the pleasure of talking obscenity and scandal, if not sedition, amid the fumes of gin and the roar of drunken associates'. This was part of a broad-brush attack on popular culture, including cruelty to animals, tobacco, snuff, 'provincial dialect' and 'coarse provincial accents'. These stood in the way of the Whig ideal of an homogenized workforce, industrious, obedient, sober and politically quiet. It would not have escaped Shuttleworth's notice that pubs were the normal venues for Chartist meetings or that some of its leaders in South Wales were beerhouse keepers.[1] Kenrick, noted that in 1840 there were 38 pubs in Trevethin parish, including Pontypool and Blaenavon, and 132 beerhouses. (He opened coffee taverns at Varteg in competition with the pubs and by the 1870s they were spreading throughout South Wales.)[2]

Of the 170 pubs and beerhouses in Trevethin parish, at least 60 were in Blaenavon; in 1970 E.J. Davies was able to list 45 which had closed and 14 which then still survived.[3] Most had names which could be found anywhere in Britain, but a few had more distinctive names reflecting life in Blaenavon – the Forge Hammer, the Miners Arms and the Jolly Colliers – or its leisure pursuits, like the Footballers or the Winning Horse. The larger ones were more than mere beerhouses. By the 1860s the White Horse Assembly Rooms and the Forge Hammer Assembly Rooms were favourite places for concerts by Alabama Sam and the Tredegar Minstrels, or (a particular favourite) the Female Christy's Minstrels. A singer from the Royal Opera at Covent Garden was billed to appear on one occasion, but missed her train, to the disappointment of her large Blaenavon audience. In 1859 a party of alleged 'Aztecs' were exhibited at the Market Tavern.

Shuttleworth ignored the fact that the public houses provided venues for such leisure activities and a range of functions apart from the selling of beer. Until the town's first postman, James Smith, was appointed in 1888, incoming private mail was delivered to public houses in each district and displayed in the window to await collection. Some pubs even issued their own three penny 'pub checks' – a form of token coinage – between about 1865 and 1900. These included the Bridge End Inn, the Forge Hammer, the Griffin Hotel in Ivor Street and the Pen Ceffyl ('Horse's Head') in King Street.[4] In the 1860s 'penny

Fig. 55 By mid Victorian times, the new town centre was evolving into a lively place, with many shops, pubs and chapels. This colourful Blaenavon shop is more recent.

readings' were popular, with programmes of music, recitations and in one case 'dissolving views' on a pair of magic lanterns, though these were more associated with chapel school-rooms and the like.

The pubs were also home to the many benefit societies in the town (see below), with lodge rooms where they met and which housed their regalia and account books. The Old Benefit Club met at the Old Crown, Dic Shon-Ffyrnig Club at the Bridgend Inn, the Phoenix Club in the New Inn and the Tumble Club in the inn at Garnddyrys.[5] Dic Shon Ffyrnig Club even operated a co-operative housing project, building a row of 'Club Houses' in Queen Street for its members. George Kenrick approved of benefit societies, but complained that they spent more money on beer and processions than on the relief of the poor. When the Red Lion was looted in the election riot of 1868, the books and regalia of the Royal Vine Tree Lodge and of another benefit society which met there were lost. Lodge rooms could even be used, when necessary, by Catholic priests for the saying of Mass.

In the early 1870s the town's thirst was served by two local breweries, John Griffith Williams' Cambrian Brewery and that of his rival entrepreneur William Burgoyne, the Ivor Castle Steam Brewery, at the pub of that name. In 1884-5 Charles Francis Westlake purchased both Williams' Red Lion Hotel and his brewery. Westlake's Brewery then bought up a series of Blaenavon pubs, owning 18 by 1907, served by his brewery in Cwmavon.[6]

Odd Fellows and Amicable Women
Town and village benefit societies developed during the 18th century. Their mechanism was simple. Members met one evening a month, usually in a public house, to collect what amounted to insurance premiums against sickness or death. Conviviality naturally accompanied such meetings and some early benefit societies put aside a small sum for beer. The societies met for an annual procession and church parade, followed by a dinner and for the

funerals of members. Each society had a pair of stewards who visited the sick, making sure that those in receipt of benefits were genuinely ill. Benefits were not paid for illness caused by dissipation and, in a not uncommon rule, members convicted of murder were not eligible for funeral benefits. By 1814 some 8,400 Monmouthshire people, mostly artisans and small tradespeople, were members. At this time, fearful of 'Jacobins', official attitudes to benefit societies were ambiguous. Some early trade unions, like the Friendly Society of Ironfounders, tried to pass themselves off as benefit societies, but on the other hand thrift and self-help reduced misery and social tension and kept down the poor rate. In 1793 The Friendly Societies Act gave official recognition to societies whose rules were registered with local justices at Quarter Sessions. A list of friendly societies registered with Monmouthshire Quarter Sessions between 1836 and 1841 has some 124 entries, though some were merely rule changes to existing societies.[7] Varteg, under the influence of the teetotal ironmaster George Kenrick had a Teetotal Friendly Society. There is no evidence that the Hibernian societies founded by immigrant Irish in Newport and Abergavenny in 1839 followed suit, though Irish benefit societies made strenuous efforts to present their members as hard working and respectable.[8]

Some societies drew members from a particular trade or work group, like the Caerphilly Furnace Society for workers at the blast furnace. Others were from a particular village or settlement or were simply patrons of a particular public house. The clubs were the centres of social life and ceremonial for working people. They reduced the ever present fear of destitution through sickness and their feasts and parades fulfilled the functions of such later events as the Sunday School 'treat' and march, the Rotarian dinner or the Trade Union 'Gala'. In May 1833 the Prince Hywel Dda Lodge of Oddfellows, founded the previous year, paraded from their lodge rooms at the Ivor's Arms to the grounds of Blaenavon House and then to the church to hear a sermon from Revd James Jenkins. This was followed by a 'sumptuous dinner', with toasts, singing and speeches.[9]

Women's benefit societies were organized along similar lines, though the insurance of women presented particular problems, since they had to cope with the sickness of family members as well as their own, and in times of hardship subscriptions to a mother's club might be among the first family assets sacrificed. Most ironworks towns had female friendly societies, and The Loyal Friendship Lodge of Odd Women at the Prince of Wales Inn, Blaenavon (not a branch of the Oddfellows despite its name) followed familiar ground, with one exception. A funeral benefit of £2, plus a shilling levy from each member, was paid on death, but no sickness payments were made. This reflected that a woman was more likely to be incapacitated by childbirth or the care of sick children than by her own illness. A cash sum, which hopefully could be set aside to cover future hardship was better protection and the Blaenavon female Oddfellows were therefore a dividing society, with the accumulated funds being shared out every two years, with a sum kept in hand to re-start the process. In March 1867 the Blaenavon Oddwomen met for tea and cakes at the Prince of Wales to distribute the surplus funds.[10]

The Blaenavon Benefit Society existed by 1813 when Samuel Hopkins left £100 to 'the sick club at Blaenavon'. It was not uncommon to belong to more than one society, just as today one might have more than one insurance. In 1826 the Blaenavon Second Society was formed 'of tradesmen and others', its sponsors at Quarter Sessions being the Anglican vicar, James Jenkins; Francis James, a substantial farmer whose family had held land in Blaenavon long before the coming of the ironworks; and the innkeeper and businessman John Griffiths, in whose Crown Inn the society met.[11] Garnddyrys had its friendly society, meeting at the Victoria Inn and Pwll Du its Prince Albert benevolent society, which met at the Lamb. Revd James Jenkins was a supporter of benefit societies, on one occasion preaching to a church parade of Oddfellows on the text 'look to the ant, thou sluggard'.

From about 1830 onwards the benefit societies were supplemented by the new 'affili-ated orders', centrally organized bodies like the Oddfellows. These had the advantage in a migrant society that an accredited Oddfellow or Forester in search of work could be assured of friendship, help and in the last resort a decent funeral from his brethren in those parts.

A number of 18th-century local societies called themselves 'Oddfellows' and references to 'Good Fellows' or 'Good Fellowship' (the last phrase appearing in the 1793 Act) show the origin of the name. From about 1814 various Oddfellows clubs around Manchester formed the Order of Oddfellows, Manchester Unity. They were followed by the Ancient Order of Foresters, whose 'Pride of Blaenavon' Lodge opened in 1845 and by Druids, Ancient Britons, Ancient Romans (founded by a schoolmaster with classical tastes), Ivorites, Free Gardeners, Shepherds and Comical Fellows. Individual branches were often combined into districts – 'Grand Groves' for the Druids, or 'Senates' for the Romans. The Oddfellows with their Lodges, Grand Masters and regalia borrowed from the Freemasons – Adam was the first Oddfellow, just as Noah was the first Druid. In 1831 the Prince Howel the Good (or Hywel Dda) Lodge, no.541 of the Independent Order of Oddfellows was established in Blaenavon, the *Monmouthshire Merlin* being quick to point out that this was not a 'Union Club'. They soon made their mark in the town. The following March they gave a funeral to a brother Oddfellow, a stranger, said to have been the finest seen since that of Samuel Hopkins.[12] In 1834 the role of Justices of the Peace in the registration of friendly societies was dropped and in 1846 John Tidd Pratt, a lawyer, was appointed the first national regis-trar of friendly societies. The Philanthropic Order of True Ivorites was a Welsh language benefit society, founded in 1836 and confined to Wales. The Blaenavon Lodge met at the Ivor's Arms and according to Lewis Browning conducted their business in Welsh for 48 years.

By 1866 there were 13 friendly societies in Blaenavon, with an overall value above £5,500 and 1,500 members. The Hywel Dda Lodge of the Order of Philanthropists (having changed Order from that of the Oddfellows) was the largest, with 236 members and a capital of over £1,500, but six others had memberships of well over 100. The Ivor Hael Lodge had 146 members and during the year had paid out £96 in sick pay and £28 in funeral benefits. The Victoria and Albert Lodge, Manchester Unity, founded in 1840, had 140 members and a value of £1,247. Over the year it had paid out over £100 in sick pay and £42 in funeral costs. Beside these were minnows like the Prince Llewelyn and the Rose of Sharon societies with around 50 members and net values of £40-£100.[13]

Browning described the benefit societies in Blaenavon as if in a procession: the Old Benefit Club, from the Crown Inn, with its brass band and banners; Dic Shon Ffyrnig's Club from the Bridgend Inn, with red ribbons tied in true lover's knots round their hats;

the Phoenix Club from the New Inn with banners and yellow ribbons tied round their hats; the Garnddyrys Tumble Club, the Ivorites, the Philanthropists and the Oddfellows.[14]

By 1875 one in five of the total population of Glamorgan, regardless of age and sex, were members of a registered friendly society. In the same decade there were 489 societies existing in Monmouthshire, plus 29 female societies, though the latter were extinct by 1910, faced with women's exclusions from some occupations and changing attitudes to the role of women in society.[15]

Processions

In many societies, an important method of affirming its unity, the status of certain individuals within it and the role of particular groups within the community is by the marking of special occasions or dates with formal processions, with costumes and regalia, with the members of those groups parading in due order according to their status. This is often accompanied by feasting or other merriment. These ceremonies could be particularly important for groups sometimes perceived as marginal to that society, as O'Leary has explained in relation to the Irish in South Wales,[16] Blaenavon was no exception. The Friendly Societies processed to mark their anniversaries with banners, regalia and bands, often making a call at the big house – Ty Mawr – to pay their respects to the ironmasters before a church service followed by a dinner, with speeches, toasts and songs.[17]

Whereas the Benefit Society parades were solely male events, the annual Sunday School Whitsun walk and the Catholic Corpus Christi parade were family occasions, with the adults in their best suits and dresses and the children in new clothes bought for the occasion. The banners which invariably accompanied the marches proclaimed the role within the community of the participants, with suitable inscriptions and (as appropriate) Biblical scenes or slogans of workers' solidarity. Until very recently the May Day 'Miners Gala' in Cardiff was a major event.[18]

Such events were essentially home grown, but Blaenavon was still a company town and some of the grandest processions and celebrations marked the marriage of a member of the Kennard family or new developments in the works. In September 1856 the opening of the new puddling forges was celebrated with a procession of 3,000 people, the firing of cannon, a roasted sheep provided by Mr D. Ely, the 'worthy landlord' of the Market Tavern, a competition to climb a greasy pole for a shoulder of mutton and a barrel of beer subscribed for by the tradespeople of the town. In 1860 the opening of the new mill on Forgeside saw the town decorated with greenery and arches across the streets, banners with appropriate slogans, cannons firing and a procession headed by the directors and agents of the company and the Blaina Brass Band. They were followed by the Oddfellows, Philanthropists and Ivorites in full regalia and the Blaenavon Fife and Drum Band, with the Blaenavon Brass Band bringing up the rear. The crowds eventually dispersed to the lodge rooms of the various friendly societies 'to drink success to the Company' with the help of 1 shilling and 6 pence given by the company to each workman. When E.P. Martin, the general manager, returned from a visit to America the following year he was greeted by a band and a choir, whilst the town was decorated with flags.[19]

Popular Entertainments

Victorian Blaenavon had a lively cultural life, with choirs and poets, brass bands and eisteddfodau. Apart from the Blaenavon band, both Pwll Du and Garnddyrys had brass bands and there was also the Good Templer brass band. That at Garnddyrys was under the blacksmith composer and bandmaster Gwilym Gwent (William Aubrey Williams) before he emigrated to Pennsylvania in 1872, and there were men like the miner composer Richard Roberts from Garn Pits. Members of the Pwll Du band also emigrated to Pennsylvania, where they founded a second Pwll Du brass band. [20]

Outside entertainment was always a welcome novelty however in this isolated community. Until late in the century, itinerant ballad singers were still visiting the town selling broadsheet ballads. Levi Gibbon (1814-1869), a blind ballad singer from west Wales, who accompanied himself on a fiddle singing songs he had composed, was led about by his teenage daughter. Converted in the 1859 religious revival, he changed what he called his 'worthless and depraved ballads' for new ones, 'pure edifying and religious'. 'Bob the Ballad Singer' was found dead in a hayloft near the Lion Inn in 1879, and when Benjamin Marsh was prosecuted over the alleged indecency of some of his ballads in 1896 he complained that he had been coming to Blaenavon 'selling songs' for 20 years without any problems.[21]

Travelling theatre companies like Poole and Young's Amusing and Instructive Entertainment or Hord's Theatre were popular. In 1886 an 'American Theatre' set up in Lion Square with a melodrama *Garcia*, based on the Llangybi murders which had caused such a sensation eight years earlier, when an entire family had been murdered by a Spanish seaman (see p.117). This played to large audiences, but later plays were less popular and the company moved to Abergavenny.[22]

The introduction of an early closing day for shops in the early 1860s increased the amount of available leisure time for many. In 1861 a 'Blaenavon early closing day amusement society' was formed, though one writer to a local paper wondered what people would find to do, since 'there is nothing to be seen here but fire and smoke and nothing to be heard but the roaring blast and the rattling forge'.[23]

Libraries and Institutes

Around 1859 a public library was started in Blaenavon. Seven years later its books were inherited by a Mutual Improvement Society founded by 'several respectable tradesmen' and housed in one of the company's mineral offices with a reading room and circulating library.[24] Edward Kennard gave £25 for books and a copy of his work *Transatlantic Sketches* (1865), whilst Queen Victoria presented a signed copy of her book *Journal of My Life in the Highlands* (1886). In 1883 the Mutual Improvement Society was replaced by an Institute in Lion Street, with a reading room on the ground floor and a billiard hall above.[25] Pontypool possessed a Mechanics Institute (the only one in Monmouthshire) and 'reading society' by 1840, whilst a library and reading room had opened at Tredegar in 1849, but it did not flourish. In 1852 Dowlais acquired a library founded by the Guests and in the same year Ebbw Vale under Thomas Brown established a Literary and Scientific Institution in a purpose-built building funded by the company. Apart from these two relatively progressive iron companies, at Tredegar a second library and institute were founded in 1869 and

Fig. 56 The Workmen's Hall and War Memorial. (Photograph by Simon Hardy)

a Literary and Scientific Society in 1877. This attracted speakers like the explorers H.M. Stanley and Frederik Nansen, as well as housing musical events and lectures on a variety of topics. Later, the young Aneurin Bevan was much involved in both institutions. New Tredegar and Merthyr Vale collieries had libraries by 1880, Blaina in 1884, Abercarn in 1888, and Risca in 1894.[26]

In 1895 the Workmen's Hall and Institute opened in Blaenavon, designed by the architect E.A. Lansdowne of Newport and built of Pennant sandstone, quarried at Newbridge near the Crumlin Viaduct, and buff-coloured Ebbw Vale brick, with stamped terracotta panels (Fig. 56). Constructed by a local builder, John Morgan, it cost £10,000, of which £9,000 had been raised by contributions of a halfpenny a week by the people of Blaenavon. The foundation stone was laid by Robert Kennard in front of a large crowd. Under the stone was a time capsule, with current coins and newspapers and photographs of royalty and of members of the Kennard family. The building soon became a popular venue for concerts and lectures, though the Sunday evening entertainment in 1908 with a bioscope was disturbed by rowdy young people in the gallery. It had a library of over 3,000 volumes, with its own salaried librarian, a reading room, magazine room, billiard hall, committee and board rooms and a theatre with balcony, capable of holding an audience of 1,500. Billiards was popular, whether for a Championship Shield or 'friendlies' between Liberals and Conservatives or Married versus Single. Subscribers paid three pence a week and Richard Kramhan was appointed to collect the dues.

In 1861, after a lecture on co-operatives, an Industrial and Provident Society (no.539) was set up, which in 1889 became Blaenavon Co-operative Society, operating out of the Workmen's Hall. Jack Jones, novelist and ex-miner from the Rhondda wrote that 'The

Workmen's Halls ... have been the political, social and cultural centres of such places as the Rhondda ... Singing festivals, Shakespearean festivals, Eisteddfodau, oratorios, operas, dramas, go-as-you-please competitions, drama week competitions, celebrity concerts, Miners Federation meetings and demonstrations, Workers Educational Association ... and Y.M.C.A. lecture courses, all at the Workmen's Halls. And ever so many other things.'[27]

Some Eisteddfodau offered prizes for a history of their town. There may have been some sort of guide or template, for they often follow a common pattern. Evan Powell's *History of Tredegar* was written as an entry for a 'chair' eisteddfod, offering a ceremonial chair for the winning poet, held in 1884. In 1902 the Tredegar Workmen's Library offered a prize for an update, bringing the history of the town down to the opening of the new century. The prize was won by Powell's brother and son. The republication of Powell's *Tredegar* with its added update may have inspired Lewis Browning, whose history of Blaenavon was published four years later. Several manuscript histories of Ebbw Vale, written as eisteddfod entries, survive in the library of the Literary and Scientific Institution there. One of these, still unpublished, was so well regarded locally that copies were borrowed by families who would then transcribe a family copy, rather in the tradition of the copying of medieval manuscripts.

Gentlemen versus Players – The Rise of Organized Sport

Popular sport had two very different origins. Spectator sports were often organized by publicans with semi-professional working class athletes and heavy betting on the outcome (to say nothing of enhanced beer sales). When a 'pugilistic encounter' took place in Blaenavon in 1868, the 'disgraceful proceedings' were stopped by the police after the fourth round. Lewis Browning recalled prizefights on the mountains between Dai Andro and Will Keare or between Tom Morgan and the shoemaker John Morris. This world of semi-professional runners, publicans and bookmakers is vividly depicted in several of Arthur Morrison's Martin Hewitt detective stories. One popular craze was 'pedestrianism' – long distance walking feats, often of an eccentric character, by semi-professional walkers, sponsored by publicans, with heavy betting on the outcome. In July 1870 one such athlete walked from Blaenavon to Pontypool and back four times, for ten miles walking backwards. On another occasion, a Blaenavon man, Walter Davies, for a bet, pushed his wife Louise in a pram from Blaenavon to the Goose and Cuckoo several miles away, whilst playing a mouth organ.[28]

Most organized sport had a very different background. Football and cricket were spread from English public schools and universities by young sporting Anglican vicars and curates, and from the alumni of Llandovery College and St David's College Lampeter.[29] Threats of French invasion in 1859 and the rise of Prussia led to concerns over the military fitness of the urban working class, leading eventually to organizations such as the Boy Scouts and the Boys' Brigade. In English cities like London and Manchester football clubs founded by church Bible classes or the Y.M.C.A, or from the workers of a particular factory developed into household names like (Woolwich) Arsenal, Aston Villa or Tottenham Hotspur. The Football Association of Wales was founded in 1876 and played its first International the same year. By the mid 1880s, Association Football had become a mass spectator sport and the English middle class retreated into rugby and cricket. In many sports, 'gentleman amateurs' sought to exclude anyone who competed for money, or any 'mechanic, artisan or labourer'. For many years, the annual Gentlemen versus Players match was a major fixture in the First Class Cricket calendar.

Cricket was being played at Blaenavon by 1859 and a cricket club was founded in 1871. The 1870s saw a huge increase in the popularity of rugby, which unlike cricket did not require expensive clothes and equipment (though in Blaenavon, cricket was often played with makeshift bats and stumps).[30] Clubs were formed at Abergavenny, Ebbw Vale, Merthyr, Mountain Ash, Brecon and elsewhere. By the later years of the century there were some 30 Rugby clubs in the town. Blaenavon Rugby Football Club (previously Blaenavon Wanderers) played its first game on 8 November 1877, against Abergavenny. The game was a draw, but by 1899 the club had produced its first Welsh international, Reg Skrimshire, a civil engineer and old boy of Monmouth School. He was the first of an illustrious series, including Ken Jones, Terry Cobner, John Perkins and Mark Taylor.[31] Meanwhile, as most of what was left of the South Welsh steel industry retreated to the coast, the new workers from the English West Midlands brought their own code of Association Football with them, resulting in the founding of Cardiff City and Newport County, 'the Ironsides', the latter by workers at Lysaghts Orb Works in 1912, with W.R. Lysaght as president and financial backer. In Blaenavon, soccer teams were formed by chapels, youth clubs and areas of the town. Blaenavon Corinthians began in 1922 from a Sunday School class in King Street Baptist Church (Bethel). In 1947 Blaenavon Blues were formed.[32]

In 1922 a new recreation ground was opened on Forgeside, incorporating the Rugby Club's playing field, replacing the older venue of Coffee Tavern field. Ken Jones, born in Blaenavon the same year, began his career as a future international rugby player, with 45 caps for Wales, and as an Olympic athlete, in the Blaenavon Schools Junior XV whilst a pupil at the Church Boys Endowed Junior School. After West Monmouth Grammar School (West Mon) and the R.A.F. he was married in St Peter's church and after a distinguished career playing for Newport and Wales was eventually buried from there.[33]

7   BROUGHT FORTH IN A HIGH PLACE: RELIGION, LANGUAGE AND THE PEOPLE OF BLAENAVON

Abergavenny had a tradition of independence in religious matters. The medieval priory of St Mary, a daughter of the French abbey of St Vincent in Le Mans, had little influence in the town. When in the 15th century the townsfolk raised funds for new bells, even performing plays in neighbouring villages, the monks, as Professor Glanmor Williams commented, 'never contributed a halfpenny. And this in their own priory church.'[1] By the 17th century, the town had a flourishing community of Catholic recusants and a pioneer Baptist cause.[2] During the so-called Popish Plot, the vicar of Abergavenny complained that more people attended the illegal Catholic chapel in the main street than went to his own church. Many families had both Catholic and Protestant branches and relations between the faiths were relaxed, save when outsiders muddied the waters. One prominent Abergavenny man felt it necessary to preface his will with the trenchant statement that he was a Protestant, and no Papist or Anabaptist.[3] This was the religious tradition which Blaenavon inherited.

The Old Dissent

Charles Herbert, vicar of Abergavenny at the time of the Civil War, was deprived of his living and replaced by a Baptist Puritan, John Abbott. In 1653, St Mary's Priory was the scene of a remarkable five-hour public debate on infant baptism between Baptists led by Abbott and John Tombes of Leominster on one side and local Anglican clergy on the other.[4] Abbott's hearers later divided on the issue of open or closed communion (whether non-members might be admitted). The closed communion group appointed a local man, William Pritchard, as Minister and first broke bread in communion in August 1652. After the Restoration, forbidden to meet in a town under the Act of Uniformity, they moved to Llanwenarth. Given land for a chapel by Christopher Price, an apothecary and coal lessee, by 1688 they had 80 members.[5]

By the time of the building of the ironworks, the members of Llanwenarth included William James and his wife, from Ton Mawr farm in Blaenavon. His brother, Francis James, was a member of Penygarn Baptists in Pontypool, which had been founded in 1727. Within a few years, ministers from the two chapels were preaching at their farmhouse.[6] By 1807 the group meeting at Ton Mawr had 30 members. Francis James sold them a piece of land, Cae William Llewelyn, for 5 shillings and Old Horeb Meeting House was built on the site for £400.[7] It bore a datestone of 1822. Three years later a quarrel over the appointment of a minister led 81 members to leave, founding Ebenezer Chapel. This was part of a wider split among the Baptists of the new industrial area between the conservative Calvinist orthodoxy of rural Wales and the slightly more liberal theology associated with the ex-wrestler Andrew Fuller and his supporter J.P. Davies of Tredegar. The Fullerite slogan 'Christ died for all men', not just the elect, had social and political overtones. If Christ died for all men, might not some argue that all men should have the vote? It also reflected the impact on Welsh rural society of the new people, and new values, of the ironfield. Both Old Horeb (not on its present site) and Ebenezer stood conveniently near the stream Nant Llywetrog, used for open air baptisms. By 1839 there were 34 Baptist churches in Monmouthshire, 20 Welsh and 14 English, with a total membership of around 4,000.[8]

The Methodists

If the Baptists represented an indigenous tradition of dissent, rooted in the Puritan ideals of the 17th century, the Methodists, in their various connections, provided a common tradition and ideology for social groups in the new industrial towns. The Wesleyans – 'the established church of dissent' – rejected Calvinist predestination in favour of universal salvation by works. High Tory in the early 19th century, they recruited among the English-speaking managers and foremen. They first appeared in the county around Chepstow at the turn of the century (Earlswood 1799, Chepstow 1807, Caldicot 1810) and only reached the industrial uplands later. In Blaenavon, they first met in a converted malt house, but in 1839-40 James Ashwell built a new Wesleyan chapel, set between two rows of houses in what became known as Chapel Row. According to Lewis Browning, this was through the influence of Thomas Deakin.

The Calvinists, equally conservative and noted for their hostility to Unions, Benefit Societies and Chartism, recruited among Welsh-speaking small contractors, artisans and colliers. They were the first Methodist group to arrive in Blaenavon. Their first chapel, Capel y Graig or Rock Chapel, was said to date from 1799, though its first register dates from 1813. Within a few years a new chapel, Penuel, replaced it, close to the ironworks, just in time to appear on Thomas Deakin's map of 1819. The move was due to the company's need to use the site of Rock Chapel as a cinder tip. Penuel remained an important centre of Welsh language culture in Blaenavon for the rest of the century. Wesleyans and Calvinists did not usually compete, since the former were English-speaking, the latter Welsh. Only when the Merthyr-based minister Edward Jones set up a Welsh Wesleyan cause in 1805 did a demarcation dispute arise. Tredegar, as usual, was the storm centre. The Calvinists brought up one of their leading debaters, the Blaenavon Calvinist Methodist stonemason, builder and coal-level owner Aaron Brute, who, according to our strongly pro-Wesleyan source, got the worst of the argument.[9]

The Primitive Methodists arrived in 1823, one of the founders being Thomas Browning, who had come to Blaenavon 30 years before from the Forest of Dean, where he had been a 'Ranter'. Their first chapel was built six years later.[10]

The Welsh Congregationalists

Among the new arrivals at Blaenavon were Welsh-speaking Congregationalists from west Wales who first met together on Christmas Day 1820 in a building on the Afon road and

Fig. 57 Bethlehem Congregationalist Chapel. The existing building is of 1864

named their chapel Bethlehem in memory of this. This was built in 1821 and enlarged in 1829. Their first ministers were Revd Harris (Harris bach Blaenavon) and Revd Thomas Griffiths (Griffiths bach Blaenavon). Lewis Browning knew Edward Williams, a miner in Dick Keare's slope and Congregationalist preacher, whose stall in the mine Browning took over when Williams felt a call to the full-time ministry. He was a well-known bard and author of prize essays on the role of the Sunday School teacher and the evils of the drink trade. In 1847, the Congregationalists of Bethlehem moved to a new chapel in the centre of town. This was rebuilt in 1864, the architect being Revd Thomas Thomas of Landore, a prolific designer of chapels (Fig. 57).[11]

The Established Church

Blaenavon's high moorland included parts of five parishes, whose medieval churches lay below in the valleys of the Usk and Afon Llwyd. A small late medieval chapel of ease, with no known dedication, served the spiritual needs of the area. The ruins of Capel Newydd are south-east of Blaenavon, beside the Llanover Road (Fig. 58). Visitors in the 19th century found a rectangular chapel, 32ft by 16ft (2 x 1 poles in medieval measures of length) within a stone-walled enclosure. It had a west porch and two small windows on the south side (as with many small Gwent churches there were no openings in the north wall). First mentioned in 1577, a deed of 1628 named four trustees – Evan William ap William, Rees Hoskyn ap Meyric, Morgan Hywel David and Jenkin Howel Loid (Lloyd). A stone bore the date of 1736. After the building of St Peter's church in Blaenavon in 1805 the chapel was seen as 'cramped, poorly maintained and unimpressive'. By 1851 services were only held in the summer, 'the situation being too stormy for winter services' and the church 'of little use

Fig. 58 The site of Capel Newydd today. (Photograph by Nathan Matthews)

since the building of Blaenafon church'. The afternoon summer services were held in Welsh by the vicar, Revd John Jones, at a time when St Peter's was wholly English in language. Capel Newydd was finally demolished in 1863, the year after John Jones died.[12]

On St Peter's Day, 29 June 1805, St Peter's church at Blaenavon was opened for worship. Paid for by Thomas Hill, it cost £3,000 (Fig. 59). The elegant cast iron font on its baluster stem, like a Georgian wine glass, bears the date 1805 (Fig. 60). St Peters was the first new Anglican church of the ironfield, just as Sarah Hopkins' school of 1815, built in memory of her brother next to the church, was the first ironworks school in Wales. In time the churchyard came to have a number of cast iron grave covers made in the works

Fig. 59 St Peter's church and churchyard. (Photograph by Nathan Matthews)

Fig. 60 The elegant cast iron font of 1805 in St Peter's church. (Photograph by Nathan Matthews)

in a West Midlands tradition. Hill took care to provide a Welsh-speaking vicar; James Jenkins was from a Carmarthenshire farming family, son of the vicar of Mydrym and Brechfa north of Llandeilo Fawr.[13] Again, West Midland influence is apparent in the provision of a church. Thomas Hill's father left £200 in 1782 to build a school at Waste Bank, Lye, an industrial hamlet of Stourbridge with a rough reputation. Thomas Hill himself added the present parish church. A kinsman of Benjamin Pratt built the little red brick church school which still stands beside Chaddesley Corbet churchyard and Sarah Hopkins was involved in founding a girls' school and almshouse in her native Rugeley in Staffordshire.[14]

The old pattern of parish and manor remained strong. Until 1860, Blaenavon was simply the Ecclesiastical district of Blaenavon with Capel Newydd. The parish was then created (in the same year that Blaenavon became an Urban District) out of parts of Llanover, Llanfoist, Llanwenarth, Aberystruth and Trevethin. James Jenkins, vicar until 1841, noted in his church register events such as the Cinder Pit disaster of 1838 and carefully recorded the birthplaces of strangers dying in Blaenavon, lest relatives should seek news of them. He also copied into the register a recipe for the cure of the bite of a mad dog.[15] Dyne Steel remembered his long sermons in Welsh as one of the trials of his boyhood. When he became vicar to the secluded ironmasters' villas at Llanfoist, many nonconformist shopkeepers joined with the Anglicans to present him with a costly piece of silver plate.[16] His successor, John Jones, was vicar until 1885. He was a fine preacher in Welsh or English and kept up afternoon services in Welsh at Capel Newydd. It was he who preached to the Oddfellows on the text 'Look to the ant, thou sluggard, consider her ways and be wise' (*Proverbs 6.6.*) praising thrift and persuading many to join the Friendly Society.

Alfred Ollivant, appointed in 1850, was the first fully resident Bishop of Llandaff since 1706. A former Professor of Divinity at Cambridge, he had learnt Welsh whilst Vice Principal of St David's College, Lampeter and when St Peter's church was re-opened in July 1851 after enlargement he preached in Welsh.[17] Under J.L. Clougher, vicar of Blaenavon from 1885, new churches were opened. St James's, Cwmafon, 'the iron church' of 1888, was built of wood, but clad in corrugated iron. After its environs had been encroached on by slag from the ironworks it was replaced in 1911 by New St James's on land given by the Blaenavon company and built of ashlar blocks stripped from the disused Nos 4 and

Fig. 60 St James's Church, uphill from the ironworks, was built in 1912-13, using stone taken from the casings of nos.4 and 5 furnaces. It replaced an 'iron' church, of corrugated iron and timber, with the same dedication. St James's became disused in 1970. (Photograph by Simon Hardy)

5 furnaces in the ironworks (Fig. 60). Dedicated in 1914, with Revd Watkin Edwards as its first curate, it closed in 1970. St Paul's, Llanover Road and St John's were built in 1893, the former from stone salvaged from Capel Newydd. Designed by the architect E.A. Lansdowne of Newport, at that time also at work on the new Workmen's Hall, and constructed by a local builder John Burgoyne, it retains architectural features from Capel Newydd, including the stone altar. The new churches were served by curates, mostly graduates of the University of Durham.[18]

New Peoples, New English Causes

Until the influx of English immigrants in the boom years of 1824-5, the chapel people of Blaenavon worshipped God in Welsh in a predominantly Welsh society. Streets had names like Heol Garegog – 'stony road' – (now Hill Street) or Heol y Nant – 'Brook street' – (now Broad Street), and people were known by names like Twm Cerrig Calch ('Tom Limestone'), Shoni Tafarn ('John the Pub') and Peggi Rysun (? Peggy the Rose). In Tredegar English language chapels opened in 1825 for Wesleyan Methodists and in 1829 for English Baptists. Many of the new immigrants came from the West Midlands, homeland of the Primitive Methodists. Their origins, like that of the Bible Christians, lay in itinerant evangelists in remote upland areas – the Cheshire-Staffordshire border for the Primitive Methodists, north Devon for the Bible Christians. Both fell out with their Methodist establishments during the Napoleonic wars, when the Government was nervous of 'Jacobins' and unlicensed preaching and legislation against nonconformity was a possibility. One characteristic feature of both – the open air 'camp meeting' – was borrowed from the pamphlets of an American evangelist. The Primitives emerged as a distinct Methodist tradition in 1812, the Bible Christians in 1815-6. By 1820 the Primitives had spread to Shropshire.

Blaenavon's Primitive Methodist chapel of 1829 was among the earliest in Monmouthshire. Elsewhere in the county they were not widespread until the mid 1840s – another reminder that Blaenavon, on the edge of the ironfield, had a high proportion of English immigrants. The baptismal register shows that over 75% of men among the congregation were colliers or labourers, with around 10% craftsmen (blacksmiths, masons, brickmakers etc) and a few small tradesmen and shopkeepers. There were few ironworkers.[19]

In 1821 the Bible Christians set out to 'send missionaries into the dark and destitute parts of the United Kingdom' and soon after began work in Monmouthshire. Their first chapel opened in Tintern in 1826. From here, they spread into the Trellech-Shirenewton uplands. In 1851 they reached Pontnewynydd at the head of the Monmouthshire canal and in January 1861 met for the first time in their new chapel at Blaenavon. They were a lively evangelical sect, with camp meetings in the Waun field. They kept up their connection with south-west England, with preachers from Cornwall or Devon at anniversaries or special services. As with the Primitive Methodists, women preachers were common. When their King Street chapel re-opened in 1861, Miss Jollow from Devonshire delivered three sermons.[20]

According to George Kenrick, the great majority of houses in Blaenavon possessed a Bible and out of a population of just over 5,000, only a tenth did not attend a place of worship. Of about 1,000 children under the age of 3, only 306 went to school (the Hopkins Free School), but 545 attended Sunday School.[21] The following decade saw a religious

Fig. 61 Horeb Baptist Chapel, 1866, designed by Thomas Thomas,
a Blaenavon civil engineer. (Photograph by Simon Hardy)

revival which, starting in America in 1858, spread across the Atlantic with a returning Welsh American minister from Cardiganshire. By autumn 1859 it had reached Gwent, spreading from Welsh Congregationalists to the English groups. Methodist colliers met for daily underground prayer meetings and Primitive Methodist tea parties attracted crowds of six or seven hundred. When, in September 1860, a brickyard girl, Martha Booth, was killed at an accident at the pugging mill, where the clay for the bricks was mixed in a hand-driven rotary mill, overflow crowds filled the Primitive Methodist chapel and the street outside. The vicar John Jones announced at the graveside a sermon which he preached the following Sunday on the text 'Two women shall be grinding at the mill. One shall be taken and one left.' This drew many to join the churches and chapels.[22] The following year, Calvinists, Primitive Methodists and Bible Christians were all enlarging their chapels. Within a few years, the Baptists of Horeb found their chapel too small and New Horeb opened opposite the parish church in 1866, designed by Thomas Thomas, a Blaenavon civil engineer, not to be confused with Revd Thomas Thomas of Landore (Fig. 61). Their old chapel was leased to the new English Congregationalists and then to the Wesleyans. Eight years later, Zion Chapel opened across the river near the present Big Pit, for the colliers and steelworkers of Forgeside.

The Roman Catholic Community and the Franciscan Mission

The 1860s also saw developments in religion and education among the Roman Catholic community, echoing what was happening in other Churches at this time. By the 18th century the Roman Catholic community in Monmouthshire, once a stronghold of recusant Catholicism, had shrunk to a small remnant. One source claimed that there were only 750 Roman Catholics in all Wales. That was to change with Irish migration. In June 1829 the *Monmouthshire Merlin* noted how day after day destitute Irish families were arriving in Newport from Bristol. 'We trust', said the *Merlin*, 'that tranquility will soon return to our unhappy sister island.' Immigration continued during the terrible famine years of 1845-51. Many Irish people settled around Pontypool, particularly in Abersychan and Varteg. In 1836 St Alban's church, Pontypool was founded and by 1840 Mass was being celebrated by a visiting priest in a room in the British Lion inn at Varteg. Other priests were saying mass in the club rooms of pubs in Merthyr and Rhymney.[23]

In 1860, at the request of Bishop Thomas Brown of the short-lived Catholic see of Newport, an Italian Capuchin Franciscan friar from Pant Asaph in Flintshire, Elzear Torreggiani, who previously had been head of a house of Capuchin Franciscans at Peckham in London and was later bishop of Armidale in New South Wales, accompanied by a lay brother, were sent to a Catholic mission in Pontypool which had been established shortly before 1846. Initially there were problems of language and culture. Many of the settlers only knew their prayers and catechism in Irish, and their children not even that, and some did not want a 'foreign priest'. Soon however mass was being said fortnightly in Blaenavon by a Father Honorius, at the house of the shopkeeper William George in King Street. When his family fell on hard times, a room over a shop – 'A wretched place ... accessible only by a sort of step ladder' – was fitted up as a chapel.[24]

In 1863 an Oxford lady, Mary Peterson, a recent Catholic convert who had felt a call to work among the poor, set up a Roman Catholic school in Abersychan, Torreggiani providing advice. The school, 'a plain, substantial gothic building on a breezy hill', opened in September that year, under the patronage of Mrs Herbert of Llanarth, with bands and benefit clubs parading with their banners. The following year she was joined by a lady member of the Third Order of St Francis and 'Blaenavon being the least attractive region of all the district was ... the one she interested herself in'. A school room and chapel dedicated to the Sacred Heart near King Street opened on 18 May 1868, with a fife band leading a procession of priests and Sisters of Mercy.[25]

Mary Peterson was probably the author of *Franciscan Missions among the Colliers and Ironworkers of Monmouthshire*. Blaenavon was a very different place to the comfortable world of Oxford and Chislehurst and the comments by an upper middle class outsider of different religious views are predictable: 'Blaenavon is completely a colony of colliers and ironworkers ... [with no] ... shops and a vast army of publicans. Dissenting chapels rival the public houses in number and variety. It is no uncommon thing for father and mother, and each member of a family, to belong to a different sect.'[26]

English and Welsh in the Chapels
By the later 1850s the English language was making significant inroads into the Welsh chapels, partly through the latter's wish to reach the immigrant English community. The Congregationalists were early in the field. Dr Thomas Rees, historian and preacher, earlier a shopkeeper victim of the Scotch Cattle and later author of *Protestant Nonconformity in Wales* (1861), was a key figure, aided by wealthy Congregationalists from Bristol and Bath, notably the tobacco brothers W.D. and H.O. Wills. English causes were founded at Ebbw Vale (1843), Beaufort (1849) and Brynmawr (1851-3), often through groups leaving Welsh language chapels to found English-speaking causes. In March 1863, 12 members of Bethlehem Chapel separated, at the suggestion of the minister, to form an English Congregational chapel. They met first in the Town Hall, then in Old Horeb, vacated by the Baptists. When Horeb was bought by the Wesleyans, they moved back to the Town Hall. The only satisfactory solution was to build their own chapel. They quickly raised £1,000 from wealthy Bristol Dissenters like Samuel Morley M.P. and the Wills brothers. The architect of the new chapel, in the restrained Gothic style favoured by the Congregationalists, was Revd Thomas Thomas of Landore, who designed many such chapels in a distinctive architectural style.[27] It opened in June 1868. The creation of a separate English Congregationalist chapel in the long run helped to preserve Bethlehem as a Welsh language chapel, the last in Blaenavon.

The Baptists, 'The most Anglicised and Anglicising denomination', founded a Monmouthshire English Baptist Association in 1857 to create 'English churches in the destitute parts of the county'. An English Baptist cause, Moriah, opened in Blaenavon's Broad Street in 1847. In 1851 it was explained that it was known as the English Baptist Chapel 'as there is no other English Baptist Chapel in the place'. After the death of Francis Hiley, 'Y Corn Arian' ('the silver trumpet') of Llanwenarth in 1860, English appeared in the oldest of Monmouthshire Baptist chapels and when Bradney wrote in 1906, Welsh was only used there on special occasions. In the countryside around Abergavenny, the Welsh Baptist church in Llandewi Rhydderch changed to English in 1850, that in neighbouring Llanvapley in 1870.[28]

Comments in the local press on the use of English and Welsh in chapels were particularly common in the 1860s. The issue was a very live one at this time. By the following decade the language issue was dividing Blaenavon chapels and spilling over into the press once again. When Samuel Owen, the Welsh Congregational minister of Bethlehem, complained of the evangelistic methods of Moriah in January 1874, he drew the reply that they were doing their best 'to instruct the ignorant and polish the rude and would earnestly invite him to attend some of the classes'. The resulting correspondence was hardly edifying.[29] Most Welsh language chapels in Blaenavon were now bilingual, often with the morning service, traditionally for members, in Welsh, the evening service, for the wider community, in English. At Horeb, an energetic young Pembrokeshire-born minister, D.E. Jones, did away with this pattern in 1880, and took both services in English. Attendances increased, though 'a few of the old Welsh members' disliked the change. Ebenezer continued as a Welsh language chapel. In 1888 Moriah (now Blaenavon Evangelical Church) in Broad Street was rebuilt in a neo-Venetian classical style – a bold statement of the strength of the English Baptist cause in the town (Fig. 62).[30]

King Street Baptists originated from quarrels within Horeb, just as Ebenezer had done. The democratic autonomy of Baptist chapels left little room for external mediation. Where a group of deacons clashed with their minister, he might find support among other members, who could circulate a petition on his behalf, or organize a straw poll. If the deacons failed to command a majority, they might be forced to resign. The minister of Ebenezer survived just such a crisis shortly before the Horeb affair, when his supporters organized a testimonial and he had withdrawn his resignation.

The Horeb affair may have involved the language issue and differences over the need to evangelise the new English immigrants. Matters came to a head on a July evening in 1878 when, after a stormy meeting, the minister, William Rees, gave notice and simultaneously the entire diaconate resigned. Rees' supporters organized a canvass, which showed that only 50 of the 240 members supported the deacons. Within a few weeks, this minority group was meeting in a schoolroom and raised money to buy the old Primitive Methodist chapel in King Street, the Primitives having moved to their new Gothic church of Bethel in Broad Street.[31] The break-away group began a

Fig. 62 Moriah, the first English language Baptist church in Blaenavon, was rebuilt in a neo-Venetian style in 1888. (Photograph by Simon Hardy)

vigorous campaign aimed at the English-speaking population. Well-heated (an attraction to many in this time of unemployment and depression), with pews replacing the old benches, the new chapel set out to attract a congregation. Their weekly 'Penny Readings', aimed at English speakers and those outside the orbit of the chapels, were hugely popular, but drew criticism from those who thought that popular music, often part of penny readings, should be left to the ungodly.

Owen Tidman, the vigorous young minister in King Street, an Englishman originally from Bradford-on-Avon in Wiltshire, was a radical and politically a leading Liberal in the town; he and his wife were active in providing food and clothing for the unemployed and their children. He was even credited with having 'healing hands' for the sick. After 14 years service to the people of Blaenavon they left when he became a Baptist Minister in Magor.[32]

The Methodists had their own separate Welsh and English traditions from the start. Even at Penuel, however, temperance meetings were bilingual by the end of the 1850s – presumably the new English immigrants were thought to be in more need of them. By the 1880s lectures and entertainments were in English, Welsh being reserved for the services. Lewis Browning's brother Thomas, a collier, led the singing at Penuel for many years, but when English replaced Welsh in the services he gave up, not being equal to leading in English. After 1884, the Welsh Ivorites benefit society no longer conducted their affairs in Welsh.[33]

By the late 19th century, Blaenavon had 13 chapels – five Baptist, five Methodist (Calvinistic, Primitive, Bible Christian and two Wesleyan), and three Congregationalist, as well as five Anglican churches. They were now almost entirely English language. The 1904-5 revival took place, so far as Blaenavon was concerned, at the time when the Welsh language and culture were in steep decline. In the first decade of the new century the population of Blaenavon rose by over 1,000 from 10,010 to 11,087, but the number of Welsh speakers fell from 857 (8.6 %) to 616 (5.6%), almost certainly all of them bilingual. A census carried out by the Welsh Church Commission showed that nearly 70% of the population claimed membership of or association with a nonconformist chapel. There were 813 church communicants (7.5% of worshippers), 2,366 members of nonconformist churches (21.8%) and 5,167 nonconformist 'adherents' (69.3%). Few of these could have followed a service in Welsh. By 1921 the percentage of Welsh speakers had halved to 2.7%. It then remained at just over 2% until the 1960s when there was another sharp decline. This may have been connected with the demolition of the housing in the old town, which may have had a higher proportion of older people, perhaps still Welsh-speaking.[34]

There were many reasons, over a long period, for the fall in chapel membership from the high point at the beginning of the 20th century – the decline of the Welsh language; mutual hostility between some ministers and deacons and the new labour leaders; and the new social clubs and cinemas, which provided rival venues for entertainments. By the time of the First World War the chapels were already in decline and the direct impact of the war may have been less than expected. However, even among those who had not experienced its horrors at first hand, the war gave many younger people wider horizons, whilst women workers were forced to use the previously sacrosanct Sabbath for household jobs such as washing, whilst in the post-war years many Blaenavon people had to leave in search of work.[35]

Among the Methodists, the quest for unity led ultimately to the closure of many chapels. Social and historical differences between the separate Methodist traditions had largely disappeared and the Calvinists of Penuel no longer worshipped in the old tongue. With union, it was no longer necessary to maintain heat and insure two or more buildings within a town, whilst the centralized organisation made it easier to amalgamate under one roof than it was for the Baptists, for whom each chapel was a self governing autonomous unit. The Bible Christians amalgamated with two other groups in 1907 to form the United Methodist Church and the term 'Primitive Methodist' ceased to be used, at least officially, in 1929. Finally the Wesleyans, the Primitive Methodists and the United Methodists merged in 1932

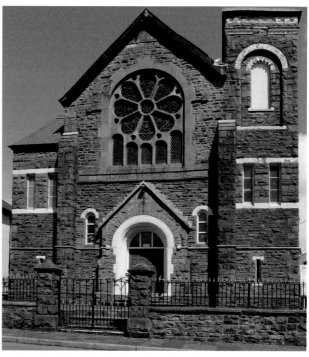

Fig. 63 The Methodist Chapel in Park Street of 1885, by the architect John Wills of Derby. (Photograph by Simon Hardy)

as the Methodist Church. The Blaenavon Bible Christians ended soon after 1907, perhaps merging with their Primitive Methodist neighbours in Broad Street, though their chapel survived as a St John's Ambulance Hall. In 1885 a new Methodist church, by the architect John Wills opened in Park Street, next to the site of the Wesleyan school of 1871 (Fig. 63). The Primitive Methodist chapel of 1879, the largest in Blaenavon, which dominated Broad Street, closed in August 1966 and Penuel was demolished in 1968. The Upper Wesleyan chapel vanished with the rest of Chapel Row in 1971.

The nonconformist decline from about 1930 onwards, resulting in the closure of many chapels, was a complex process, as the centrality of the culture of the chapels was eroded from many directions. Statistics are difficult, since chapels included both full communicant members and a larger looser body of adherents, and it was often the latter who fell away.[36] The experience of different churches varied. The Baptists had broadly the same membership in Monmouthshire in 1950 as in 1900 – just over 15,000 – though between 1950 and 2000 the number of Baptist chapels in the county declined from 146 to 60. In Blaenavon, Horeb, Garn-yr-Erw closed in 1971, Ebenezer in 1988. Ebenezer's site is now marked by a plaque in Market Street car park. Other denominations suffered severely. The Calvinistic Methodists halved in numbers in the county between 1930 and 1950, though much may have been due to chapel mergers. Congregationalists declined by two-thirds between 1900 and 1950.[37] The English Congregationalist chapel in Lion Street closed in 1982 and was demolished five years later. Its parent chapel, Bethlehem, closed in April 2009.

8   SIDNEY GILCHRIST THOMAS, PERCY CARLYLE GILCHRIST AND THE BASIC BESSEMER PROCESS

On 24 May 1847 a new railway bridge over the river Dee at Chester, designed by no less a person than Robert Stephenson, suddenly collapsed as a local train to Ruabon was crossing it. Five people were killed. This was only one of a series of such accidents and they exposed a basic flaw in railway engineering. The bridge used cast iron girders in three large sections dovetailed together. Cast iron, with its crystalline structure, is brittle and liable to fracture under pressure or vibration. Wrought iron was better, but expensive. It was later used very successfully for example in the Crumlin Viaduct, built by one of the Kennard ironmasters of Blaenavon. What was needed was a new material, at a cost-effective price.

With existing techniques steel could only be produced in limited quantities, mostly in crucibles by the Huntsman process. It was possible, by combining the contents of a series of crucibles in a mould, to produce cast steel, though this needed precision and careful timing. In 1874 the production of a steel ingot at Sheffield as material for forging a heavy gun barrel at Woolwich Arsenal took 584 crucibles, but this required a regimented workforce working in close discipline. In Germany, Krupp in Essen and Meyer in Bochum built up a reputation for cast steel.[1] There was a need for cheap bulk steel for a range of uses, from railways to girders and shipping to heavy guns, and one of those who tried to provide the answer was Henry Bessemer (1813-98).[2]

His father, Anthony Bessemer, was an inventor who had settled in Paris, producing dies for the French mint. He fled Paris at the Revolution and later settled in Hertfordshire, where his son, Henry, was born. Henry was to become a prolific inventor and is described by his latest biographer as 'over six feet tall, with (at least in photographs) an unsmiling persona', and looking 'every inch the Victorian man of iron' (Fig. 64). Henry Bessemer worked on the problem of manufacturing cheap steel for ordnance

Fig. 64 Sir Henry Bessemer (1813-98), inventor rather than scientist, used low phosphorus Blaenavon pig iron in his experiments and was initially unaware of the problems caused by phosphorus in his 'mild steel'.

production in the early 1850s and in 1856 he gave a paper 'On the manufacture of malleable iron without fuel' to the British Association during their conference at Cheltenham. This explained the technique he had developed for the production of steel by blowing oxygen through molten pig iron in a special converter, removing the carbon, silica and manganese by oxidation and leaving molten steel. The process occupied only 20 minutes, after which the steel could be run off into ingot moulds, without the back-breaking, wasteful and dangerous toil of puddling. Steel could now be produced at 20% of its previous cost and in much greater quantities.[3]

Within a month Bessemer had been paid £27,000 for licences to use the process, even though it was by no means perfect. Thomas Brown of Ebbw Vale offered £50,000 for the patent rights, which Bessemer refused.

Fig. 65 A Bessemer converter in operation

Ebbw Vale had produced steel a year or two earlier, using the American Martiers process and Bessemer now paid the company £30,000 to abandon this in favour of his own process. In 1862 Ebbw Vale built one of the first two Bessemer plants in Britain, with six 10 ton converters (Fig. 65). Bessemer licensed his invention to five ironmasters, but he was an inventor rather than a scientist and the process needed further refinement and could only be used with great difficulty, as the lessees soon discovered. Dowlais took out a licence in 1856, but only made its first Bessemer steel rail in 1865 and came to regard the first decade of use as 'an unfortunate transaction'.

One of the problems, that of absorbed oxygen, was solved by R.F. Mushet at Darkwell in the Forest of Dean by the addition of ferro-manganese in the form of spiegeleisen or of manganese rich pig iron. But the main problem was the retention of phosphorus, which could make the steel brittle. The problem had not been immediately apparent, for Bessemer had used low phosphorus Blaenavon pig iron in his experiments. He now brought in eminent scientists, including Edward Riley, an eminent metallurgist, as consultants and tried a variety of fluxes to remove the phosphorus, but without success. One French report of 1859 even claimed that the Bessemer process had been abandoned.

Both the Bessemer process and the alternative open hearth method of Pierre Martin and Werner Siemens could only be used with non-phosphoric ore – haematite from Cumberland or northern Spain, the spathic ores of Germany or the iron ore of Elba. This greatly limited the application of either process, while the price of haematite ore doubled.[4]

Krupp was forced to import pig iron from Cumberland or Scotland for his Essen steelworks in the Ruhr. Bessemer's 'mild steel', as it became known, did not replace puddled wrought iron or the 'Sheffield' steel used for edged tools. Its main use was in engineering, particularly for railway rails, a major product both for domestic use and for export made by the South Welsh ironworks.

In 1870 the scientist George Challenor remarked in a lecture at the Birkbeck Institute in London that 'the man who eliminates phosphorus by the Bessemer converter will make his fortune'. Sitting in the audience was a 20-year-old police court clerk, Sidney Gilchrist Thomas.[5]

Sidney Gilchrist Thomas and the Basic Bessemer Process

Thomas had been born in London in 1850, the son of a London-Welsh civil servant who worked in the solicitors' department of the Inland Revenue and a Highland Scot mother, Melicent Gilchrist, daughter of a nonconformist minister.[6] His family moved to Camberwell so that the children could attend Dulwich College. Sidney's uncles were clergymen and the family spent summer holidays with them in North Wales, at Corwen or with his godfather, the Revd Thomas Hughes, at Llandrillo near Rhos. His headmaster and parents hoped that he would go up to Oxford or Cambridge, but Sidney preferred the University of London, either because of better scientific teaching available there or because of the religious tests at the older universities, which discriminated against non Anglicans, including nonconformists like Sidney. He originally hoped to be a doctor, emulating his elder brother Llewellyn, but when Sidney was 17, his father died suddenly. He therefore left university in order to support his mother, working as a police court clerk at Marlborough Street and later at Thames Police Court, Stepney at a salary of £90 a year. In 1870 he attended a course of lectures by Challenor, where he heard the fateful words and set to work to improve his scientific knowledge. Whilst still working at the police court he attended lectures at the School of Mines, where he took a series of examinations, set up a small laboratory in his bedroom fireplace at home and contributed articles to the journal *Iron*, edited by Challenor, including one on early blast furnaces. Challenor also gave Thomas the use of his own laboratory.

Sidney's cousin, Percy Carlyle Gilchrist (1851-1935), was the son of Alex Gilchrist, a Scottish poet and writer, whose sister was Sidney's mother, and Anne Burrows, a wealthy woman of artistic and scholarly tastes. Both parents were published writers and moved among the intellectual elite of Victorian London. Alex greatly admired the essayist and historian Thomas Carlyle, who became a close friend and next door neighbour in Cheyne Walk, Chelsea. He corresponded with Pre-Raphaelite painters like Rossetti and Ford Madox Ford, while Alfred Tennyson was a frequent caller at the house. Anne Gilchrist was a correspondent of the American poet Walt Whitman and after her husband's death moved to America where she became a close friend of Whitman.[7] Percy had greater scientific training than his cousin. From Felsted School he attended the Royal School of Mines from 1868 onwards, where he trained as a metallurgist and analytical chemist, becoming a member of both the Institutions of Civil and Mechanical Engineers. Appointed to a post as analytical chemist at Cwmafon ironworks above Port Talbot, he began to work with his cousin towards a solution of the problem of eliminating phosphorus in Bessemer steel.

By the end of 1875 a theoretical solution to the problem was emerging from the cousins' work. The key lay in replacing the original Bessemer converter lining of firebrick, silica brick and fused sand (the 'acid' Bessemer process) with a lining of bricks of Dolomite (Magnesium limestone) fired to white heat and with additional basic limestone in the mix, able to absorb phosphorus (the 'basic' Bessemer process). The two cousins were not alone in the race. George Snelus (1837-1906) had been appointed works chemist at Dowlais in 1868 and by 1870 had made small-scale experiments with a basic lining of hard burnt magnesium limestone on which he had taken out a patent. However (as he recalled years later) he did not follow these up after being appointed to a post in Cumbria, where the low phosphorus haematite made the matter less relevant. Snelus was Alfred Russell Wallace to Thomas's Darwin; as often with a scientific problem, several people were working towards a solution but only one is remembered in popular memory.[8]

In August 1876 Sidney wrote to his cousin at Cwmavon from Thames Police Court about his experimental converter which was testing their theoretical work,[9] and that summer he made a tour of German mines and ironworks. Soon after his return, the post of works chemist at Blaenavon was advertised. Both cousins applied, but Percy, with his greater formal education and practical experience of ironworks, was appointed. In December Sidney wrote to Percy that he still thought 'our idea has something auriferous about it. Whether we shall either of us be able to devote the time to it is quite another matter. I always expect some wretch to walk in and do it.'[10] The following October Percy invited Sidney 'to come down so that we can get some experiments made. I can manage the analysis all right, but I should like your assistance in the experiments – so say that you will come.'[11] During 1877 Thomas travelled down from London on the Thursday midnight train to Newport and thence to Blaenavon, before returning to his police court duties on Monday morning; over the long weekends he was conducting secret experiments with his cousin. That December

Fig. 66 Edward Pritchard Martin, manager of Blaenavon and later of Dowlais, who encouraged the Thomas-Gilchrist cousins in their experiments.

he wrote to another cousin, Elizabeth Burton: 'My first trial comes off in January down in Wales, some experiments on a small scale having given results remarkable in a scientific point of view. The problem is the separation of phosphorus in the manufacture of Bessemer and Martin steel.'[12]

Early in 1878, Edward Pritchard Martin (Fig. 66), Blaenavon's General Manager (1844-1910), spoke to Percy: 'I know you young men have some secret work in hand. I think it would be well if you put confidence in me.' They did and the company then built a small experimental converter, initially of 3-4 cwt, later of 12 cwt on Forgeside. That March Sidney attended a lecture by Lothian Bell, 'On the separation of phosphorus from pig iron', at the Iron and Steel Institute. In the discussion that followed, Sidney announced 'it may be of some interest to members to know that I have been enabled by the assistance of Mr Martin at Blaenavon to remove phosphorus entirely by the Bessemer converter ... I have the results in my pocket of some hundred and odd analyses by Mr Gilchrist, who has had almost the entire conduct of the experiments ... and I hope that we have overcome the practical difficulties that have hitherto stood in the way.' His intervention made little impression and George Challenor recalled 'the sneers and smiles of incredulity ... [when] an unknown youth ... presumed to proclaim the solution of a problem which leading metallurgists had pronounced well-nigh impossible.' During the same discussion, George Snelus drew attention to his own valid patent.[13]

Martin continued his support and helped Gilchrist and Thomas to obtain their own patent. In September the two cousins prepared a paper, 'The elimination of phosphorus by the Bessemer converter', for the autumn meeting of the Iron and Steel Institute. Due to pressure of time, it was not read until May 1879, and in it they paid tribute to the help they had received from E.P. Martin and the Blaenavon company. By this time, the cousins had learnt how to convert the limestone for the converter lining into hard, dense and impermeable blocks by heating at over 1,500°C.

In the meantime, at the Paris meeting of the Iron and Steel Institute timed to coincide with the Great Exhibition of 1878, Thomas had met Edward Windsor Richards, the Merthyr-born manager of Bolckow Vaughan and Co. of Middlesborough, during an exhibition excursion to the Creusot steelworks. At Middlesborough, Richards had one of the largest steelworks in the world, but was unable to use the local ores for Bessemer steel because of their high phosphorus content. On his return Richards visited Blaenavon to see Thomas' work at first hand and witnessed three 'blows' in the experimental converter. Richards then took out a licence for the process, which could be used both with the Bessemer converter and the Siemens-Martin open hearth method. Richards persuaded Thomas and Gilchrist to move to Middlesborough to continue their work, where he made an old fixed cupola available and built a pair of small Bessemer converters, which were ready by the end of 1878. Thereafter, the process took off. In 1878 only 20 tons of steel were made by Thomas and Gilchrist's Basic Bessemer process. By 1880 this had risen to 10,000 tons and by 1890 around 500,000 tons of steel were produced in Britain by the Basic process.[14]

In December 1878 Thomas wrote to Elizabeth Burton with news that the Blaenavon Company, had failed, but that Middlesborough was 'besieged by a large array of continental metallurgists' and that foreign patents were being taken out.[15] Alfred Krupp tried to use the process without patent rights on technical and legal grounds, but Thomas pursued him through the courts and won his case. In 1879 patents were taken out in the Ruhr, France, Luxembourg and Austria and Thomas was at last able to give up his job in the police court (Fig. 67). The following January he wrote to E.P. Martin at Blaenavon, where a new company had been formed, 'You will be quite safe now in starting Blaenavon on basic Bessemer. It is a success.'[16] Rhymney had started Bessemer production in 1877, Blaenavon and Tredegar in 1882 and Cyfartha in 1885. By April 1882, 14 works in Britain, France, Belgium,

Fig. 67 Sidney Gilchrist Thomas on a Luxembourg stamp of 1979, commemorating the 'Thomas process'.

Germany, Austria and Russia were using the Thomas-Gilchrist process. Before long, 'most of the ironworks which did not convert to steel soon closed'.[17] Edward Pritchard Martin had moved to the Merthyr ironworks at Dowlais in 1878 as general manager, 'head hunted' by the polymath ironmaster-scholar G.T. Clark, now best remembered for his magisterial studies of medieval castles.[18]

The effect of the Bessemer process was described many years later by a Middlesborough steel maker. 'A new phenomenon appeared ... every few minutes the town became illuminated with brilliant lights ... making the long winter evenings at intervals as light as day ... [from] the after blow of the basic Bessemer plant ... and we became aware that a new industry was being started.'[19] There were still problems to be overcome. The all-important converter lining was made of bricks of calcium carbonate and dolomite (magnesium limestone), but as these shrank and lost weight in the intense heat of the process they tended to work loose and come apart. The search for a durable lining material was long and difficult. The two cousins tried a variety of binders, including sugar, molasses and even horse manure, in a preparation known in the works as 'Mr Gilchrist's Special'. Eventually it was found that hot tar, already used locally as a binding agent in puddling furnaces, was the solution. A major problem in the viability of the 'Thomas Process' had been overcome. In April 1879 the success of the new process was announced in *The Times*.[20]

Success and Later Years

Among the principal beneficiaries were Alfred Krupp of Essen in Germany and Andrew Carnegie of Pittsburg in the United States, who both possessed large phosphoric ore fields, now available for steelmaking. Carnegie, canny Scot and American steel baron, acting as Thomas' agent, persuaded the American Bessemer Steel Association, of which he was a member, to purchase the patent for $300,000 (at no cost to himself) and then charged Thomas a commission of $50,000. He was thus not only paid a handsome sum to use the process, but ensured that the production of basic Bessemer steel in America remained within his cartel. It was little wonder that he could afford to endow public libraries on such a generous scale. His praise of Thomas and Gilchrist was not disinterested. 'These two young men ... did more for Britain's greatness than all the Kings and Queens put together. Moses struck the rock and brought forth water. They struck the useless phosphoric ore and transformed it into steel – a far greater miracle.' In 1881 Sidney stayed with Carnegie in Pittsburg for two months.[21]

When, in the following year, one of the major iron companies in the Austro-Hungarian Empire, the Prager Eisenindustrie Gesellschaf, presented Sidney, who was visiting Vienna, with an elaborately decorated casket containing a congratulatory message, it was fitting that it was made of 'Thomas Steel', but equally significant that the presentation came from the Austrian steel industry rather than the British. The company, based near Prague, had begun Bessemer steel production in 1875, but it only began major expansion in 1879 when it obtained the monopoly for the Thomas-Gilchrist process in the Czech lands. It subsequently obtained a dominating position in the production of railway rails within the Empire.[22] In 1883 the Iron and Steel Institute awarded Sidney their Bessemer gold medal.

In 1879 the two cousins set up their own steelworks at Middlesborough, which they sold to the steelmakers Dorman Long when Percy Gilchrist retired from business in 1903 and instead established a company with George Snelus, with Percy Gilchrist as Managing Director, to exploit their foreign patents and those of Edward Riley.

The basic process could also be applied to the Siemens-Martin open hearth process and in 1884 the first basic open hearth furnace was blown in at Brymbo in Flintshire. From about 1890 the superior quality steel of the Siemens-Martin process took over much of the market. Ironically, at the outbreak of the First World War, over 60% of German steel was being produced by the Thomas process. Sidney Gilchrist Thomas had not sought riches for himself, but rather to support his widowed mother and to enable her to continue her charitable work. Nevertheless, he was now a very rich man.

From an early stage, Sidney realized the potential if the phosphorus and other chemicals retained in the slag from the hearths could be released and used as agricultural fertilsers. In March 1878 he wrote to Percy that they should keep quiet about this, in the hope of including a clause in licences giving them its exclusive use. Much of Thomas's last four years were spent in developing and marketing a process to achieve this, though there were problems in making the insoluble phosphate soluble in the soil and it was not Sidney but the Germans who finally solved this problem by finely grinding the slag.[23] In 1889, 700,000 tons of basic slag worldwide were ground up for fertilizer.

Sidney continually looked for new projects. He began work on a new and improved typewriter and spent several years travelling in Europe and America on business. In 1882 he visited Vienna and the following year Germany in connection with phosphate production. Sadly, his health was frail, his lungs affected by the fumes from his experiments and by his long hours spent in an ill-ventilated East End police court. Writing to his friend and former tutor George Challenor, he said that he had thrown his health and much else into his basic Bessemer process, but thought he might not live to see the harvest. He consulted his cousin, Dr Burnie, in Bradford who diagnosed lung disease. He spent a winter in Algiers and set off on a long sea voyage around the world

Fig. 68 Sidney Gilchrist Thomas, from R. W. Burnie Memoirs and Letters of Sidney Gilchrist Thomas *(London 1891).*

Fig. 69 The bronze portrait medallion of Sidney Gilchrist Thomas by the sculptor Fred Mancini on the obelisk in Fig, 71.

in an attempt to recover his health, visiting South Africa, Mauritius, India and Ceylon. Politically a radical Liberal, who had turned down a well-paid post at a Burton on Trent brewery in 1873 on moral grounds, he visited the Egyptian nationalist Arabi Pasha in Ceylon, where he had been exiled by the British government after being overthrown in the Egyptian campaign of 1882 and the battle of Tel el Kebir. From here, Sidney travelled over the Pacific to Australia and across America, but when he returned home his health was visibly failing. He spent further time in Egypt, but died in the Avenue Marceau in Paris, where he had gone in hope of a cure, in February 1885 at the age of 34, and was buried at Passy in the city. His sole executrix was his sister Lilian, who shared his radical views and, in accordance with his wishes, disbursed money 'doing good discriminately' in causes including improving working conditions in the East End of London, women's suffrage and workers' housing.

Fig. 70 The only known photograph of Percy Carlyle Gilchrist.

Sidney Gilchrist Thomas, with his pale drawn face and lock of hair over his forehead, fulfilled the Victorian idea of the young romantic hero dying of lung disease, like Keats or Chopin (Fig. 68). His own words make it clear that Percy Carlyle Gilchrist played a much larger part in the experiments than is usually admitted. Percy lived on full of years and honours, a Fellow of the Royal Society and a Chevalier of the Legion d'Honneur until 1935, when he died aged 84, having outlived his cousin by 50 years. In contrast to Sidney, of whom many images exist, there is only one known portrait of Percy Gilchrist, a photograph in an obituary in the Proceedings of the Royal Society (Fig. 64).[24] As the *Dictionary of National Biography* put it, he was overshadowed by his 'romantic innovative cousin, his vivacious mother and his talented brother', the fashionable Victorian painter Herbert Gilchrist. In 1960 a granite obelisk with a bronze plaque bearing a portrait of Sidney Gilchrist Thomas by Fred Mancini was erected in front of Coity House on Forgeside. This was later moved to a site adjacent to the ironworks (Fig. 71) and in 1985 the American Society of Metals unveiled a plaque within the ironworks commemorating his experiments. It is thus Sidney Gilchrist Thomas, not his cousin, who today has a memorial in Blaenavon near the site of the former ironworks and an industrial estate there named after him.

Fig. 71 The red granite obelisk memorial to Sidney Gilchrist Thomas which now stands in the ironworks car park. (Photograph Simon Hardy)

9 HIGH VICTORIANS: BLAENAVON 1870-1900

> But iron – cold iron – is master of them all.
> Rudyard Kipling *Cold Iron*

Decline and Fall: The South Wales Iron Industry 1870-1880

In 1870, Blaenavon entered the new decade with eight furnaces in blast, increasing to ten three years later. R.W. Kennard died at his London house that January, and when his son Edward Kennard returned to Blaenavon soon afterwards with his new bride, a Miss Laing of Brighton, he was met between Varteg and Blaenavon by 2,000 members of various Friendly Societies. They were in full regalia with their banners, together with the Cyfartha Band in their green uniforms, the Garnddyrys brass band and the band of the 4th Rifle Volunteers. In the town were floral arches, more banners and fireworks. Cannon were fired off from the Coity, though sadly one exploded, killing the old regular soldier, Robert Lechman, who fired the guns on such occasions. Samuel Laing, Chairman of the London, Brighton and South Coast Railway, presumably Kennard's brother-in-law, became Chairman of the Blaenavon Company. [1]

In 1870 the townspeople could enjoy such diverse events as a troupe of female minstrels, a 'panorama of African scenery' at the White Horse assembly rooms, a reception hosted by Edward Kennard and his wife at the Big House, various missionary events or a lecture on Moses to raise funds for the new Wesleyan School. Amenities in the town were also improving. In 1872 the Blaenavon Gas and Water Company began supplying piped water to the town and in 1895 the Blaenavon Company agreed to sell water to the council from its new Forgeside reservoir under the Public Health Act. There had been plans to introduce gas lighting to the streets of Blaenavon by 1870, though this was opposed by some on grounds of cost. When it was finally introduced in 1874, this 'longed for improvement' was greeted with brass bands and the ringing of church bells.[2]

This optimistic picture was misleading, for the iron industry in Monmouthshire was in recession. In 1870 the company reformed itself as The Blaenavon Iron and Steel Company with some new directors, but continued to be held back by the lack of capital which had plagued its predecessors. It hoped to diversify into steelmaking and tried to raise capital for this, but few shareholders wanted to buy the 10% preference shares. It did diversify into coal and in 1873 was the third largest coal company in South Wales, with an annual production of over 900,000 tons, but a boom in the coal trade in 1871-3 was followed by a prolonged slump from 1874 onwards. With the failure of the West of England and South Wales District Bank in December 1878 the company was forced into liquidation, with debts of £80,000, mostly owed to its own directors, and a mortgage of £125,000.

Thanks to the Bessemer process, South Wales was briefly the world's largest steel producing area, but this meant a decline in wrought iron production disastrous for those without the capital or resources to change over to steelmaking. Between 1869 and 1877 the annual production of wrought iron rails for railways fell from 534,000 tons to 100,000 tons,[3] and Crawshay Bailey sold up at Nantyglo and Beaufort in 1870 and retired to Llanfoist, where he died two years later. Commentators noted that his works were old-fashioned, with obsolete machinery and that he had failed to diversify into Bessemer steel or coal. Bailey still produced coke in open heaps rather than in coke ovens and his coal pits still had water balance head gears, by that time something of an historical curiosity. Double chains on colliery winding gear were by now mandatory, but Bailey continued to use single chains long after they had been abandoned by everyone else, only replacing them after being prosecuted over a fatal accident when a chain broke. It may be that he suffered from a lack of capital – an obituary noted his serious financial losses in a commercial crisis in 1866 – but he may have become more interested in his substantial Breconshire landed estate than in ironmaking and kept his industrial investment to a minimum. Beaufort finally closed in March 1873 and Nantyglo a year later.[4]

'The Battle must be fought to the bitter end' – Coal and conflict, 1868-1875

The early 1870s saw other changes. The election riot of 1868 had taken place at a watershed moment. It was the last general election before the introduction of the secret ballot and many working men in towns (but no women of course) now had the vote. The aims of the Chartists were starting to come about. That year also saw the first of a series of increasingly hard-fought colliery strikes and lock outs over wage cuts and working practices. The Miners National Association had been founded in the north of England in 1863 and one of the four South Welsh participants at their first conference was Reuben Price of Blaenavon. Soon afterwards Price moved to Abertillery, where he was dismissed for Union activity the following year.[5]

There had been strikes over wage reductions at Blaenavon in 1867 and 1868. In 1869 the Lancashire miners resolved to send delegations to South Wales and Staffordshire with the aim of discussing co-operation in the event of strikes. In April 1871 representatives from throughout the Monmouthshire coalfield, including Blaenavon, Abersychan and Varteg, were addressed at the King William Inn at Blaina by Thomas Halliday of the new Amalgamated Association of Miners. Halliday was soon pitted against the coalmine owners' Monmouthshire and South Wales Collieries Association in a struggle which neither side could afford to lose.

In 1871-3 there was a boom in the coal industry but fluctuations in prices led to a series of strikes, which did not initially involve Blaenavon. However in 1872 the Blaenavon miners were on strike demanding a nine-hour day at the time of a 'coal famine', when demand outstripped supply. The Blaenavon miners were again on strike from January to the end of March in 1873 amid much suffering, though John Paton, the Blaenavon General

Manager, permitted striking workers to dig coal from the 'patches' for use in their houses. As the boom ended, the price of coal fell and May 1874 saw the first of two 10% wage reductions. When a third wage cut was announced for January 1875, this precipitated a further strike.[6]

'The battle must be fought to the bitter end' was one comment from a coalowner in 1875, when starving miners in Abersychan and Tredegar were set to work breaking stone for new parish roads so as to receive parish support. In May 1875 the miners capitulated at a meeting in the Royal Hotel, Cardiff between the South Wales Collieries Association and what was pointedly described as 'a deputation on the part of the working men of the district' – there was no mention of Thomas Halliday or of the Amalgamated Association of Miners, which had been destroyed by the lock out and bankrupted by strike pay. The miners accepted a 12.5% reduction for three months and the introduction of a sliding scale, tying wages to the selling price of coal whilst fixing a minimum wage. Sadly, the price of coal and the quantities of pig iron produced continued to fall.

The benefits or otherwise of the sliding scale were hotly contested by miners in subsequent years. William Abraham (1842-1922), also known by his Bardic name of Mabon, had helped found the Amalgamated Association of Miners. He favoured the sliding scale and dialogue with coal owners after he saw the union's funds depleted as a result of the strike, which he saw as then leading to the coal owners' ability to cut wages. After the strike, Abraham helped form the Cambrian Miners Association at Rhondda from a branch of the Amalgamated Association of Miners that had managed to struggle on, and in 1885 he was elected Liberal-Labour M.P. for the Rhondda, one of 12 M.Ps. elected on the dual party ticket. One of the leaders of the opposition to the sliding scale was the Risca-born William Brace (1865-1947), who had started work underground aged 12, and had become the miners' agent of the local branch of the Miners' Federation of Great Britain. Relationships between the two men became such that Abraham successfully sued Brace for libel in the 1890s. By the time of the conclusion of another strike in 1898, the two men had managed to patch up their differences and when the South Wales Miners Federation was formed that year, Abraham became its president and Brace its vice-president.[7]

In the winter of 1878-9 the Blaenavon Iron and Steel Company was forced into liquidation by the failure of the West of England Bank, which also caused the closure of the Crumlin Viaduct Works. This coincided with a period of acute distress throughout South Wales, which was particularly severe in Abersychan. Subscription lists and soup kitchens were opened for 'the starving poor'. The *Monmouthshire Merlin* reported: 'It is heartrending to see the little ones trudging from door to door without shoes and clothing to warm them' and that 'at Abersychan people were to be found by scores crowding together in the almost empty houses without fire and with little clothing'.[8] One of the few distractions came later in the year, when an entire family at Llangybi were knifed by a Spanish seaman, who had sailed from Bilbao on a vessel with a cargo of iron ore and was newly released from Usk prison. Unemployed workers flocked to the scene of the murders and a local paper complained that the road outside the cottage was like a funfair.

The Blaenavon Company Limited, 1878

After its collapse the Blaenavon Iron and Steel Company was sold to a financier, W.C. Quilter, for £75,000 and the payment of its debts. In its place, the Blaenavon Company Ltd was formed, with W.G. Dowden as Manager and Samuel Laing retained as Chairman. Three Old Side furnaces were still in use. Number 2 furnace, where the cast house still survives, produced cold blast pig iron. When the Bessemer steelworks opened in 1882, the cast houses of nos. 4 and 5 furnaces were demolished and the tapping areas remodelled (Fig. 72). Rail lines were laid to the furnaces and the molten iron ladled into ingot moulds set on trucks and transported across the valley to the Bessemer works to supply ingots as raw materials for the steelworks. A number of ingot moulds were found close to Number 4 furnace and can be seen on site. This may have been a short-lived expedient, though a mosaic in the former South Wales Institute of Engineers in Cardiff shows a similar arrangement, with railway lines and trucks leading from an open-fronted furnace (Fig. 73).

In January 1880 a new blast furnace was blown in on Forgeside (Fig. 74). The following year the Company produced an advertisement for its products – three grades of cold blast pig iron, various grades of forge iron, Bessemer steel, weldless railway tyres, and steel rails. The rails were marked BLAENAVON STEEL with the date, and examples have been reported as far afield as Sweden and Australia (Fig. 75).[9] Wrought iron was everywhere

Fig. 72 When the Bessemer plant came into operation the casthouses of nos. 4 and 5 furnaces were demolished and the tapping area of Furnace 4 remodelled to supply iron ingots to the steelworks across the valley. (Photograph by Simon Hardy)

Fig. 73 This mosaic in the former South Wales Institute of Engineers in Cardiff shows a late 19th-century blast furnace, with a railway track to convey the iron ingots to a steelworks. The arrangements at nos. 4 and 5 furnaces were similar.

Fig. 74 In the 1880s the ironworks moved across the valley to Forgeside, seen in the distance in this view from the top of the balance tower in the old works. The freehold land avoided the heavy royalties payable to Lord Abergavenny.

Fig. 75 'Blaenavon steel 1885' Railway rails made in Blaenavon steelworks have been reported worldwide, from Australia to Scandinavia. This example is from Sweden. (Photograph by Arnold Paul)

Fig. 76 The Forgeside furnaces in 1896. Three circular furnaces with round piercings in the parapets, with four slightly lower hot blast stoves between.

being replaced by cast steel – in 1881 the Ebbw Vale company dismantled a hundred puddling furnaces and in August 1882 Tredegar started its Bessemer furnaces, to be followed a month later by Blaenavon, with two Bessemer converters.[10] In January 1886 another large blast furnace was blown in on Forgeside, where four were now in blast, one for 'ordinary pig' using local ore, and three for 'haematite pig' using imported ore. The Old Side furnaces were now described as 'wholly idle'. A photograph of 1896 shows three of the Forgeside furnaces, solid iron-clad structures, topped by parapets (Fig. 76). Between them are the lower cylinders of four hot blast stoves.[11] The old furnace yard remained in use as a maintenance depot, employing some 170 men, and later as a sale coal yard, saving it from demolition and re-development, though one furnace may have been in intermittent use until 1904.

Martyn Kennard – An Egyptian Interlude
Henry Martyn Kennard (1833-1911), younger son of R.W. Kennard, ran the Crumlin Viaduct Works from the date of his brother Thomas' departure for America in 1858 until 1872, after which he lived in retirement in Crumlin Hall. He met the Egyptologist Flinders Petrie by chance in London in 1887. The previous year Petrie had fallen out with his previous sponsors, the Egypt Exploration Society, and after a spell of anthropological work in Egypt for the British Association for the Advancement of Science was seeking new sponsorship to continue his excavations. Kennard was a prominent Freemason and his portrait, by W.W. Ouless, which is surrounded by Egyptian symbols, now hangs in the Hall of the Kennard Lodge in Pontypool. Greatly interested in ancient Egypt, Kennard offered to fund Petrie's work in return for a share of the finds – an arrangement common at the time.

In 1888 Kennard arrived from Cairo at Hawara, south of Arsinoe at the entrance to the Fayyum depression, with tents, an English manservant, a dragoman, a cook, two donkey boys and two hangers on. Petrie had uncovered a vast Roman period cemetery which produced a spectacular series of painted mummy portraits of high artistic quality – the 'Fayyum portraits', now divided between the Cairo Museum and the British Museum. Kennard presented one, with the inscription 'O Arthenidorus Farewell', to the British Museum and hired the Egyptian Hall in Piccadilly for two months to exhibit his collection. This aroused great public interest and drew large crowds. Petrie sent regular bulletins to Kennard and his other backers and in 1892 promised them a hopeful-looking unopened tomb. The following year Petrie shifted his activities to Coptos, north of Luxor, where Kennard visited him in the winter of 1893-4 and watched the uncovering of the foundation deposits of a temple. He also supported Petrie's work at Amara on the Nile in northern Sudan and on the pre-dynastic cemeteries at Naqada on the west bank of the Nile below Abydos. By 1896 Kennard's association with Petrie had come to an end and Petrie's interests were in any case shifting towards Palestine, but Kennard remained a generous contributor to Egyptian research.

Kennard presented much of his share from Petrie's work to the Ashmolean Museum in Oxford, where it forms the basis of their important collection of early Egyptian material. He gave other material to the British Museum, Manchester and Newport Museums. After his death, his remaining collection was sold at Sotheby's in July 1912, the sale of the 743 lots occupying four days.[12]

Endgame

Despite the new blast furnaces on Forgeside and investment at Tredegar and Ebbw Vale, by 1880 the inland South Wales iron and steel industry was in terminal decline. In 1890 America introduced the McKinley tariffs on imported goods, including steel, sponsored by the future President William McKinley. In the same year the United States steel industry, aided by the new tariff and by the highly advantageous terms under which Carnegie and his cartel could produce Bessemer steel, overtook Britain as the world's largest steel producer. By 1902 Britain was in third place, behind America and Germany. It was claimed that before the tariff, Blaenavon had exported 1,000 tons of steel billets (lengths of cast steel) a week to America, but that after the tariff was introduced the trade was killed. The production figure may be exaggerated, but the effects were real enough and immediate. They were made worse by competition from Siemens-Martin open hearth steel and by the dumping of American steel bars on the British market, undercutting locally produced steel. In 1891 the Rhymney Iron Company closed its Bessemer steel plant, opened as recently as 1883, and retreated into coal production. Tredegar had flourishing Bessemer steel production until 1890, but the plant closed in the autumn of 1895, throwing 1,500 men out of work. As has been remarked elsewhere, after 1885 the history of the Monmouthshire iron industry consisted of the absorption of what remained of earlier works by Ebbw Vale and the 'increasingly tenuous survival of the Blaenavon Company'.[13]

In addition to American competition, British industry was backward in technical education compared with Germany. Bismarck realised that German military strength needed to be supported by industrial innovation and encouraged research in engineering and science. At a time when British middle class education was dominated by Oxford and Cambridge, with their predominantly classical curriculum of Greek and Latin, Germany had *Technische Hochschulen* (technical universities) and engineers enjoyed high social status, sometimes as personal friends of the Kaiser.[14] Britain was to pay a high price for its scientific and technical backwardness. When war came in 1914 she was dependent on Germany for chemicals such as toluene and acetone essential for explosives manufacture, precision optical instruments and pharmaceuticals needed for the drugs and anaesthetics to treat, among others, the war wounded.[15]

By this time, most iron ore used in the furnaces was imported haematite, much of it from northern Spain, where the company had links in Bilbao – 'the Manchester of Spain'. Though ironstone mining on a limited scale continued until 1903, most accessible seams of the 'Welsh mine' that had attracted Hill and Hopkins had long been worked out. Five bands of ironstone had once been mined in Blaenavon, with an iron content of 28-35%. Metal mining techniques were sometimes rough and ready.[16] John Whitney, who had worked in the Three Quarter Ball seam earlier in the century, recalled how it overlay the Three Quarter Coal, which was worked by the pillar and stall method, leaving the ironstone as a roof. The pillars were then cut away, leaving the ironstone to be collected from the rubble, though sometimes the amount of debris was too great to allow the iron ore to be recovered. This, to say the least, was a precarious and dangerous method of mining. John Burchall and Isaac Davies had worked the Bottom Vein seam in various Blaenavon mines and described the mining technique in detail. Though less dramatic, their accounts make clear what a difficult and labour-intensive process ironstone mining had become. As late as 1922 the colliery agent Kemp Cartwright and a surveyor looked at the feasibility of re-starting ironstone mining, but after interviewing some former miners concluded that it was a lost art and one that was, in any case, not economically viable.[17]

In these circumstances, it made little sense to transport iron ore from Newport to Blaenavon on the congested valleys rail network. Instead, new steelworks were begun around Newport and Cardiff by firms new to South Wales, the precursors of the 20th-century coastal steelworks at Llanwern and Port Talbot. In 1887, E.P. Martin, who had encouraged the experiments of Thomas and Gilchrist at Blaenavon and who was now general manager at Dowlais, played a central role, with G.T. Clark, in the momentous decision to move steel production from Dowlais to East Moors steelworks in Cardiff, a process completed in 1891. The following year, Nettlefolds opened their works at Rogerstone outside Newport producing Bessemer steel with bought in pig iron. Lysaghts, a steel firm based in Staffordshire and Scunthorpe, established steel rolling mills at the Orb works in Pillgwenlly, Newport, in 1897, in time coming to specialize in motor body sheets and other automotive parts.[18] Blaenavon soldiered on and in 1899 opened new Siemens furnaces.

Garnddyrys and Pwll Du

With the closure of the Garnddyrys forges in 1860, the mountaintop communities lost much of their reason for existence, but the Pwll Du tunnel still carried limestone from the Blorenge quarries to the ironworks. Garnddyrys Square – 20 houses in three rows around a central triangle – was partly demolished by 1870 and Garnddyrys Row, which existed by 1827, was abandoned by 1938. The Queen Victoria survived until August 1946, when at 10.15 at night the floor collapsed in the middle of a lively sing song, depositing the customers in a cellar. It was finally demolished in 1953.[18] In 1971 the Abergavenny and District Steam Society carried out an excavation on the site of the forges, uncovering the remains of a puddling furnace.[19]

Pwll Du was a community of some 300 people, the men miners and quarrymen. Of its two rows of housing, Lower Rank was the earlier, built shortly before 1819. Close to it were the Anglican Chapel of Ease of St Catherine's and Pwll Du school. To the west was Upper Rank, of 1827, with a Methodist Chapel on one end. The Lamb Inn (which happily still survives as the Lamb and Fox) was conveniently sited between the two rows. There was a second pub, the Prince of Wales, to the west, along with a general stores and the cottage of Mr Button the cobbler.[20]

The two communities lacked plumbing, sanitation and piped water, but they were remarkably self sufficient. Water was from a spring. (Dolly Parton once remarked that of course her family had running water – they just had to go outside to fetch it.) The rows were equipped with bakehouses for bread and, according to Lewis Browning, the first question asked of a prospective bride was 'Can you bake?' Long Row also contained a village library and a vegetable and sweet shop. There was a series of pigsties in front of Long Row and in the allotments, and each family had a wash-tub for scraps, collected by the pig owners, those who contributed to the feeding receiving a share of the meat. This not only gave a range of meat products but could provide a cash crop in the form of a litter of piglets. The family pig was an important asset. Martin Lawler, who did fieldwork in Pwll Du in 1978 and toured the site with Mr Stan Jones, who had been brought up there, heard a story of a man who had once been prosperous, but took to drink and finally crossed the threshold – 'He sold his pig'. Pwll Du was demolished in 1963, shortly after the village had finally been connected to mains electricity, and its inhabitants were moved to new council houses in Govilon.[21]

10   BLAENAVON IN WAR AND PEACE, 1900-1945

The Blaenavon Company Ltd, 'Iron and steel manufacturers and colliery proprietors', struggled on in their Forgeside works, across the valley from the old town and ironworks, despite
a prolonged steelworkers strike in 1900-01 (Fig. 77).[1] In 1902 Forster Martin, a nephew
of E.P. Martin and formerly of East Moors steelworks in Cardiff, was appointed General
Manager. The following year Garn Pits closed, marking the end of ironstone mining, and in
1904 the last furnace in the old works was finally blown out. By 1906 only two coal mines
were working in Blaenavon, Big Pit and Milfraen. It was little wonder that many young
men from Blaenavon rushed to enlist for the Boer War; James Attwell of Forgeside, son of
a blast furnace foreman and a veteran of the battle of Omdurman in the Sudan, died in
South Africa and there were said to be four Blaenavon men in the siege of Ladysmith.[2] As

*Fig. 77 The ironworks in about 1900-1910. To the left is a cylindrical iron clad Cowper's hot
blast stove. Furnace no.2 has a crane for a 'cap and cone' closed top. The circular no.6 furnace
was added in 1860. Massive blast mains cross the furnace yard in front of the balance tower.*

a result the company faced a temporary labour shortage and in April 1900 had to advertise for men in Cork and Waterford.

Despite the closures, the population of Blaenavon peaked around 1910 at 13,000. Its inhabitants could enjoy musical comedies and melodramas by travelling companies, concerts from the Treorchy Male Voice Choir, and hear a performance of the cantata *Ruth* by the Forge Side choir and Blaenavon Orchestral Society with four guest soloists, all in the Workmen's Hall. They could play in the Blaenavon Town Silver Band, sing in the newly founded Blaenavon Male Voice Choir, or inspect a waxwork of Dr Crippen at the Forge Hammer. The last was a reflection of how mass media (in this case the new popular newspapers) were beginning to make themselves felt in Blaenavon. By 1911 the patrons of the 'Electric Picture Palace' could enjoy weekly films, mixed with variety acts and films of such outside events as the siege of Sydney Street, the state opening of Parliament or the 'Gaumont Gazette of interesting events' – an early newsreel.[3]

The company could still claim 'two blast furnaces of the most recent design, three Siemens open hearth furnaces, a steel tyre mill etc' and in 1911 acquired 'The Ottos', new coke ovens named from the German Otto-Hilgenstock Company which installed them. They provided gas to central Monmouthshire towns until the Second World War, when a larger plant was built in Pontypool, as well as producing profitable by-products such as tar, pitch, napthalene and benzol.[4] By now, however, Blaenavon was in the depths of a trade depression. The tyre mill and Bessemer plant were closed for a lengthy period for lack of orders and for a while the works shut down altogether. Shareholders complained that there

Fig. 78 In 1911 the outer casings of furnaces 4 and 5 were stripped to provide building material for the building of St James' church. The photograph shows the workforce, the curate in the centre, and the furnace casings behind.

Fig. 79 The demolition work in progress, providing a unique view of the original exteriors of nos.4 and 5 furnaces.

was no director resident in South Wales and no one with any experience of steel production. In 1911, as an unemployment relief scheme, the masonry casings of nos.4 and 5 furnaces were dismantled and used to build St James's church, uphill from the ironworks, replacing a previous corrugated iron church. Two photographs show the work in progress, supervised by the curate (Figs. 78 & 79).[5] In March and April 1912 there was a colliery strike throughout South Wales, forcing a shutdown of the blast furnaces. In the same year the Stack which gave its name to Stack Square was deemed to be dangerous and demolished by the simple expedient of attaching two locomotives to it by hawsers – a process carried out without damage to any of the houses. That summer there was a brief recovery, but it did not last. In 1913 the company had only one small furnace in blast.[6]

The Brickyard Girls

Two remarkable photographs show the women workers of Upper Brickyard, above the ironworks, grouped in front of the circular 'beehive' brick kiln. The date of the photographs is unknown, but they are similar to those of the men stripping the outer casings of nos.4 and 5 furnaces in 1912 and this may give the approximate date (Fig. 80). Bricks would have been needed for furnace linings from the earliest days of the ironworks and Upper Brickyard appears on the map of 1814. An earlier generation of brickyard women had been interviewed by Munby in 1865 when he described them as 'wellgrown, healthy lasses aged from 15 to 21, working three to a kiln with a shoveller and a gaffer in charge'. Sadly, a few years before Munby's visit, two of them had been killed when their clothes caught

Fig. 80 *The brickyard women c.1911*

in the machinery of the pug mill used for grinding and mixing the raw materials. Another photograph, taken in the last years of the 19th century, shows earlier brickyard workers, male and female, grouped in front of a large kiln, the women wearing the shawls and pinafores described by Munby. A photograph of Ebbw Vale brickyard women of around 1900 shows them in flannel 'turnovers' (shawls), sacking aprons and scarves (known to be red from written accounts) to keep the brick dust from their hair. In late Victorian times the brickyard, though owned by the Blaenavon Company, was operated by William and John Burgoyne, from a versatile family of contractors and builders who even produced the memorial to Samuel Elmes Steel in Blaenavon church.[7]

Mrs Howells, the last occupant of Brickyard Cottage, born about 1906, was interviewed by Martin Lawler in 1978. She remembered the last phase of the brickyard's operation. The centre of the yard was occupied by four kilns set in a square, three rectangular in shape, the fourth a circular 'beehive' kiln, with another circular kiln to the west. Between the kilns were two drying sheds, where the unbaked bricks were pre-heated on cast iron plates. To the north were the boiler house and engine house. A feeder pond to the west fed water to the boilers through a series of vaulted brick culverts, traces of which remain.

The clay was mined from an area to the west, on Garn Slope, and brought to the brick-yard along a tramway and dumped near the engine house. The hand-driven pugging mills, which had caused the fatal accidents recounted on p.75, had been discontinued. Instead, the clay was fed down a chute into a moving set of brick moulds. Mrs Howells remembered a human chain passing the bricks from the bottom of the chute to the drying kilns. Before the installation of the automatic brick moulds, the clay had been hand-shaped in moulds and then sanded to prevent the bricks sticking together in the kiln. The brickyard and brickyard cottages were surrounded by company-owned allotments, their boundaries made up of waste from the brickyard, including many firebricks, Bessemer tuyères and hot blast pipes. These now form an open air museum of industrial brickwork. Until 1913, the brickyards made a modest annual profit, delivering bricks to other sections of the works, but thereafter, particularly during the Great War, they made a sometimes substantial loss. The reasons for this are obscure, but they probably caused their closure soon after 1918.[8]

Blaenavon and the First World War

The outbreak of war found the blast furnaces and coke ovens at Blaenavon shut down and the collieries only working intermittently, leading a local paper to report that 'before long, not many men will be at work in Blaenavon'.

There had never been a shortage of old soldiers in Blaenavon ready to regale young men with tales of their travels and adventures, men like William Osborne, who after 12 years in the South Wales Borderers and fighting in the Zulu War became a miner in Big Pit. As had happened at the start of Boer War, many of those young men now rushed to enlist to fight in a war which 'would be over by Christmas'. Soon, however, wartime demand for steel and coal lifted Blaenavon from its economic trough. By January 1915 the company had a large contract from the French government for shell cases. The 'big blast furnace' on Forgeside was in operation, two Siemens steel furnaces were working and 700 men were employed at Milfraen Pit alone.[9]

The Blaenavon reservists of the 2nd Battalion, the Monmouthshire Regiment, the old Rifle Volunteers, under Captain Arthur Edwards, left for war by rail from Blaenavon station. When some 500 volunteers followed, they were seen off by cheering crowds with a procession headed by the Blaenavon silver band and the Boy Scouts.[11] They were soon serving in the Ypres salient near Armentières, where one company took part in the famous Christmas truce of 1914.[10] They had arrived in France earlier than the other two battalions and were assigned to the 12th Brigade of the 4th Division. The 1st and 3rd Monmouthshires, the latter with many Abergavenny men, were in the 28th Division.

From the autumn of 1914 onwards local papers reported a melancholy catalogue of deaths in action. One of the first was Arthur Birkin of Forgeside, a Lance Corporal in the 2nd Monmouthshires. The first officer killed was 2nd Lieutenant J.E. Paton, son of the former General Manager.[11] The skills of the former miners were often put to use digging tunnels under the German lines, and a mining unit, the 4th Divisional Mining Company, was formed under a Blaenavon man, Captain (later Major) Arthur H. Edwards, son of Ben Edwards, Commercial Manager of Blaenavon, with two N.C.O.s and 12 men. Their first task was the setting of a mine below a row of cottages at Le Touquet known as 'sniper's cottage', which the Germans were using as a strongpoint by means of which they were causing many casualties. The mine was successfully detonated – the first of the war. Captain Edwards was awarded the Military Cross and a fellow Blaenavon man, Private Jack Lewis, the Distinguished Conduct Medal – the first awarded to a Territorial. In 1915 a specialist tunnelling company of Royal Engineers, the 171st Tunnelling Company, was formed in the 28th Division from civilians experienced in digging sewers and railway tunnels and miners from Welsh units, including the 1st and 3rd Monmouthshires. These went on to dig mines at Hill 60 at Ypres and on Messines Ridge.[12]

All three battalions were engaged in the second Battle of Ypres in April and May 1915, in which casualties were heavy, the 2nd Battalion being reduced to half its strength. The battle brought grief to families of all classes at Blaenavon. Edward Pritchard Martin's only son Charles was a scientist with a growing European reputation, a biologist who had held posts at Glasgow University and at Oxford, author of several books (and Master of the Crickhowell Harriers). He enlisted as a Lieutenant in the 3rd Monmouthshires under a family friend, Captain Owen Dyne Steel, son of Colonel W.D. Steel who had commanded the Blaenavon Territorial Volunteers. Charles, then the battalion machine gun officer, was killed at Ypres in May. He has no known grave. (Owen Dyne Steel survived the war, ending with the rank of Lieutenant-Colonel.) John Paton Worton, killed the same month aged 22, grandson of John Worton of the Blaenavon Company, had been manager of the Victoria furnaces at Ebbw Vale. George and Esther Cairnes were prominent Primitive Methodists. One of their sons, Frank, was killed in the 2nd Monmouthshires and his brother Albert badly wounded and invalided home.[13]

At the end of May the survivors of the three battalions were amalgamated into a single battalion under the command of Major W.S. Bridge, though their combined strength was less than that of a single pre-war battalion. In July, the 2nd Monmouthshires were re-formed, with a strength of 12 officers and 476 men, under the command of Captain Edwards. By now, the casualty lists were swelled by men of the other local regiment, the 2nd South Wales Borderers, who were taking part in the Dardanelles campaign, including a Blaenavon Boer War veteran, Leonard Caddick. The following January the 2nd Monmouthshires were moved into reserve before becoming a pioneer battalion of the 29th Division.

The first day of the Somme offensive in July 1916 had seen massive slaughter, the highest loss of men in any day in the history of the British army, for pathetically small gains. Among the dead was Lieutenant-Colonel Maurice Nichol Kennard, commanding the 18th Battalion of the West Yorkshire Regiment, who had won the Military Cross and been mentioned in despatches three times. On 7 July, the untested and poorly trained volunteers of the 38th (Welsh) Division were sent to attack Mametz Wood, held by the elite Prussian Guards Lehr Division. Two brothers from Blaenavon steelworks, Henry and Charles Morgan, originally from Cardiff, had volunteered in late 1914 for the 16th (Cardiff City) Battalion of the Welsh Regiment. Both were killed that day, one of several pairs of brothers who fell at Mametz. The initial assaults failed, with heavy losses, but three days later, too late for the Morgan brothers, the Welsh took most of the wood. The poet Robert Graves, who was severely wounded on the Somme whilst serving with the Royal Welch Fusiliers wrote 'Last night I saw in Mametz Wood / A Certain cure for lust of blood'. The battle is now commemorated by what is perhaps the most striking memorial of the western front. A proudly striding red dragon, the work of Welsh artist blacksmith David Petersen, atop a high granite plinth, tears at a tangle of barbed wire as it gazes at the fields across which the Welsh advanced, towards Mametz Wood.

After the Battle of the Somme, the 3rd Monmouthshires were disbanded and their men distributed among other units, many to the 2nd Monmouthshires, who served the remainder of the war as a pioneer battalion. They continued this hard and dangerous work, digging communication trenches, mending roads cut by shell fire and constructing railway lines, at Ypres and on the Somme, where their C.O. Colonel A.J.H. Bowen D.S.O. and bar, from a well known Usk and Pontypool family, was killed by a sniper on 2 March 1917 near Bapaume.[14] Later that year the battalion took part in the offensives at Arras and at Third Ypres (Passchendaele) until they were relieved in October. In the spring of 1918 they were caught up in the final German offensive and on 12 April were overrun, many being killed or captured.

Shortly after the war, an Usk man, W.G. Sweet, who had been sergeant in the 2nd Monmouthshires, wrote an account of the activities of the battalion in the final phase of the war, starting in the Ypres salient in August 1918. The Armistice on 11 November found them at Celles in southern Belgium (where over 30 years later the German Ardennes offensive of 1944 was halted). From here, they advanced via the field of Waterloo and the Ardennes to Cologne, which they occupied under the terms of the Armistice. The 2nd Monmouthshires had been the first Territorial battalion to be given the task of holding a front line trench, were one of only ten Territorial battalions that had been awarded the 1914 Star and were now the only Territorials to march into Germany at the war's end.

During the course of the war over 40 Blaenavon men died serving in the regiment.[15] Of those who had survived, many Blaenavon men were among the earliest to return home from the battalion since, with the need for coal, miners were given priority in demobilization.[16]

The Home Front – We Stood in Queues for Apples, for Paraffin and Jam

An immediate effect of the outbreak of war was the partial stoppage of shipping. There was a drastic reduction in exports, including coal, and of the import of wheat, meat and other essential foodstuffs. Food prices increased sharply. At some stages in the war, particularly during the U-boat blockade of 1917, there was a fear that Britain might be starved into submission. Despite this, the war years saw a decline in the high levels of pre-war infant mortality. These, like adult mortality rates, were already falling before the war due to medical advances, the import of cheap food and better sanitation, but the side effects of the war increased this trend. With higher wartime wages and women at work, more money was coming into the family and a higher proportion of it was reaching mothers, resulting in the better nourishment of small children. In Newport, infant mortality fell from 118 per thousand live births to 80, in Merthyr from 128 to 89 and in Swansea from 135 to 88.[17]

In 1914 the average wage of women in industry was a third of the average industrial male wage. At the outbreak of war, 3,400 women were employed nationally in the iron and steel industry, 1% of the workforce.[18] Initially, there was reluctance to employ women in the munitions industry. Amongst the concerns, unions feared possible 'dilution' of the workforce by lower paid workers. However, the 'shell scandal' of May 1915, when there was a shortage of munitions on the western front, resulted in the creation of a Ministry of Munitions under Lloyd George, whilst the introduction of conscription in 1916 led to a labour shortage. Given the circumstances, the unions agreed to female workers, provided that they were paid at the same rate as men and on an understanding that they would be sacked when the war ended. In the event, through a loophole in the agreement, they were paid roughly half the male wages, though this was more than most working women were used to receiving. By November 1918 the number of working women in the iron and steel industry had increased to 39,000 or 11% of the workforce.[19] Manual labour was no novelty to many women of Blaenavon. The Blaenavon furnaces produced shell steel and a poorly preserved photograph shows a group of some 75 women munitions workers in uniform overalls and head coverings, one holding a shell. When a Pontypool woman, the wife of a serving soldier, was fatally injured in February 1918, she was given something akin to a military funeral, with her coffin carried by soldiers, followed by a column of Blaenavon munitions women in work overalls. Middle class women were employed as 'lady superintendents', the Blaenavon women working under a 'Lady Supervisor', Miss Henrietta Griffiths of Pontypool.[20]

Throughout the war, there was conflict between the needs of army recruitment and those of armaments production. With the acute wartime need for coal and steel, both increasingly became reserved occupations; in the first fully industrialised war, supply was the essence of victory. In the early months of the war coal owners complained that the government was at one and the same time demanding greater coal output and sending recruiting sergeants into mining areas. Later, skilled men exempt from military service were issued with badges to show their status in the war effort. In 1914-15, 22% of recruits nationally were miners. With the need to retain skilled manpower in essential industries, this fell to 4% after October 1915. At Blaenavon a new Siemens-Martin open hearth furnace was built in 1917 and the railway sidings near the furnaces enlarged to carry the all-important shell steel and the finished shells.

There was one minor addition to the wartime population of Blaenavon – refugees from German-occupied Belgium. These were something of a feature of wartime Britain, one even inspiring Agatha Christie to create her Belgian detective, Hercule Poirot.[21]

The wartime rise in food prices would have hit many in Blaenavon hard. Before the war, Britain had imported most of its food – wheat from America (80% of bread wheat was imported), meat from Australia and New Zealand. Expenditure on food took two-thirds of the income of a normal working-class family. The diversion of shipping and the U-boat blockade quickly drove up food prices and restricted supplies. In the early months of the war, the price of a loaf rose from 5.5 pence to 8 pence and by February 1915 flour was 75% dearer than a year before and sugar 72% dearer. By 1917 food queues had become a familiar sight. 'We stood in queues for apples', recalled Idris Davies, 'for paraffin and jam'.[22] The prices of cheaper staple foods, particularly imported meat, rose more quickly than those of better quality produce. A lack of storage space and facilities (with no refrigerators) meant that working-class housewives needed to buy smaller amounts and more often. There were serious fears of starvation. All cultivatable land was pressed into service for growing food and one unexpected but permanent result of the war was the family allotment. In January 1918 food rationing was introduced. One other wartime legacy would have been unpopular for quite other reasons. In an effort to save grain, increase munitions production and please Lloyd George's nonconformist supporters, restrictive opening hours for pubs were introduced, long to outlast the war.

The war effort led to greater state involvement in the coal industry, in the longer term paving the way for nationalisation. The coal owners drew large windfall profits from the war and unions demanded a share as a 'war bonus'. This led to strikes. The South Welsh miners were in a strong bargaining position, with a near monopoly on the supply of steam coal for the Royal Navy. In February 1918 the Coal Mines Control Act regulated profits, with any excess going to the Treasury. At the same time, miners' representatives were appointed to the committee of the Government Coal Controller. William Brace, the Risca-born former collier and now miners' leader thought that the war had advanced the position of the miner by 25 years.[23]

Hard Times – Blaenavon Between the Wars

On 11 November 1918 the guns finally fell silent along the western front. The demand for coal and steel for reconstruction in Europe initially turned a war-boom into a post-war boom that lasted until 1921 with good wages and profits. In 1919, faced with demands from miners for a 30% wage increase, a reduction in hours and nationalization of the coal industry, the government asked Sir John Sankey to make recommendations. The resulting Sankey Report conceded higher wages and a seven-hour day and recommended the setting up of the Miners Welfare Fund, with a levy of a penny per ton of coal – 'the magic penny'. This, through the Mining Industry Act of 1920, helped pay for much needed leisure facilities in Workmen's Institutes such as billiard halls and cinemas and for such amenities as pithead baths. In 1922 Blaenavon's first council housing estate, already planned before the war, was built at Elgam, followed in 1923 by an open air swimming pool.

This post-war optimism did not last. Newly rebuilt iron and steel plants with modern equipment were coming into production in Belgium and northern France, undercutting Welsh steel in world markets. The decline of the steel industry left the area even more dependent on coal, which relied heavily on export, with 57% of its output going overseas.[24] On 31 March 1921 government wartime control of the coal industry ended. Coal prices had already halved due to French competition and a fall in demand for steam coal – many steamships had been sunk by German U-boats and the new ships that replaced them were mostly oil driven. After the war the Admiralty changed over to oil for its ships, removing an important and prestigious market. Elsewhere, coal was giving way to electricity and the internal combustion engine.

Under the Treaty of Versailles, the French occupied the Ruhr coalfields in compensation for wartime damage to their collieries in Nord and Pas de Calais. France has only limited coal deposits, save in the north-east, and pre-war there had been a lucrative export trade in coal from South Wales, whilst the empty coal ships returning from Breton ports carried the Breton onion sellers (Shoni Wnions), long to be a familiar presence in South Wales. Such exports now ended. In 1921 Milfraen Pit closed (albeit briefly), along with Kay's Slope, one of four drift mines still working, the others being Dodd's Slope, Forge Slope and Tunnel Level. At Merthyr, Cyfartha, once the largest ironworks in Wales, which had closed down in 1910 and re-opened in 1916 to produce shell steel, was finally abandoned in 1921. In Monmouthshire, the Rhymney Iron Co. Ltd, now basically a colliery company, was bought by the Powell Dyffryn Combine in 1920.

With the end of the war, the women munitions workers were made redundant as men returned from the front. One estimate is that nationally 750,000 women lost their jobs.

As Deidre Beddoes wrote: 'Women swept chimneys and roads, dug graves and fields, drove trams and buses, laboured in shipyards and engine sheds, assembled aeroplanes and tanks and manufactured shells and bullets. When the war ended, women were expected to down tools and return quietly to the house.' Newspapers campaigned against women taking the jobs of unemployed ex-servicemen, while middle class householders grumbled that women, having tasted the freedom, pay and camaraderie of factory work had no wish to return to domestic service, creating what was called a 'servant problem'. By 1921 only 13% of adult women in Blaenavon were in paid work, well below the Welsh national average. Only a few places, including Nantyglo and Blaina, had a lower figure. Between 1921 and 1938, 440,000 people left Wales in search of work, out of a population of 2.5 million.[25]

The Blaenavon furnaces and steelworks were briefly re-started in 1924-5, but coal output was falling sharply as were miners' wages. The Monmouthshire and South Wales Coal Owners Association demanded further wage cuts, changes to working conditions and a return to local wage bargaining. The government-appointed Samuel Commission of 1926 accepted the coal owners' case and recommended a 13.5% cut in wages, local wage bargaining and the withdrawal of government subsidy. The owners then threatened a lock out if the men did not accept these terms by 1 May. Since the miners were joined in a 'triple alliance' with the rail and transport workers, when the miners went on strike, the General Strike of 1926 followed. The subsequent lock out by the coal owners lasted until November, with great suffering to the miners and their families. In mid May contingents of workers from Blaenavon, Abersychan and elsewhere, led by bands and with banners reading 'Workers of the World Unite' and 'Give Us Our Daily Bread', converged on Pontypool to protest about the inadequacies of relief. The Wall Street crash of 1929 brought about a world crisis and in 1931 the British Government raised income tax, cut unemployment pay by 10% and introduced a means test for the payment os state relief to families. This scrutinised a family's income and resources, often including their personal possessions, to determine whether they were eligible for state aid. This assessment, often carried out with great rigour by unsympathetic local officials, caused much bitterness and resentment, and in April the Relieving Officer at Blaenavon was besieged in his office for several hours by an angry crowd 2,000 strong.[26]

In 1925 the directors leased Blaenavon House to Blaenavon Medical Society for use as a hospital and gave up their shooting rights on the Blorenge, the most southerly grouse moor in Britain. There would be no more shooting parties for local gentry at the Big House. Since the early days of the ironworks Blaenavon had the medical services of the Steel(e) family of doctors from Abergavenny. The Blaenavon Medical Society, however, developed from within the community and was financed by weekly contributions from the people of Blaenavon; it was acknowledged by Aneurin Bevan, along with the Tredegar Medical Aid Society, as one of the models for the post-war National Health Service.[27]

In 1929 Robert Kennard died at his London house. Though he had not been actively involved in Blaenavon for many years, this marked the end of an era that had started in 1836. There were other signs that the world had changed. In the first decade of the century the Liberal Party and their Labour allies had dominated Welsh politics, holding between 26 and 28 of the 34 Welsh seats. Reginald McKenna had been Liberal M.P. for North

Monmouthshire since 1886 and as Home Secretary a hard line opponent of Women's Suffrage. An early rival of Churchill, he was described by Roy Jenkins as 'not at all like Churchill ... prim, even prissy, efficient but with almost nil charisma'. Coal miners had been fully unionized by 1895 and the old Liberal-Labour alliance was destroyed by a bitter coal strike in 1898, leading to the creation of the South Wales Miners Federation, which affiliated with the Labour Representation Committee, the forerunner of the Labour Party, in 1908. In the same year, branches of the Trade and Labour Council and the Labour Representation Committee were founded at Blaenavon.[28] In the 1918 election for the new seat of Pontypool, McKenna lost to a Labour candidate, Thomas Griffiths, Divisional Officer of the Iron and Steel Trades Federation, who held the seat until 1935, when he was succeeded by Arthur Jenkins (1882-1946). McKenna finished in third place, behind the Conservative. Nationally, Labour won 10 seats. The Liberal programme of church disestablishment, temperance and hostility to landlordism no longer had any relevance to the concerns of industrial society.[29]

On 10 July 1929, three years after the trauma of the General Strike, Blaenavon experienced a mining disaster at Milfraen Pit. This took the lives of eight miners, mostly young men in their early 20s. Milfraen had been opened by John Jayne, a member of a long-established local family, in 1865 and was taken over by the Blaenavon Company in 1884. Some years after the disaster a survivor, James Daniel Matthews, who had been working in the pit on the morning of the explosion, wrote a vivid and moving account of the tragedy and of the heroic rescue attempts which followed. The cause was probably a faulty coal cutting machine, which ignited an accumulation of gas.[29]

In 1931, Blaenavon erected its war memorial next to the Workmen's Hall on a site previously occupied by a captured German field gun. The tall white obelisk of Portland stone, modelled on the Whitehall cenotaph but topped by a clock, carries the names of 118 men who had fallen in the war, with no rank or regiment. Several chapels and churches followed suit, with bronze plaques or illuminated scrolls, often giving more detail than the bald list of names on the cenotaph. Sadly, the long melancholy list of names has since been added to by a second World War and by conflict in Korea and Northern Ireland.[30]

The Garnddyrys Tunnel

At Garnddyrys, Thomas Hill II's tunnel was still in use, with close to its exit a shed housing three small saddle tank locomotives for the quarries. In 1978 Martin Lawler interviewed Stan Jones, who had lived in Long Row at Garnddyrys and remembered the final years of the tunnel's operation. Trains of 15-20 trams, each laden with seven tons of limestone, conveyed material from the quarries to the steelworks. By the 1920s a system of battery-operated electric signalling wires had been installed. John Powell, who operated the main stationary engine at the Blaenavon entrance to the tunnel, was an amputee, having lost both legs in an accident when the haulage rope came off the shears. The 'tail' engine at Pwll Du was operated by William Watkins, also disabled. In bad weather, women from Pwll Du were allowed to use the tunnel to go shopping in Blaenavon, riding through on the trams; if Powell saw a Pwll Du woman approaching, he would delay the trams. After the General Strike in 1926, the limestone quarries closed and the tunnel fell into disuse.

Fig. 81 Restoration of the Pwll Du tunnel in 2012. (Photograph by Tim Davies)

The Angry Summer – Films, a Novel and Self Help

> And on the roads arterial,
> As London died away,
> The poets of the Thirties,
> Were singing of decay.
> Idris Davies   *I Was Born in Rhymney*

Each year the directors expressed hope that when conditions improved, a furnace might be put into blast and each following year the same hope was repeated. By July 1927 the percentage of unemployed workers at Abertillery was 36%, at Blaina nearly 38% and at Blaenavon 40.3%. Two years later, the Wall Street Crash led to a global financial crisis and by 1932 the percentage in both Glamorgan and Monmouthshire reached a total of over 40%. At Merthyr Tydfil the figure stood at over 60% and at Brynmawr in 1934 at 74%.[31] The National Unemployed Workers Movement organized a series of hunger marches to London and in October 1936, 500 hunger marchers left South Wales in protest against the Means Test regulations. The march had the support of a broad range of local civic and religious organizations and the Blaenavon contingent were seen off with a religious service.[32]

Despite the hardships and suffering of the 1920s and 1930s, South Wales saw a remarkable flowering of writing and film, in which Blaenavon played its part. In 1922 the British Broadcasting Company (later Corporation) began wireless transmissions. Though possession of a wireless set remained something of a status symbol for some years, this widened horizons for many people.[33] Idris Davies, an ex-miner from Rhymney, a poet praised by no less a critic than T.S. Eliot, is worthy to stand alongside the better known poets of the thirties, who came from a very different public school and Oxbridge background, of whom he was not uncritical. In 1921 a Blaenavon miner and mine rescue worker, William Henry Taylor (*c*.1891-1980) published a novel, *The Cheated Death*, set in a thinly disguised 'Garnavon'. Its main themes are the conflicts of culture and society in a community on the margin between England and Wales. The father of Taylor's heroine, Crystal Westwood, is an immigrant from Somerset, whilst Jack Owen, whom she eventually marries, is caught between pit management and unions and between older nonconformist Welsh-speaking traditions and newer socialist ideals. The impending pit disaster which forms the climax of the novel reflects Taylor's firsthand experience as a member of the Blaenavon mine rescue team. The novel deserves re-publication.[34]

Later in the decade, a group of Blaenavon people made a remarkable and successful venture into film making. The arrival of the 'Talkies' in 1927 began a golden age of the cinema and in time there were over 70 cinemas in Workmen's Institutes in Wales. The Miners Welfare Fund ('the magic penny') helped to pay for projectors and keep the cinemas open during the depression, when contributions from members dropped off.[35] In Blaenavon Workmen's Hall, the programme was changed twice weekly. In 1928 a young engineer, W.H. Fleet, obtained a secondhand film camera and A.S. Northcote, secretary of the Workmen's Hall wrote the script for a silent film edited by a Pontypool journalist J.R. Payne, who was also producer and actor. The resultant *By the Aid of A Rogue* was an 18th-century costumed elopement drama, with Doris Evans as the heroine and Albert E. Parsons as the wicked squire. Sadly, one actor, Ernest West, was killed in a mining accident two weeks after shooting finished. The film was sold to the European Motion Picture Company and saw a number of successful screenings. The team planned to make a longer film, *The Reckoning*, the following year, starring a local beauty queen, but this never materialized.[36]

These years also saw a Quaker-inspired self-help project, the Eastern Valleys Subsistence Scheme. Westlake's brewery had opened down the valley at Cwmavon in 1900, but it closed in 1928, a victim of the slump. In March 1935 the building and its grounds were taken over for the Subsistence Production Society, led by a Newport member of the Society of Friends, Peter Scott. A bakery was opened, producing a thousand loaves a day, pigs were reared for meat, bacon and sausages, milk and eggs produced and vegetables and fruit grown. Men were able to use their skills – cobblers repaired footwear, suits were made by tailors. Six hundred acres of land around Pontypool, Cwmbran and Brynmawr were farmed and Ayrshire cattle reared on land at Llandegveth near Caerleon, providing beef for families rarely able to afford meat. Scott began a subsistence production society, with 300 members. Instead of cash, members acquired credit for working so many hours, which could be exchanged for goods. Scott was succeeded by Jim Forrester, otherwise James Grimston, later 5th Earl of Verulam. They were later joined by a refugee German education-alist Minna Specht and a group of children from a progressive school forcibly shut down by the Nazis. The scheme was seen as no more than a temporary expedient, but gave the 400 men involved a new sense of their own value (Fig. 82).[37]

In 1937 this co-operative venture was the subject of a documentary film, *Eastern Valley*, financed by Jim Forrester and the Society of Friends and made for Strand Films by Donald Alexander, a Scottish Cambridge graduate involved in the Workers Film Movement. It was

Fig. 82 Westlake's Brewery, Cwmavon, scene of the remarkable Quaker co-operative venture of the 1930s. (Photograph by Simon Hardy)

produced by Stuart Legg and directed by Alf Jenkins, who was also, with S.D. Onions, the cameraman. It told how in the past the people of the valley had gone from being agricultural workers and skilled rural craftsmen to being ironworkers and miners, huddled together in rows of housing close to their place of work. The story was told through the person of Dai Williams, an unemployed miner, and explained how men were rediscovering an older, slower and quieter way of life. In an epilogue, a Mrs Whetton described the problems of raising three children on 30 shillings a week. Her husband, a miner, unemployed for ten years, now worked as a roundsman, delivering milk and bread for the subsistence co-operative 'to unemployed houses like ours'. The film was praised by no less a critic than Graham Greene.[38]

In 1934 much of the obsolete Forgeside plant was sold for scrap. The Bessemer process had died out in Britain by 1928 in favour of open hearth furnaces like those at Blaenavon. Re-introduced in the 1930s at Ebbw Vale and Corby, when these closed in 1966 and 1968 it marked the end of Bessemer steel. A new steel plant opened at Blaenavon in 1937-9, with assistance from the Nuffield Trust, when fears of an impending war saw the beginnings of a rearmament programme, but this used imported pig iron – a sign of how radically things had changed.

On 20 November 1936 Blaenavon received a visit that was to be long remembered. King Edward VIII had travelled from Usk via Cwmbran, where he was met by the Quaker Peter Scott, who showed him around the Subsistence project and its bread making, boot repairing and carpentry schemes. His stop in Blaenavon had not originally been included in the itinerary, but the king spent some time talking to local councillors and unemployed workers. In the course of conversation with A.H. Holder, Chairman of Blaenavon Council, he made the remark that was to be so widely quoted: 'Something must be done for you'. He then left for lunch in Garn yr Erw Welfare Hall. Within a few weeks the abdication crisis intervened and in 1938 the last Forgeside furnace was blown out.[39]

Blaenavon and the Second World War

One Sunday morning in September 1939, the Prime Minister, Neville Chamberlain, gave one of the most momentous radio broadcasts in history: 'I have to tell you now', he concluded, 'that Britain is at war with Germany.' Much of what followed for the people of Blaenavon – gas masks in their cardboard boxes, identity cards (drab green-grey rectangles with their holder's details) and ration books – was shared with the rest of Britain. Many Blaenavon miners or steelworkers were in reserved occupations, but others faced call up for the armed forces. Older men joined the Local Defence Volunteers, the later Home Guard. Near Big Pit a row of upended colliery trams, filled with concrete, formed an optimistic anti-tank barrier. The whole nation moved into uncharted waters.

In July 1940 a train full of children evacuated from the bombing and cross-Channel shelling of Dover and the east end of London arrived in Blaenavon. John Lockyer, then a 12-year-old, recalled the event many years later:

> I was one of several hundred children who arrived in Blaenavon after a 14-hour train journey. We were there in total darkness, due to the strict blackout regulations. We were tired and confused – some distressed – but the people of Blaenavon were there

for us. Comforting voices and outstretched hands gave us a sense of hope and a sense of security which ... we will never forget.

In all, something like a thousand children were evacuated to Blaenavon and the over-stretched local schools had to operate a double shift system. John Lockyer lodged with the Jenkins family in 65 High Street, whose own son, Tom Jenkins, was an airman reported missing, presumed killed, over Dunkirk. John Lockyer went on to study in a Welsh University and to have a successful career as a graphic designer. In 2010, aged 82, he led a group of surviving evacuees back to Blaenavon to express their thanks. In some cases, apart from the trauma of leaving home, the move from crowded inner cities to rural villages or from southern English middle class homes to working class families in the valleys was a culture shock, with sheep wandering the streets, and tin baths before the fire in place of the privacy of bathrooms. Len Street of the W.E.A. Blaenavon History Group has now collected the reminiscences of children from Dover and Walthamstow evacuated to Blaenavon. Apart from their own memories, these give a lively picture of Blaenavon in the 1940s as seen by a group of perceptive young people from a different environment.[40]

The war began to intrude on Blaenavon in other ways. On 22 September 1940 a flight of three Blenheim light bombers from 17 Officer Training Unit (90 Squadron) on a cross-country training flight became lost in fog. One became separated and crashed on Garn Wen between Pontypool and Abersychan, killing the crew of three. Evacuee Eric Turner many years later recalled the shocked reaction in the town as news of the accident spread. A memorial stone now marks the site (at Grid ref SO 285046).[41]

The following month the Light Alloys Control Office contacted the Blaenavon Company, since they were planning to install drop stamping equipment for aircraft production. In 1941 the Ministry of Aircraft Production extended the machine shop and installed new forging hammers and other machinery. The Ministry was putting production on a war footing, requisitioning 24 factories at the Treforest Industrial Estate alone. Blaenavon acted as agents for a Slough-based company, High Duty Alloys, involved in aeronautical engineering. There was some debate about the solid wheel and axle plant, since the Ministry of Supply had powers to transfer any unused plant and machinery elsewhere. There was other armaments production, with an assembly line for 17 pounder guns in the 'black shed' on Forgeside. These were Britain's most effective anti-tank weapons, and enabled Sherman tanks, upgraded to 'Fireflies', to compete more equally with German Tiger tanks and the feared 88mm anti-tank guns.[42]

It was not only men who were conscripted for the war effort. In May 1941 women aged between 19 and 40 were required to register at employment exchanges and that December single women between 20 and 30 were conscripted for industry or the armed forces. Many women from the Gwent valleys worked in the Royal Ordnance Factory at Glascoed outside Usk, which by 1942 had 13,000 workers, many of them women. This involved long hours of travel by bus or train in difficult wartime conditions. In 1942 the Mass Observation Survey, a private organization which recruited volunteers to record conversations and details of everyday life, sent Mollie Tarrant to Blaina and Nantyglo. She found that the relatively high wages of the munitions factory gave women greater independence, with a breakdown of pre-war restrictions and taboos, though they could also cause domestic friction when a woman's take home pay was greater than that of her miner husband. The survey also found fears among the more thoughtful of a possible post-war depression and of how far things would actually change after the war.[43]

Even after Hitler's assault on Russia, fears continued of an invasion. In the spring of 1942 instructions were issued for the immobilization of the works in such an eventuality and specific managers were nominated to carry this out. Essential machine parts were to be hidden, plans and blueprints destroyed and all power plants immobilized. Blaenavon was made a 'key point of national importance'. Damage from enemy action was to be reported on an official form, special visitors' passes issued, checks on lorries instituted and precautions against spies and saboteurs brought in. A steel anti-aircraft flak tower was mounted on Forgeside, with a Home Guard sergeant in charge, perhaps in reaction to a raid by a flight of Dornier 17 German bombers which dropped incendiaries on Coity mountain near Forgeside, starting a fire. The four foreign refugees in Blaenavon, two Spaniards, Celestine Sancho and Jean Pullido, and two Belgians, were given clean bills of health.[44]

In 1942, though only one furnace was working, Blaenavon was producing steel ingots, sprocket rings and tyres, as well as aluminium and magnesium alloys for the Ministry of Aircraft Production. There were 700 workers, including 50 women and 1,800 in the collieries, producing 550,000 tons of coal a year.[45] Above Pwll Du, Canadian soldiers with heavy machinery and expert in open cast mining, then a novelty in Britain, stripped 500 acres of moorland, producing 3 million tons of coal a year, 5% of Britain's wartime needs. The resulting spoil heaps are still known as the 'Canada Tips'. Two ruined Bronze age cairns were excavated in advance of this by W.F. ('Peter') Grimes, an early case of rescue excavation funded by the state, but nothing significant was found. Graham Sutherland, then an official war artist, drew this extraordinary landscape, which still survives (Fig. 83).[46]

A fortnight before D Day, on the evening of 21 May 1944, Halifax bomber MH-V (serial no LK 835) of 51 Squadron, took off from its base at Snaith in Yorkshire. At 20,000 feet a starboard engine burst into flame. The pilot put the plane on to 'George' (automatic pilot) and the crew of eight baled out and landed safely around Blaina and Nantyglo. Maisie Peters, a girl of 14 living in Milfraen Cottages, saw the plane plunge down nose first

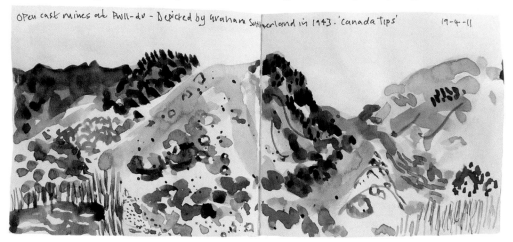

Fig. 83 The Canada Tips painted by Graham Sutherland

139

into a bog 200 yards from Milfraen House, narrowly missing her father's greenhouses. After the war, the navigator, Sergeant David Biddie, emigrated to Perth in Australia, but came back in 1985 and visited the crash site. He met Maisie, by then Maisie House, landlady of the Whistle Inn and recorded his memories of the event in the pub's visitors' book. Some wreckage can still be seen on site.[47]

The 2nd Monmouthshires, as part of the 53rd Welsh Division, landed in Normandy on 28 June 1944 and were involved in the fighting around Caen and in the Falaise Gap before advancing into Holland, where they took part in the liberation of the town of 's-Hertogenbosch. After further heavy fighting in the forest of the Reichswald, where they took heavy casualties, they were in Hamburg by the time of the German surrender. Cyril McCann, originally from Upper New Rank, a medical sergeant, has given a vivid first hand account of his experiences from the Normandy beaches to the German capitulation.[48]

In 1944, with the war nearing its end and a coal shortage at home, miners serving in the forces were offered the chance of early release, though not all took the option.

11 REINVENTION: BLAENAVON IN THE POST INDUSTRIAL WORLD

Brave New World?

On 7 May 1945 Blaenavon, for the second time within living memory, entered a post-war world, though the war with Japan continued for some months. After the V.E. 'Victory in Europe' celebrations, reality resumed. Food was scarce and rationing continued until 1953, with bread rationed for the first time. Blaenavon was still an isolated upland community and in the 30-hour blizzard and snowstorm of March 1947 food supplies for the Milfraen cottages had to be taken underground at Kay's Slope colliery and carried along mine galleries. When a midwife was needed, she had to be taken to the cottages in the bucket of a tracked JCB.

In 1949 the obsolete solid steel and axle plant on Forgeside was sold to a French firm for £160,000 and nine years later the Blaenavon Company Limited was finally wound up. The previous year Daniel Doncasters had moved into the empty Forgeside works, part of an international engineering group making specialist forged rings, castings and blades for the aerospace, gas turbine and petrochemical industries, with such clients as Boeing, Rolls Royce and Volkswagen. When Ebbw Vale steelworks ceased production in the 1970s and converted to a tinplate works (which itself closed in 2002), Blaenavon became the last survivor of the iron and steel industries along the heads of the Valleys. Even the newer coastal steelworks were in difficulties. East Moors closed in 1978, though Ebbw Vale's successor Llanwern was until the late 1990s the largest single site manufacturer of tinplate in Europe.

This Proud Land – Alexander Cordell and the Mortymers

Like most valley towns, Blaenavon has a tradition of local historians, from Lewis Browning onwards, who have a pride in the history of their community and its people and a local knowledge which few outsiders can match. The first of those outsiders to take a sustained interest in the history of Blaenavon was George Alexander Graber (1914-97), better known as Alexander Cordell, a former Major in the Royal Artillery born in Ceylon and latterly a civil servant living in Llanellen. In the 1950s a local newspaper, the *South Wales Argus* ran an annual competition for local historians, *Pages from the Past.* In 1957 this was won by Graber with a work *Life Among the Ironworkers of Garnddyrys and Blaenavon 1810-1836,* now put in print by Blaenavon Community Heritage Museum.[1] He was already at work on the historical novel which was to make his name, *Rape of the Fair Country*, published in

1959, extracts from which appear in his competition entry, together with a pioneer map of the historical landscape and a series of photographs of surviving buildings.

Cordell's ability to create vividly-drawn characters that stay in the memory recalls Charles Dickens. His Welsh trilogy, *Rape of the Fair Country*, *The Hosts of Rebecca* (1960) and *Song of the Earth* (1969) begins in 1826, but he later added a prologue or 'prequel'. *This Proud and Savage Land*, also set in Blaenavon, tells how young Hywel Mortymer had come from rural mid Wales in 1800 to work in the South Welsh ironfield. The story opens in rural Carmarthenshire, around Llandovery and Dolaucothi. Cordell uses the Dickensian plot formula of a young man from a gentry family fleeing from villainous relatives and finding himself in very different company. *Rape of the Fair Country*, set in Blaenavon, Nantyglo and Garnddyrys, has been translated into many languages and has seen a number of stage adaptations. Hywel Mortymer and his two children, Iestyn and Morfydd, live in a world of child labour, exploitation and suffering, where even the river is polluted by industry. It is also a world of growing political consciousness, of Scotch Cattle and Chartists, culminating in the 1839 Newport Rising, brought to life both by characters such as Iestyn Mortymer and his sister Morfydd and by Cordell's historical research.

The Hosts of Rebecca deals with another Welsh radical movement of the early 19th century, as small farmers in west Wales banded together in nighttime attacks on the hated toll gates, often disguised as women and taking their name from a Biblical text 'The daughters of Rebecca shall possess the gates of their enemies'. *Song of the Earth*, the third of the trilogy, is set in Merthyr and the Neath Valley, with the Evans family living in a turbulent world of cholera epidemics, Irish immigrants and early trade unionism, as the world of the Neath Canal is threatened by Brunel's new railway.

The immense success of Cordell's books showed that the historical importance of the town was beginning to be recognized and influenced powerfully what was to follow.

The Death of the Old

Development of the present town in mid Victorian times had left the older core around the ironworks – Shepherd Square, Staffordshire Row, Bunker's Hill and the rest – isolated. At the same time this saved it from re-building and renewal. In the 1960s these old houses still stood, increasingly dilapidated, often derelict and unsuitable for modern living. They provided the essential background for Cordell's story of the Mortymer family, but in 1951 over 60% of houses in many industrial communities in Gwent, including Blaenavon, were without fixed baths or internal bathrooms and relied on a tin bath in front of the fire. This was a time when newspapers and magazines were full of advertisements for refrigerators, washing machines and dish washers.[2] There had long been concerns about the effects of poor housing conditions in Blaenavon on public health, with infectious diseases, high rates of infant mortality from scarlet fever and measles and what an observer in 1877 referred to as the 'inadequate disposal of human excreta'. As long ago as 1909 Shepherd Square had been described as 'dank, damp, dirty, squalid ... slum property'. The 17 houses stood around a triangular court with a central latrine block without fixed plumbing. One visitor in 1951 wrote of Shepherd Square: 'The most deplorable housing conditions I have seen are in Blaenavon, by the old derelict works.'[3]

The Labour Party election victory of 1945 was part of a post-war determination to create a brave new world in which such relics of the past as slum housing and obsolete industrial plant would be swept away. In 1963 the isolated community high on the Blorenge at Pwll Du was evacuated, ironically just after it had at last been connected to mains electricity. Its residents were re-housed in new council houses in Govilon or on Forgeside and the rows of early housing demolished, though the Lamb Inn (now the Lamb and Fox) happily survived. At one time, Pwll Du had been a flourishing community, but when the quarries closed in 1926 that community was no longer viable.

By the 1960s, with a new generation which had not known the sufferings of the 1920s and 1930s at first hand, attitudes to the industrial past were beginning to change. Industrial landscapes were now seen not as relics of a dark age before the brave new post-war world, but as the visible relics of generations of struggle for political and social advancement, epitomized in Cordell's novels. Where such historic landscapes could not be preserved, at least a proper record of them should be made.

Blaenavon as History – Preservation and Record

In 1970 Blaenavon Urban District Council drew up a redevelopment plan which involved the wholesale demolition of most of the housing around North Street and the old town.[4] The recording of below-ground archaeological remains before destruction by 'rescue

Fig. 84 Stack Square: the interior of the re-furnished cottage of the Macarthy family from County Cork, who were here in 1841 (see Fig. 17). (Photograph by Simon Hardy)

143

*Fig. 85 Stack Square: the interior of a refurnished cottage of a later family.
(Photograph by Simon Hardy)*

*Fig. 86 Stack Square: the family's table, as laid for afternoon tea sometime
in the mid 20th century. (Photograph by Simon Hardy)*

archaeology' was well established, but there was no similar framework for recording standing buildings. The Welsh Archaeological Trusts which today might have taken on such a task, did not then exist. Jeremy Lowe of the Welsh School of Architecture of the University of Wales Institute of Science and Technology and I realized the importance of recording this early housing before demolition and in 1969 we devised the idea of a recording survey for industrial housing in Blaenavon. The Royal Institution of British Architects agreed to fund the work with a grant of £1,000, leading to the appointment of a research student, David Anderson, and the recruitment of a group of student volunteers.[5]

It was planned to begin with the recording of Shepherd Square, but when Jeremy Lowe arrived on 30 July 1970 to begin the survey, he found demolition already in progress, the Urban District Council being under the misapprehension that the survey had already been carried out. Between 1970 and 1972 there was a large-scale clearance of the older housing, as the remaining inhabitants were re-settled. Shepherd Square, Bunker's Row, Staffordshire Row and Chapel Row disappeared. The site of Shepherd Square is now occupied by Kennard Place, whilst Chapel Row has been replaced by the Sidney Gilchrist Thomas Industrial Estate. Apart from Stack Square (Figs. 84, 85 & 86), one of the few groups of early workers' housing still existing is Forge Row at Cwmavon. When its final occupant left in 1975 it faced demolition. However, thanks to the vision of the Torfaen Museum Trust under its Director Adrian Babbidge, the houses were purchased for preservation and in 1987 the British Historic Buildings Trust and the National Trust, with help

Fig. 87 The furnace yard before conservation. Furnaces 4 and 5 after clearance of rubble that had reached halfway up the structures can be seen in the background. A support pillar for the hot blast pipe stands on the right.

Fig. 88 The cast house prior to restoration

from Cadw and the Prince of Wales Committee, restored the cottages at a cost of £200,000, installed modern facilities and re-sold them to new owners, under covenants to prevent unsympathetic alterations.

In the 1960s the old furnace yard, with its blast furnaces and cast houses, was still in use as a small scale engineering workshop by Ferrous Fabrications Ltd and as a coal yard. There was a proposal by the Welsh Development Agency to level the ironworks as part of a land reclamation scheme and reduce the site to a grassy slope. Fortunately this was delayed since Alexander Cordell had sold the film rights of his novel and the actor Richard Burton wished to use the site to film *Rape of the Fair Country.* The film was never made, but it gave time for attitudes to change. David Morgan Rees, Keeper of Industry in the National Museum of Wales had written a pioneering article on industrial archaeology in Wales in *Archaeologia Cambrensis* for 1964. He and Michael Apted, Inspector of Ancient Monuments for Wales, opened negotiations in 1970 for the preservation of the ironworks. Much needed urgent conservation work began in 1974, leading to the site coming into the care of what is now Cadw: Welsh Historic Monuments two years later (Figs. 87 & 88).

Tourism and Leisure – The New Industry
In February 1980 Big Pit, the last deep mine in Blaenavon, closed. It had produced the coking coal which had originally brought Blaenavon into being, but from the late 1950s oil had been replacing coal for domestic heating and in industry and in the 1960s North Sea Gas had begun to come ashore. Big Pit incorporated a complex of earlier mines and levels, one of which, Forge Level, originally an ironstone mine, went back to 1812. Big Pit itself

Fig. 89 Big Pit. (Photograph by Nathan Matthews)

may have begun as a balance pit of the 1830s[6] but its immediate origin was Kearsley's Pit, sunk in 1860 and deepened to 300 feet in 1860. Big Pit's closure also marked the end of rail in Blaenavon. Though the passenger line to Newport had closed in 1962, the line as far as Pontypool had been kept open for coal traffic.

This however was far from being the end of the story. Following negotiations between the National Coal Board and Torfaen Museum Trust, Big Pit reopened as a museum under a charitable trust in April 1983, since when it has had well over three million visitors (Fig. 89). In 1999 it was taken over by the National Museum of Wales. After a programme of restoration in 2004, with funding from the Heritage Lottery Fund, The Welsh Assembly Government and the Wales Tourist Board, it is now the National Coal Museum of Wales. One other South Welsh coalmine followed a similar route. In 1983 the Wales Tourist Board issued a report: *Realising the Tourist Potential of the South Wales Valleys*. The following year, after the closure of Lewis Merthyr colliery, a process began (with a lunchtime meeting of interested parties in a pub in the middle of the 1984 miners' strike) which ended in its rebirth as the Rhondda Heritage Park, with exhibitions telling the story of the 'black gold' of the Rhondda and the communities it created. Blaenavon had known visitors and tourists since the time of William Coxe and had been described as 'the famous iron works of Blaenavon ... a principle object in the tour of Monmouthshire'. Now it was to become part of 'the brave new world of leisure'.

One prominent feature of the new 'heritage industry', following the Beeching axe which had closed so much of Britain's rail network, was the rise of steam railways, run by volunteers and directed not at normal passenger traffic, but at tourism and holidaymakers. Between the wars there had been 13 or more trains each way daily between Newport and Blaenavon. High Level station and the line to Brynmawr had closed in 1941 and in April 1962 the last train from Blaenavon Low Level station had left for Newport, shortly before the wholesale closures of the 'Beeching axe', though the line from Blaenavon to Pontypool carried coal from Big Pit until 1980. Twenty years after the last passenger train had run from Blaenavon, the Brynmawr and Blaenavon Railway, built in 1866 to carry coal to the Midlands, was reopened in 1983 by the Pontypool and Blaenavon Railway Company. It had been closed to passengers in 1941 and to goods traffic in 1964. The company now runs steam and diesel trains from its main station at Furnace sidings to the Whistle Halt, next to the Whistle Inn, the highest railway station in England and Wales, Big Pit and Blaenavon High Level station near the town centre, from April until Christmas. There are also special events like the annual 1940s weekend, with groups of re-enactors in period costume and a variety of wartime uniforms and vehicles.

Other areas of the industrial landscape were also changing. The Aberfan disaster of October 1966, when a coal tip collapsed on to a school resulting in the deaths of 116 children and 28 adults, gave an added impetus to the removal of colliery waste tips and the reclamation of derelict land from coal workings. In 1979 the three large pyramidal coal tips near Big Pit, known locally as 'Little Egypt', were removed[7] and in the 1990s a large area of old coal workings west of Blaenavon below the Brynmawr road was the subject of a land reclamation scheme by Torfaen Borough Council. The Kays and Keares opencast site took its name from two of the early drift mines named after their operators – Joseph Kay's Slope and Dick Keare's Level. An area of 148 acres was stripped, 32,000 tons of coal extracted, and two lakes, known as Garn Lakes, created. These are now a wildlife habitat and recognized bird watching venue, with lapwings, mallard, widgeon, tufted duck, coot, moorhens, little grebe, redshank and common sandpipers recorded. Adjacent is the Kay and Keares Industrial Estate. Meanwhile, the Afon Lwyd below Blaenavon, once a black river, not only heavily polluted with coal waste, but an open sewer which stank in hot weather, is now a home for otters, wagtails and dippers.

In conserving the remains of the ironworks, the Inspectorate of Ancient Monuments faced formidable problems. The crumbing, often fire-damaged and dangerous masonry was very different from the medieval castles and abbeys with which they were more familiar. Big Pit had been maintained to the highest Coal Board standards of safety until the day it closed (as it still is). The miners left one day and the museum staff moved in the next. At the ironworks things were very different. The Stack Square cottages were ruinous, in poor structural state and rapidly losing their roofing. Nos.4 and 5 furnaces resembled nothing so much as volcanoes – cones of rubble crowned by a gaping furnace top. Many hundred tons of stone and debris had to be removed before conservation could even begin. The retaining wall at the rear of the furnace yard was in a dangerous state and visiting English colleagues expressed surprise at the problems this presented.

Gradually, these problems were overcome. Architects drew up plans for the conservation of the cottages, the furnaces were cleared of the accumulation of rubble, their stone and brick were conserved and they were made safe – itself a work of engineering. Eventually, the site was gradually made safe for visitors. A programme of documentary and archaeological research informed the conservation process and made possible the interpretation of the site to the public. This task has continued over the years, as a guidebook was produced and facilities and interpretation provided for visitors. The Stack Square cottages were imaginatively refurnished to show living conditions at various periods of their history.

In 1997 Torfaen County Borough Council, established the previous year, organized a major conference to discuss the importance of Blaenavon and its industrial landscape and the feasibility of a bid for UNESCO World Heritage status. The Blaenavon Partnership, led by Torfaen Council began to work for the inscription of the Blaenavon Industrial landscape on the list of World Heritage sites. The partnership included a wide range of interested parties – Cadw, local authorities, Blaenavon Town Council, the Royal Commission on the Ancient and Historical Monuments of Wales, the National Museum of Wales and a range of heritage and amenity bodies. John Rodger, previously Director of Planning and Economic Development with Gwent County Council, became the Director of Blaenavon Industrial Landscape World Heritage site and of the linked Blaenavon Regeneration Project.

In 1999 Blaenavon Industrial Landscape took its place on the list of sites to be put forward by the British Government for consideration for World Heritage status. It finally attained that status on 30 November 2000. The area constituted

> an exceptional illustration in material form of the social and economic structure of nineteenth century industry ... the components together make an outstanding and remarkably complete example of a nineteenth century industrial landscape ... The area around Blaenavon bears eloquent and exceptional testimony to the pre-eminence of south Wales as the world's major producer of iron and coal in the nineteenth century. All the necessary elements can be seen in situ: coal and ore mines, quarries, a primitive railway system, furnaces, the houses of the workers and the social infrastructure of the community.

The news was beamed via a live video link from the UNESCO Committee meeting in Cairns, Australia to a gathering of Blaenavon people in the Workmen's Hall. Ten-year-old

Joshua Williams was sent across the road to tell the church bellringers and the bells of St Peter's church rang out as they had done on other notable occasions in the town's past. The following day newspapers were full of Blaenavon and its new status. The *Independent's* headline announced that Blaenavon was 'Up there with the Taj Mahal', with a map of British World Heritage sites, including Blenheim Palace, Stonehenge and Hadrian's Wall.[8]

Booktown and Cheesetown

Blaenavon's new World Heritage status was a matter of great local pride, but it was hoped that it would also serve as a catalyst, bringing to the town new businesses and new prosperity. Blaenavon, despite its new status, was at a low ebb. Then an improbable would-be saviour appeared. An American, James Daniel Hanna, had sold up his bookshop in New Orleans and became a business partner of Richard Booth, the eccentric self-proclaimed 'King of

Fig. 90 The logo of the Blaenavon World Heritage Site

Hay', who had turned Hay-on-Wye into a secondhand book emporium, which later led to the annual Hay Festival. Attracted by the low rents and boarded up shops of Blaenavon and by a transatlantic 'Can Do' attitude, James Hanna set about creating the 'Blaenavon Booktown' project, based on the success of Hay-on-Wye. Owners of bookshops opening in Blaenavon were invited to sign up to his scheme on payment of a substantial fee. In 2003 seven shops, specializing in a variety of topics, opened and a large supply of books was stored in a warehouse ready for distribution. Over the next four years the journalist Maeve Kennedy kept up an often wry commentary in the *Guardian* on this brave experiment, though like many Metropolitan outsiders she was clearly bemused by this unique community and its remote location.

Fig. 91 Steam Hammer in the ironworks car park, originally from Daniel Doncasters who are based in Forgeside, Blaenavon

In 2004 the new Blaenavon was put on display in a conference organized by the Institute of Welsh Affairs, the National Museums and Galleries of Wales and Torfaen County Borough Council. The emphasis was on the refurbishment of Big Pit and the Book Town development rather than the ironworks (Fig. 90). There were lectures in the Workmen's Hall, a cultural programme of poetry and history in Bethlehem Chapel and guided tours of the bookshops and Big Pit.[9]

Bookshops like Broadleaf Books, specializing in Natural History, and Browning Books, named after the miner historian Lewis Browning, brought new life to central Blaenavon, but sadly for the Book Town project as a whole, as had happened several times in Blaenavon's earlier history, an idealistic project of expansion coincided with a fatal downturn in the market. Throughout the country, bookshops were closing in great numbers as on-line booksellers like Amazon took an increasing slice of the market. Hanna left the area and returned to America, where he was later given a lengthy prison sentence for sexual offences.

Though sadly the bookshops did not flourish, this was not the only enterprise attracted to Blaenavon by people who recognized its unique quality. In December 2006, Susan Flander-Woodhouse and Gerry Woodhouse, previously based in Abergavenny, but attracted to Blaenavon by its world heritage status and unique character, established the Blaenavon Cheddar Company in Broad Street, making a range of cheeses (Fig. 91a & b). They used James Ashwell's balance tower in the furnace yard, Big Pit and other Blaenavon buildings as logos, whilst their Pwll Mawr Cheddar is matured underground at the bottom of Big Pit. As a spin off from the Blaenavon Railway, a railway shop opened in the middle of town, with an array of model railway equipment and other railway related material.

*Fig. 92 Blaenavon Cheddar Company shop and their cheese label,
with Ashwell's Water Balance Lift as logo*

With help from the Heritage Lottery Fund, local volunteers set up the Blaenavon Community Heritage and Cordell Museum, a small but vibrant museum incorporating a local history centre with a family history research archive including census returns, trade directories and a book of remembrance for the town's war dead. Apart from its collection of local artefacts, it also houses material relating to Alexander Cordell, including his desk

Fig. 93 Blaenavon streetscape, with the slopes of Coity Mountain in the background

151

Fig. 94 The World Heritage Site visitor exhibition centre in the old National School building next to St Peter's Church. (Photograph by Simon Hardy)

and typewriter. It is currently in the course of re-location from Blaenavon Library to a new home in the Workmen's Hall, due to re-open in the autumn of 2015. At the same time, the Blaenavon branch of the Workers Educational Association set up a History Group, who meet weekly to research the history of the town. Their detailed historical research, incorporating studies of many aspects of Blaenavon's history, has now resulted in a fine study of the town in the first half of the 20th century, *Funeral to Festival,* with lively illustrations by their resident artist Mary Challenger and a book dealing with Blaenavon and its people in the First World War.

Both Big Pit and the ironworks have become favourite locations for a wide range of television programmes. In 2007, Blaenavon attained its own reality television series, Coalhouse, when BBC Wales moved three volunteer families, including a geologist, an astrophysicist and a Welsh-speaking family from west Wales into the refurbished houses of Stack Square, to live for a month as mining families. This was set in 1927, a particularly hard time after the collapse of the General Strike and the colliery lock out the previous year. For the modern families there was the initial shock of finding no baths, showers or running water, of hand-washing nappies and using mangles rather than washing machines, whilst the men experienced work as colliers on performance-related pay. The programme proved popular and generated both a Christmas special and a second series in 2008, Coalhouse at War, set in 1944, complete with evacuees and Bevin Boys. Time Team came here looking for the lost viaduct depicted by Sir Richard Colt Hoare and Big Pit became a familiar television image on programmes about industrial South Wales. In 2007 the Heritage Lottery Fund and the Welsh Government set up a multi-disciplinary study of the Blaenavon Industrial landscape and its ecology, the Forgotten Landscape Project. This was concerned both with the industrial remains of the Blaenavon uplands and the ecology and wildlife of its heather moorland. On the archaeological and industrial history front five sites were selected for detailed study and conservation proposals – The Dyne Steel Incline, the Engine Brake Wheel, the ruins of Hill's Pit Cottages, Ty'r Abraham Harry and the southern portal of the Pwll Du tunnel.

Much of the experience of Blaenavon and of other valley communities since the 1950s was similar to that of other former industrial areas such as Clydeside or north-east England. The departure of heavy industry – coal and steel or shipbuilding – has created a post-industrial community which, whilst still coping with intractable and chronic social problems, has also developed more positive outcomes. The Afon Llwyd, like Glasgow's Clyde and Kelvin rivers, is no longer a black coal-polluted river and supports new life. Blaenavon, whose falling population at one time seemed to threaten the future existence of the town, now supports a more stable and viable community, supported by the advent of new food- and craft-based enterprises and by affordable housing for younger people setting up house. The moorlands of the Blorenge attract walkers, mountain bikers and families, with guidebooks, tourist information and marked trails interpreting the industrial and natural landscapes for the visitors who are increasingly discovering this unique place. Though this new phase of recovery is perhaps still fragile, Blaenavon has been transformed since mid century, when its future seemed to consist only of demolition and what was euphemistically called 'land reclamation'. This unique community may hopefully at last have found the assured future which it so richly deserves.

Fig. 95 Celebrations during Blaenavon America Week

Appendix   Monmouthshire Ironworks

Blaenavon was the most easterly of the chain of ironworks which stretched across the heads of the Monmouthshire valleys as far as Merthyr and beyond. Along the west side of the Afon Llwyd below Blaenavon were Abersychan, Varteg, Pentwyn, Golynos and Pontypool. To the west along the Ebbw Fach were Nantyglo, Coalbrookvale, Cwmcelyn and Blaina while, in the Ebbw itself were Beaufort, Ebbw Vale and Victoria. To the west again, in the Sirhowy and Rhymney valleys, were Sirhowy, Tredegar and Rhymney. Many of these have been mentioned in the text, but the histories of some of the others can help put the story of Blaenavon into context.

Beaufort
Beaufort, at the head of the Ebbw Valley, was begun by the Kendalls in 1780. Named after its ground landlord, the Duke of Beaufort, it was known in Welsh as Cendl after its founders. By 1833, when it was bought by Joseph and Crawshay Bailey of Nantyglo, it had five furnaces in blast.

Coalbrookvale
At Coalbrookvale, south of Nantyglo, a single furnace was built in 1818 by George Brewer, Hopkin Perkins of Newport and Thomas Vennor of Abergavenny. A second furnace was added in 1824, but quarrels among the partners led to the latter two publicly disowning Brewer and dissolving the partnership in the 'ironworks, colliery and shop'. This also included a public house, the Royal Oak, built by the company in 1826 and kept by the Chartist leader Zephaniah Williams. By 1852 the partnership had passed to the next generation and comprised William Brewer, a Newport surgeon, Henry Vennor and Margaret Brewer of Llanfoist, widow of George Brewer. The manager, Tom Llywelyn Brewer, retired in 1855.

Cwm Celyn, Blaina
The 19th-century mining settlement of Blaina, lower down the valley, exemplifies the changes that industry brought to Gwent. The church of the large mountain parish of Aberystruth was here, with medieval wall paintings and lively parish fairs. Rebuilt in Victorian times, it was finally demolished in the 1960s. The ironworks of Cwm Celyn at its upper end was a late-comer, its three furnaces built by Thomas Brown and Co. in 1824. In 1866 the works became bankrupt and in 1873 it was bought up by the Nantyglo and Blaina Iron Company.

Ebbw Vale

In 1789 Jeremiah Homfray, brother of Samuel Homfray, became a partner in a forge at Ebbw Vale with two local men – Walter Watkins, owner of a forge near Crickhowell and Watkins' son-in-law Charles Cracroft – and built a blast furnace By 1791 he was sole owner but five years later disposed of it to the Bristol Quakers James Harford and John Partridge, with the latter as resident partner. By 1810 Ebbw Vale had three furnaces. When Harford and Co. went bankrupt in 1842, Ebbw Vale was purchased by Abraham and Alfred Darby and their innovative manager Thomas Brown.

Pentwyn and Golynos

Two ironworks in the Afon Llwyd valley below Blaenavon were eventually, like their neighbour the British Ironworks at Abersychan, swallowed up by Ebbw Vale. Pentwyn was built by the Hurst brothers in 1825 with three hot blast furnaces, at a cost of £35,000. Like the Victoria ironworks at Ebbw Vale it was a creation of the speculative boom after the repeal of the 'Bubble Act'. Based in Bath, its investors were drawn from Somerset and Devon. Initially abandoned by 1850, two furnaces were briefly put in blast in 1865-8 before being finally abandoned. Its neighbour Golnos was founded in 1837, but its two furnaces (later three), blown by a Neath Abbey beam engine, were worked jointly with Pentwyn from the following year. It had limited success and in 1860 there was an attempt to sell it and some of its machinery was moved to Varteg. Two furnaces were briefly put in blast in 1863-6, using Northamptonshire ironstone, but thereafter production ceased.

Sirhowy and Tredegar

Sirhowy, at the head of the Sirhowy Valley, was established in 1778 with speculative merchant capital from the City of London, combined with an input from the Cumbrian iron industry, with its long-standing Welsh connection. The partners included three wholesale grocers and tea merchants – John Sealy, Bolton Hudson and William Barrow – and a former South Carolina merchant Thomas Atkinson, then resident in Skipton in Yorkshire and involved with Henry Kendall in the Ulverston ironworks in north Lancashire. Barrow became resident manager, along with Kendall's brother-in-law Revd Matthew Monkhouse, vicar of Selside in Westmoreland (presumably served by a curate in place of the absentee vicar, though Monkhouse established a school there in 1783). In 1794 Barrow and Monkhouse described themselves as 'ironmasters'. Other partners included two Clapham builders, Richard Fothergill and John Hanscomb. In 1818 Sirhowy was acquired by the Ebbw Vale Company.

Tredegar, on the opposite bank of the Sirhowy, was founded in 1800 by a partnership which included Richard Fothergill of Sirhowy and Samuel Homfray of Penydarren. Homfray, son of a Staffordshire ironmaster brought to Merthyr by Anthony Bacon, was son-in-law to Sir Charles Morgan of Tredegar House, on whose estates the new ironworks lay. William Thompson, another partner, was a London iron merchant who the previous year had leased the Tintern Abbey Works. He may have given Tredegar access to London capital and the new company had a working capital of £30,000.

Rhymney

On the borders of Monmouthshire and Glamorgan, the first iron furnace in the Rhymney Valley was built in 1801 by a Bristol-based partnership of David Evans, Thomas Williams, John Ambrose and Thomas Cunningham, each contributing £1,000, with a promise of £6,000 more if required. The first three partners were bought out by Richard Crawshay of Cyfartha. Cunningham was retained by Crawshay, but later removed for alleged irregularities in his accounts. Crawshay then gave the furnace, which produced pig iron for Cyfartha, as a wedding present to the father of Sir Benjamin Hall, who had married his daughter Charlotte. Hall became sole owner on Crawshay's death in 1810. This single coke-fired furnace, the lower part of which survives, stands at the junction of Monmouth, Glamorgan and Brecon and was known as the Union Furnace, Rhymney Old Furnace and Upper Furnace. Hall's son, Sir Benjamin Hall M.P, later Lord Llanover was known as 'Big Ben'. As First Commissioner of Works he gave his name to Parliament's famous clock.

Other furnaces were later added further down the valley. In 1824 William Forman of Penydarren, Thomas Seaton Forman and Thomas Johnson built Bute Ironworks, noted for their Egyptian Revival style furnaces and cast houses, designed by the architect John Macculloch and modeled on the ruins of the Temple of Hathor complex at Dendera ('Dendrya') in Egypt, drawings of which had been exhibited at the Royal Academy. These picturesque industrial structures attracted artists, and paintings are known by Penry Williams (1825) and John Petherwick (c.1830). In the latter year the Bute Ironworks and the Old and New Rhymney furnaces were amalgamated as the Rhymney Iron Company. In 1837 this became a new company, with the Lord Mayor of London on the board and a capital of £500,000.

BIBLIOGRAPHY

Parliamentary Papers

1842 (380) XV-XVII *Report of the Commission of Inquiry into the Employment of Children in Mines and Manufactures*

(381) *Appendix Part 1*

(382) *Appendix Part 2 Inquiry into the Employment of Females and Children in Mines and Factories*

1844 (16) *Report of the Commission of Inquiry into civil disorder, south Wales*

1846 (737) *Report of the Commission Appointed ... to Inquire into the State of the Population in the Mining Districts*

1847 (27) *Report of the Commission on the State of Education in Wales*

1850 (23) *Report of the Commission on the Mining Population*

1871 (36) *Report of the Commissioners Appointed to Inquire into the Truck System*

Maps and Plans

1792 Dadford Monmouthshire Railway and Canal Company : Newport to Pontnewynydd Canal. Gwent Archives D 38.41

1801 Plan, railroad and tramroad Newport to Varteg etc. Gwent Archives D 179.2

1806 Map with lease Lord Abergavenny to Thomas and Samuel Hill (*sic*). Gwent Archives D 713

1812 Plan of Blaenavon Mine East of the Large fault 1 May 1812, redrawn 1939. Gwent Archives D 38.41

1813 Ordnance Survey Surveyors sketches for draft map. British Library 194 (E)

1814 August Plan of Blaen Afon Iron Works, Monmouthshire, William Llewellin. Gwent Archives GRO 1814

1818 Plan of land at Warren Farm purchased for construction of tramroad D 751/ 306

1819 29 September. Plan of the Tram Road from Blaenavon furnaces to Pwll Du and Garn Ddyrys, Thomas Deakin. Gwent Archives Mon/A/2/0273.

1821 'Blaenavon Iron Works in the liberty in the parishes of Llanover and Llanwenarth'. NLW Marquess of Abergavenny Estate Plan 29 MAP 10630

1824 'A section of Blaenavon deep mine work' Thomas Deakin 29 July 1824, Showing 'Ingin Pit', Cinder Pit, Kear's Slope and 'Slope near the coke ovens'

1824 'Plan of land for road from Blaenavon ironworks to Abergavenny' Gwent Archives D 751.81

1829 30 July 'Blaenavon Mine Work' (re-drawn 1939) ex National Coal Board. GRO 1829

1830? Map attached to indenture Gwent Archives D 751, 213-4

1836 'Plan of the Tram Road from Pwll Du tunnel mouth to Llanfoist Coal Yard'

1837 Map, Thomas Deakin. Gwent Archives D 591. 112. 27

1843 Tithe map, Llanover Upper Parish. Gwent Archives DPA 149/6

1843 Jean Prujean Map of the ironworks and collieries ... Railroad Tramroad and Canal with the Ports of Newport and Cardiff

N.D. Plan of Blaenavon Property showing freehold, leasehold and tramroad. Gwent Archives D 591. 112. 27

Documentary Sources
Gwent Archives

1779	16 October Lease of Beaufort Ironworks. D 397.1664
1787	6 November Agreement to lease, Lord Abergavenny to Hill and Pratt. D 7.13
1789-1811	Leases, Lord Abergavenny to Hill, Hopkins and Pratt. D 7.12-17
1789	Hill, Bates and Robins, loan to Blaenavon Ironworks Co. D 751-57
1791	Will of Thomas Hopkins. D 7.232
1793	Land near railroad leading from Blaenafon ironworks near Pontnewynydd. D 751-29
1794	Will of Benjamin Pratt Npt 1800. M 350
1796-1819	Harford Memorandum Book (Ebbw Vale). D 2472, 1-4
1801, 1811	Leases Lord Abergavenny to Hill and Hopkins. D 7 12-17
1806	Lord Abergavenny, Thomas Hill and Samuel Hopkins re exported coal. D 7.235
1804-19	St Peter's Church Register of baptisms and burials. DPA 74.1
1814-37	Register of baptisms. DPA 74.2
1813- 84	Registers of baptisms. DPA 3-5
1813-42	Registers of burials. DPA 17-18
1815	Will of Samuel Hopkins. D 751.297
1816	Miscellaneous correspondence. D 7.148
1818 March	Purchase of land for tramroad and incline plane. D 7.226, D 751, 305-6
May	Agreement with Brecon and Abergavenny Canal Co. for embankments and bridge across canal. D 751.53
1818-49	Miscellaneous correspondence. D 7.149
1819-31	Miscellaneous correspondence. D 7.150-151
1824	Land for construction of carriage road, Blaenavon ironworks to Abergavenny. D 751/81
1825	Will of Thomas Hill I of Dennis. D 751, 295, 298
1826	R. Court *A Letter to the Shareholders of the British Iron Company*. 038.415
1827	Articles of partnership, Hill, Hill, Wheeley and Morgan. D 591.3217
1830	Articles of partnership, Wheeley and Morgan. D 591.3221
1833	Particulars of sale, Blaenavon ironworks. D 7.194
1835-58	Miscellaneous correspondence. D 7.152-154
1836	Prospectus Blaenavon Iron and coal company. D 591.6.2
1836-64	Minute book of the Blaenavon Iron and Coal Company. D 751. 356
1838	Deed of settlement re Blaenavon Iron and Coal Company. D 751.325
1838	Thomas and Waldon Hill re sale of works to James Ashwell and fellow directors. D 751.69
1851	Henry Hartop 'Report on the Blaenavon minerals'. D 7.301
1854	William Llewellin Report on the Blaenavon mineral property. D 591.112
1861	*General and specific rules to be observed at Blaenavon Iron and Coal Company.* Bythway Mss 283
1870	Prospectus, Blaenavon Iron Company. D 591.16.1
1870	Sale of ironworks. D 480/15-16, D 591/112/31
1870-78	Minutes of Directors meetings, Blaenavon Iron and Steel Co. Ltd. D 2133.2
1873	Pay cheques etc, Charles Nutt, Dodd's Slope. D 591.112
1880-1948	Minute books Blaenavon Company Ltd. D 480/1-12
1911-42	Ledgers and balance sheets. D 751.357-9
1920-36	Balance sheets and accounts. D 751.340-355
1927	Churchwarden's Memorandum Book. D.Pa.74.31
1890-1955	Big Pit colliery records. D 2732
1880-1962	Big Pit colliery records. Accs 2891, 2903,2921, 2943

National Library of Wales
Abergavenny Mss
1585-6   Mines on Blorenge and Ebbw valleys

852 1701   lease of 'thirty acres of land called Blane-Avon' to William Lewis

900 1701   lease of 'hamlet of Blane-Avon' to Llywelyn John

Cyfartha Mss 2
733-742 1833   Correspondence of William Crawshay re possible purchase of Blaenavon

Clenennau Mss
2 (E) 1697   Letter of Edward Lhwyd re finds of fossil fish on the Blorenge

Maybery Mss
255 1771   Deed of co-partnership Thomas Hopkins and Kendalls

254 1792   Deed of co- partnership (Nantyglo) Thomas Hill and Co., Harford Partridge and Co.

1901 1794   Agreement Hill Hopkins and Co., Nantyglo with ironstone miner

797-813 1802   Correspondence re attempts to force Blaenavon to use only the Monmouthshire Canal

Newport Reference Library
1805   Act for establishing a new church ... at Blaenavon. Haines Collection Pf M250 270 LAW

1816   Monmouthshire Assizes, 19 August 1816- Papers re Powell and Yeates versus Hill and Hill. Also pamphlet concerning the Lords of the Manor of Parc Lettice, Llanover and Blaenavon Ironworks
Haines Collection px M 250.672

1844   R.J. Blewitt *New Monmouthshire Railway from Newport to Nantyglo and Blaenafon through Pontypool.* M 000 (625), 656 '4 vols, of which this is vol 4'

1845   Sale Catalogue, Victoria Ironworks Ebbw Vale. Haines Collection Px M 240.672

1855   Report of the Committee of investigation appointed to inquire into the affairs of the Blaenavon Iron and Coal Company in pursuance of a resolution of the shareholders passed at the Annual Meeting held in the Blaenavon offices on April 27, 1855 (London, preface dated 20 June 1855). Haines Collection, M.250.672

1872   *Blaenavon and Abersychan Railways Act: Bill for Making Railways in the Parish of Trevethin.* 625 pq M00

1957   G.A. Graber *Life among the ironworkers of Garndyrus and Blaenavon, 1810-1836.* q. 417.8.900

Newspapers
Blaenavon Express and Monmouthshire Gazette 1871-73
Monmouthshire Merlin 1829-91
Monmouthshire Weekly Post 1908-22
Pontypool Free Press and Herald of the Hills 1859-93
Pontypool Free Press 1909-
Free Press of Monmouthshire 1909-10
South Wales Argus 1892-
South Wales Daily News 1872-1900
South Wales Times and Star of Gwent 1889-1903
Star of Gwent 1854-89

Unpublished Manuscript Sources

Lawler, M. and Knight, J. *Landscape Survey of Blaenavon* Card index and maps, held at Cadw : Welsh Historic Monuments

Lawler, M. article on pre-industrial land use in Afon Llwyd valley – copy in letter to the author 13.9.1989

Lawler, M. letter and enclosures to Clive Gardner 20 March 1999

Van Laun, J. *Mineral Exploitation at Blaenavon.* Fieldnotes, Longtown outdoor education centre 1979

In Private Possession at Blaenavon

Blaenavon Co, Ltd. Minute Book no1, 1864-70

Blaenavon Iron and Coal Company Minute Book no 5, 1860-64

1877 Plan 'Blaenavon shops July 1877' (Messrs Caddick)

Printed Sources

Abergavenny and District Steam Society n.d. *Garnddyrys* (Abergavenny)

Almond J.K. 1978 'Cleveland and the basic process of steelmaking' *Historical Metallurgy Society* (conference papers) 8/1-16

1979 'Making steel from phosphoric ore in the convertor – the "Basic Bessemer" process in Cleveland in the years from 1879' Hempstead (ed.), 117-196

2004 'Thomas, Sidney Gilchrist' *Oxford Dictionary of National Biography* ed H.C.G. Matthew and Brian Harrison, Vol 54, 373-5

Anon 1876 *Franciscan Missions Among the Colliers and Ironworkers of Monmouthshire* (Burns and Oates)

Ashton, T.S. 1924 *Iron and Steel in the Industrial Revolution* (Manchester)

Atkinson, M. 1983 *Blaenafon Ironworks: a guide to its History and Technology*

1986 'The supply of raw materials to the south Wales iron industry 1800-1860' Baber and Williams ed., 43-52

Atkinson, M. and Baber, C. 1987 *The Growth and Decline of the South Wales Iron Industry 1760-1880* Cardiff, Board of Celtic Studies

Babbidge, A. 1984 'The development of the constabulary in the Eastern Valley 1830-1890' *Gwent Local History* 57, 30-36

Baber, C. 1986 'Canals and the economic development of south Wales' Baber and Williams, 24-42

Baber, C. and Williams L.J. 1986 *Modern South Wales : Essays in Economic History*

Bailey, Peter 1978 *Leisure and Class in Victorian England*

Barber, Chris 2002 *Exploring Blaenavon Industrial Landscape World Heritage Site* (Abergavenny)

Barber, Chris and Blackmore, M. 1996 *Portraits of the Past* (Blorenge Books, Abergavenny)

Barraclough, K.C. 1978 'The British steel trade from 1840-1880' *Historical Metallurgy Society* (conference papers), 3-10

Beckett, I.F.W. and Simpson, K. 1985 ed. *A Nation in Arms: A Social Study of the British Army in the First World War* (Manchester)

Beck, P.J. 2003 'Leisure and sport in Britain 1900-1039' Wrigley ed., 453-469

Beddoes, Deidre 1991 'Munitionettes, Maids and Mums: Women in Wales 1914-1939' in Angela V. John (ed.) *Our Mothers Land: Chapters in Welsh Womens History 1830-1939* (Cardiff)

Berry, David 1994 *Wales and Cinema: The first hundred years* (Cardiff)

Birch, A. 1967 *The Economic History of the British Iron and Steel Industry*

Birnie, R.W. (ed.) 1891 *Memoirs and Letters of Sidney Gilchrist Thomas, Inventor* (reprinted Cambridge University Press 2011)

Blaenavon Community Heritage Museum 2014 *Blaenavon and the First World War 1914-1918: A Welsh Industrial Town at War, Home and Abroad*

Blaenavon History Group 2011 *Funeral to Festival: A History of Blaenavon 1901-1951*

Bradney, J.A. 1904-1993 *A History of Monmouthshire from the Coming of the Normans into Wales down to the present time* (5 vols, 10 parts)

    1926 *A Memorandum, being an attempt to give a chronology of the decay of the Welsh Language in the Eastern part of the county of Monmouth* (Abergavenny)

Brett, G.A. 1933 *A History of the 2ⁿᵈ Battalion the Monmouthshire Regiment* (Pontypool)

Brock, W.H. 2004 ' Gilchrist, Percy Carlyle' *Oxford Dictionary of National Biography* Vol 22, 221-2

Browning, Lewis 1906 *Blaenavon: A Brief Historical Sketch* (Abergavenny), reprinted D. Brown and Sons, Cowbridge 1989

Burnie, R.W. 1891 *Memoirs and Letters of Sidney Gilchrist Thomas, Inventor* (reprinted Cambridge University Press 2011)

Buxton, N.K. 1978 *The Economic Development of the British Coal Industry from the Industrial Revolution to the Present Day*

Carpenter, H.C.H. 1936 'Percy Carlyle Gilchrist 1851-1935' *Obituary Notices of Fellows of the Royal Society* 1936, 2, 19-24.

Chadwick, Owen 1966, 1970 *The Victorian Church* (2 vols)

Church, Roy 1977 'Family and failure: Archibald Kenrick and Sons 1900-1950' *Essays in British Business History* ed. Barry Semple (Oxford)

Colebrook, Kim 1983 'A history of the British ironworks, Abersychan' *Gwent Local History* 54, 5-29

Coleman, D.C. 1973 'Gentlemen and Players' *Economic History Review* 26, 92-116

Collis, R. 1976 'O happy English children: coal, class and education in the north east' *Past and Present* 90 (February 1976), 136-165

Colt Hoare, Richard 1983 *The Journeys of Sir Richard Colt Hoare in Wales and England 1793- 1810* ed. M.W. Thompson (Alan Sutton)

Cornwell, John 1985 *Enter the World of Big Pit, Blaenafon South Wales* (Cowbridge)

    2001 *Collieries of South Wales 1* (Landmark Press)

    2002 *Collieries of South Wales 2*

Court, W.H.B. 1938 *Rise of the Midland Industries 1600-1838* (Oxford)

Cox, N. and A. 1994, 2012 *The Tokens, Checks, Metallic tickets, Passes and Tallies of Wales 1800 -1993.* Vols 1 and 2 (Cardiff)

Coxe, William 1801 *An Historical Tour in Monmouthshire* (reprinted with new introduction Cardiff 1995)

Davies, E.J. 1967 *Blaenavon: Its People and its Iron*

    1970 *A Short History of Blaenavon*

    1975 *The Blaenavon Story* (Torfaen Borough Council)

Davies, E.T. 1965 *Religion in the Industrial Revolution in South Wales* (Cardiff)

Davies, T. Gray 1978 *Blaenavon and Sidney Gilchrist Thomas*

Davidoff, Leonore 1979 'Class and gender in Victorian England: The Diaries of Arthur J. Munby and Hannah Cullwick' *Feminist Studies* 5.1, 86-141

Denner, S.G. 1978 'The pursuit of crochets: an appreciation of Sidney Gilchrist Thomas' *Historical Metallurgy Society* 5/1-15.

Dicks, Bella 2000 *Heritage, Place and Community* (Cardiff)

Dixon, J. and J. 1991 *With Rifle and Pick* (Cwm Press, Abertillery)

Dixon J. 2000 *Out Since 14: A History of the 2nd Battalion the Monmouthshire Regiment 1914-1917* (Cwm Press)

Doyleruish, E. 2008 *Rocks in the Clouds: High Ground Aircraft Crashes in South Wales*

Drower, Margaret S. 1985 *Flinders Petrie: A Life in Archaeology*

Dyne Steel, T. *Memoir Autobiographical Memoir* Manuscript formerly in the possession of the late Fred Percy, Blaenavon, printed by R. Nichols *Presenting Monmouthshire* 28 (Autumn 1969), 42-47

Edmunds, O.P. and F.L. 1963 'An account of the founding of H.M. Inspectorate of Mines and the work of the first Inspector, Hugh Seymour Tremenheere *British Journal of Industrial Medicine* 1963, 210-217

1965 ed. *I Was There: The Memoirs of H.S. Tremenheere* (University of California Press)

Edwards, Reese 1951 'Percy Carlyle Gilchrist' *British Steelmaker* November 1951

Elliott, John 1996 'The Crumlin Viaduct Works: from world leader to Welsh tragedy' *Gwent Local History* 80, 4-19

2004 *The Industrial Development of the Ebbw Valleys* (Cardiff)

2011 'The iron and steel industry' *G.C.H.* 4: 73-86

Elsas, M. 1960 *Iron in the Making: Dowlais Iron Company Letters 1782-1860* (Cardiff)

Evans Chris 1993 *The Labyrinth of Flames: Work and Social Conflict in Early Industrial Merthyr Tydfil* (Cardiff)

1994 'Iron puddling: the quest for a new technology in eighteenth century industry' *Llafur* 6.3, 44-57

Evans, E.W. 1961 *The Miners of South Wales* (Cardiff)

Evans, J.A.H. 1996 'The witness and testimony of ordinary people in the vicinity of Blaenavon between 1810 and 1816 through the journals and correspondence of Walter Osland' *Gwent Local History* 81, 4-19

2000 'Big Pit, Blaenavon: A new chronology?' *Gwent Local History* 88, 53-68

2003 'The Evolution of Blaenavon town' *Gwent Local History* 94, 34-54

Evans, L.W. 1961 'Ironworks schools in Wales 1784-1960' *Sociological Review* 14

Fox, Cyril and Lord Raglan 1951-4 *Monmouthshire Houses Vol 1 Medieval Houses* (1951); *Vol 2 Sub-Medieval Houses c.1550-1610* (1953); *Renaissance Houses c.1590-1710* (1954) Cardiff, National Museum of Wales

Frances, Hywel and Smith, David 1980, 2nd ed. 1998 *The Fed: A History of the South Wales Miners in the Twentieth Century* (Cardiff)

Gale, W.K.V. 1967 *The British Iron and Steel Industry* (Cardiff)

Gilchrist Thompson Lilian 1940 *Sidney Gilchrist Thomas : An Invention and its Consequences*

Gosden, P.H.J.H 1961 *The Friendly Societies of England 1815-1875* (Manchester)

Gray-Jones, A. 1970 *History of Ebbw Vale* (Risca)

Guiseppi M.S 1913 'Some fourteenth century accounts of ironworks at Tudeley, Kent' *Archaeologia* 64 (1912-13) 145-64

Gunther, R.T. 1945 *Early Science at Oxford. Vol XIV. Life and Letters of Edward Lhwyd* (Oxford)

Hadfield, E.C.R. 1967 *The Canals of South Wales and the Border* (David and Charles, Newton Abbot)

Harbord, F.W. 1937 'The Gilchrist-Thomas Basic process 1879-1937' *Journal of the Iron and Steel Institute* 136, 77-97.

Harris, F. 1981 'From the industrial revolution to the heritage industry' *Geographical Magazine* 61.5, 38-42

Harrison, J.K. 1979 'The production of pig iron in north-east England 1577-1865' Hempstead (ed.) 49-79

Hempstead, C.A. 1979 ed. *Cleveland Iron and Steel: Background and Nineteenth Century History* (British Steel Corporation)

Hilling, J.B. 2006 'The migration of people into Tredegar in the nineteenth century' *Gwent Local History* 100, 19-39

Hilton, G.W. 1960 *The Truck System, including a history of the British Truck Acts* (Cambridge)

Historical Metallurgy Society 1978 *Annual Conference: Sidney Gilchrist Thomas ; Centenary of the basic process of Steelmaking 1878-1978*

Howell, R. 1995 'Ironworking in the medieval borough of Trellech, Gwent' P. Crewe and S. Crewe (eds) *Iron for Archaeologists: A review of recent work on the Archaeology of early iron working in western Europe* (Plas Tan y Bwlch)

Hudson, D. 1974 *Munby: Man of Two Worlds: The life and diaries of Arthur J. Munby 1828-1910*

Hutchings, C. and Frame R. 2015 '"In the Pink" Private Percy James Scammell and the Monmouthshire Regiment during the First World War' *Mon Ant* 31, 85-101.

Hyde, C.K. 1973 'The adoption of coke smelting by the British Iron industry 1709-1790' *Explorations in Economic History* 10 no 4, 397-418

Ince, Laurence 1991 *The Knight family and the British Iron Industry 1695-1902* (Solihull)
   1993 *The South Wales Iron Industry 1750-1885* (Cardiff)

James, H. 1924 *Freemasonry in Monmouthshire from 1764* (Newport)

Jenkins, Rhys 1925-6 'Iron making in the Forest of Dean' *Trans. Newcomen Society* 6, 42-65

Jennings, Hilda 1934 *Brynmawr: A study of a distressed area*

John, A.H. 1995 *The Industrial Development of South Wales 1750-1850* (Cardiff, Merton Priory Press, 2nd ed.)

Johnson, R. 1970 'Educational policy and social control in early Victorian England' *Past and Present* 49.1 (November 1970), 96-119

Jones, A.H. 1950 *The Industrial Development of South Wales* (Cardiff)

Jones, David 1973 *Before Rebecca: Popular Protests in Wales 1793-1835*

Jones, Dot 1984 'Self help in nineteenth century Wales: the rise and fall of the female friendly society' *Llafur*   6.1, 14-26
   1985 'Did friendly societies matter? A study of friendly societies in Glamorgan 1794-1910' *Welsh History Review* 12.3, 324-49

Jones, Edmund 1789 *A Geographical, Historical and Religious Account of the Parish of Aberystruth* (Trevecha)

Jones, L.G. and Williams D. 1976 ed. *The Religious Census of 1851: A calendar of returns relating to Wales. Vol 1 : South Wales* (Cardiff)

Jones, Oliver 1969 *Early Days of Sirhowy and Tredegar* (Tredegar)

Jones, R. Merfyn 2003 'Wales and British politics 1900-1939' Wrigley (ed.) 87-103

Kelleher, S. 2009 'Identifying, remembering and restoring forgotten landscapes : Recent archaeological work at and around the Blaenavon World Heritage site' *Archaeology in Wales* 49, 39-52

Kenrick, G.S 1840 'Statistics of the population of the Parish of Trevethin (Pontypool) and at the neighbouring works of Blaenavon in Monmouthshire, chiefly employed in the iron trade and inhabiting part of the district recently disturbed *Journal of the Statistical Society of London* 3, 366- 375
   1840a *The Population of Pontypool and the Parish of Trevethin, situated in the so called 'disturbed districts': their moral, social and intellectual character* (London, Simpkin, Marshall and Co.)

Kirby, M.W. 1977 *The British Coalmining Industry 1870-1946. A Political and Economic History*

Knight, J. 1967 'Blaenavon Ironworks 1789-1967: A preliminary survey' *Journal South East Wales Industrial Archaeology Society* 2.3 (1967), 26-38
   1970 'The Blaenavon Iron and Coal Company, 1836-64; A Victorian Joint Stock Company, *B.B.C.S.* 28.4, 631-44
   1970a 'Odd Fellows and Amicable Women : Friendly Societies in Nineteenth Century industrial Monmouthshire' *Mon. Ant* 4, 1-2, 50 -53
   1989 *Blaenavon Ironworks: A Bicentennial Guide* (Cadw) 2nd revised ed. 1992

2000 'Brought forth in a high place: Religion, Society and language in nineteenth century Blaenavon' *Mon. Ant.* 16, 121-130

2004 'A Nonconformity of the gentry? Catholic recusants in Abergavenny in the seventeenth century' *Mon. Ant.* 20, 145-152

2007 'A lease of the Hills: Hill, Hopkins and Pratt at Blaenavon' *Mon. Ant* 23, 51-59

2007a 'Rural industries in pre-industrial South Wales' *Arts and Crafts in the Medieval Rural Environment : Ruralia VI 22-29 September 2005, Szentendre, Hungary* (Brepols, Turnhout), 321-326

Lambert, W.R. 1983 *Drink and Sobriety in Victorian Wales c.1820-1895* (Cardiff)

Lapsley, G.T. 1899 'The account rolls of a fifteenth century ironmaster' *English Historical Review* 14, 509-29

Laurence, Ray 2013 *The Coal Workings of the Blaenavon Area* (Blackwood)

Lewis, H. 1980 Monmouthshire and the Welsh language censuses 1901-1971 *Gwent Local History* 48, 18-24

Lewis, Steve 2011 *Ken Jones: Boots and Spikes* (Cheltenham)

Llewellin, W. 1863 'Some account of the iron and wire works of Tintern' *Arch. Camb.* 1863, 291-318

Lloyd, John 1906 *The Early History of the Old South Wales iron works 1760-1830*

Lovering, G.W.J. 2001 'The Monmouthshire elections of 1868 *Gwent Local History* 90, 17-34

Lowe, Jeremy 1977 *Welsh Industrial Workers Housing 1775-1875* (Cardiff)

1978 'The first forge at Blaenavon' *Journal South East Wales Industrial Archaeology Soc.* 3, 1 31-40

1978a 'Industrial houses and settlement patterns at Nantyglo 1811-1845' *Mon. Ant.* 3, parts 3-4, 196-208

1982 'Housing as a source for industrial history: A case study of Blaenavon' *Journal of the Society of Industrial Archaeology* 8.1

1998 'Stack Square' *Archaeology in Wales* 38, 160-62

Lowe, J.R and Anderson, D.N. 1972 *Iron Industry Housing Papers* 1-9 Cardiff, University of Wales Institute of Science and Technology:

1 Stack Square and Engine Row, Blaenavon

2 'Two prototype house'

3 Standard four room houses in Garndiffaith

4 Standard houses of the first Blaenavon Company : Forge Row, Cwmavon

Lowe, J.R. and Lawler, M. 1980 'Landscapes of the iron industry at Blaenafon, Gwent' *Landscape History* 2 (1980), 71-82

Marwick, Arthur 1977 *Women at War 1914-1918*

Mass Observation 1970 *The Pub and the People: A Worktown study by Mass Observation*

McDermot, E.T. 1964 *History of the Great Western Railway* (revised edition, ed. C. Clinker)

Mitchell, T. 1904 *The Monmouthshire Iron and Steel Trade* (Newport)

Morris, E.H. 1946-8 'Abergavenny and Hereford tramroads: Some of the earlier history of the undertaking' *Trans. Woolhope Naturalists Field Club* 32, 65-72

Morris, Jeremy 2013 'Religion' *Gwent C.H. 5,* 241-256

Morris, J.H. and Williams L.J. 1958 *The South Wales Coal Industry 1841-1875*

Needham, William 1831 *The Manufacture of Iron*

Nicolas, D. 2014 *They Fought with pride: First World War Experiences of the 2nd Battalion The Monmouthshire Regiment*

O' Leary, Paul 2000 *Immigration and Integration: The Irish in Wales 1798-1922* (Cardiff)

2004 (ed.) *Irish Migrants in Modern Wales*

2004a (ed.) 'The cult of respectability and the Irish in mid-Nineteenth century Wales', 119-138

Osborne, B.S. 1976 'Patching, scouring and commoners: the development of an early industrial landscape' *Industrial Archaeology Review* 1, 37-42

Palmer, Roy 2004 *The Folklore of (Old) Monmouthshire* (Logaston, 2nd ed.)

Parr, H.W. 1933 'The furnaces at Coed Ithel and Trellech' *Bulletin of the Historical Metallurgy Group* 7, 36-9

Parr, H.W. and Tucker, D.G. 1975 'The old wireworks and ironworks in the Angidy Valley at Tintern, Gwent *Historical Metallurgy* 9, 1-14

Parry, A., Keen F. and Bowen, R. 1986 *Blaenavon in Old Picture Postcards*

Picken, J. 1982 'Excavations at Abbey Tintern furnace' *Historical Metallurgy* 16, 1-21
1982a 'The ironworks at Tintern and Sirhowy' *Gwent Local History* 52, 3-9

Pounds, N.J.G. and Parker, W.N. 1957 *Coal and Steel in Western Europe*

Powell, Evan 1884, 1902 *History of Tredegar* (Newport, reprinted 2008)

Prescott, G. 2011 *This Rugby Spellbound People : Rugby Football in Nineteenth Century Cardiff and South Wales* (Cardiff)

Pryce, W.T.R. 2013 'Population and language' *Gwent C.H.* 5 157-187.

Rattenbury, G. 1977 'The Cwm Ffrwd rail road' *Gwent Local History* 42, 12-21
1980 *Tramroads of the Brecknock and Abergavenny Canal* (Oakham)

Reed, S.J., Juleff, G. and Buyer, O.J. 2006 'Three late Saxon iron smelting furnaces at Burlescombe, Devon' *Transactions Devon Archaeological Society* 64, 71-122

Rees, D. Morgan 1964 'Industrial archaeology in Wales: an introduction' *Arch. Camb.* 1964, 129-49
1969 *Mills, Mines and Furnaces*

Rees, W. 1950 'Accounts of the Ministers for the lordship of Abergavenny 1256-7' *South Wales and Monmouthshire Record Society* 2, 68-125
1957 'Accounts of the Ministers for the lordship of Monmouth' *South Wales and Monmouthshire Record Society* 4 ,5-29
1968 *Industry Before the Industrial Revolution* (Cardiff 2 vols)

Richardson, F.O. and Jeffries, J.H.E. 1980 'Sidney Thomas's Invention and its late impact' *Ironmaking and Steelmaking* 7, 222-226

Riden, P. 1993 *A Gazetteer of Charcoal-fired blast furnaces in Great Britain in use since 1660* (Merton Priory Press)

Riden, P. and Owen J.G. 1995 *British Blast Furnace Statistics 1790-1980* (Cardiff)

Ridgwell, S. 1995 'South Wales and the cinema in the 1930s' *W.H.R.* 17.4, 590-615

Rimmer, D. 2015 'Colonel Bradney: a Monmouthshire soldier's Great War' *Mon. Ant.* 31, 103-123

Robb, G. 2002 *British Culture and the First World War*

Roberts, B. 1992 'A Mining town in wartime: the fears for the future' *Llafur* 6.1, 82-95

Schubert, H.R. 1957 *History of the British Iron and Steel Industry to A.D. 1775*

Scourfield, J. 2003 'The Chapels of Blaenavon' *Capel* 41, 1-5

Scrivenor, Harry 1841 *A Comprehensive History of the Iron Trade, from the earliest records to the present period* reprinted Cass and Co – Cass Library of Industrial Classics 1967

Simmonds, A.G.V. 2012 *Britain and World War One*

Spencer, Colin 2009 *The Miners and Coal Levels of Gwent* (History Press)

Strange, Keith 2005 *Merthyr Tydfil, Iron Metropolis Life in a Welsh Industrial Town* (Tempus, Stroud)

Strong, Peter 2013 'The First World War' *Gwent C.H. 5,* 1-16
2013a 'The Second World War' *Gwent C.H.* 5, 17-33

Svedenstierna, E.T. 1973 *Svedenstierna's Tour Great Britain 1802-3: The Travel Diary of an Industrial Spy* (David and Charles, Newton Abbot)

Tamplin, R. and Teulon, A. 1974 'A general history of Garnddyrys ironworks' *Presenting Monmouthshire* 37, 38-47

Taylor, A.J. 1960 'The sub-contract system in the British coal industry' *Studies in the Industrial Revolution presented to T.S. Ashton* (ed.) Presnell, 215-35.

Taylor, William Henry 1925 *The Cheated Death*

Thomas, Brinley 1993 *The Industrial Revolution and the Atlantic Economy: Selected Essays*

Thomas, Malcolm and Lewis, John (1987-1993) *Blaenavon Through the Years* vol 1, 1987, vol 2 1987, vol 3 1993

Thornton, Harry 2011 'Bygone ironmasters of Amblecote and Rugeley and their industrial legacy of global acclaim' *Staffordshire History* spring 2011, 1-10

Thompson, Lilian Gilchrist 1940 *Sidney Gilchrist Thomas: An Invention and its consequences*

Thompson M.W. 1983 *The Journeys of Sir Richard Colt Hoare through Wales and England* (Gloucester)

Tylecote, R.F. 1965 'Blast furnace at Coed Ithel, Llandogo, Mon *Journal Iron and Steel Institute* 204, 867-74, reprinted *Mon. Ant.* 2. part 3 (1967), 149-160

Van Laun, J. et al. 1978-9 'Hill Pits, Blaenavon' *Industrial Archaeology Review* 3, 258-275

 1981 *Mineral Extraction at Blaenavon* (Northamptonshire County Council)

 2001 *Early Limestone Railways: How Railways developed to feed the furnaces of the Industrial Revolution in South East Wales* (Newcomen Society)

Wakelin, P. 1996 'Scouring the land: Early iron ore extraction at Blaenavon' *Mon. Ant.* 12 (1996), 62-67

 2006 *Blaenavon Ironworks and World Heritage Industrial Landscape* (Cadw)

Walker, Lesley 1997 'Your fair and sunny land... an emigrant family from Blaenavon' *Gwent Local History* 82, 10-15

W.E.A. History Group 2001 *Funeral to Festival: A History of Blaenavon 1901-1951* (Gomer Books)

Webb, R.K. 1955 'A Whig Inspector' (H.S. Tremenheere) *Journal of Modern History* 27.4., 352-364

Wilkins, C. 1908 *The History of the Iron, Steel, Tinplate and other trades of Wales* (Merthyr)

Wilkinson, J.F. 1886 *The Friendly Society Movement, its origins, rise and growth*

Williams, Chris 1998 *Capitalism, Community and Conflict: The South Wales Coalfield 1898-1947* (Cardiff)

Williams, L.J. 1960 'A Welsh ironworks at the close of the seventeenth century' *National Library of Wales Journal* 11, part 3, 266-272

Williams, Mari 2002 *Female Munitions Workers in South Wales 1939-1945* (Cardiff *Studies in Welsh History* 19)

Williams, Sian Rhiannon 1998 'The Welsh language in industrial Monmouthshire c.1800-1901' Geraint H. Jenkins (ed.) *Language and Community in The Nineteenth Century* (Cardiff), 203-29.

Wrigley, C. (ed.) 2003 *A Companion to Early Twentieth Century Britain* (Oxford, The Historical Association)

REFERENCES

Abbreviations

Arch. Camb.	*Archaeologia Cambrensis*
B.B.C.S.	*Bulletin of the Board of Celtic Studies*
Bradney *History*	J.A. Bradney *A History of Monmouthshire from the Coming of the Normans into Wales down to the Present Time* (5 volumes in ten parts 1904-1933 and 1993)
D.N.B.	*Oxford Dictionary of National Biography* ed. H.C.G. Matthews and Brian Harrison (Oxford 2004)
Gwent C.H.4	*Gwent County History Volume 4, Industrial Monmouthshire 1780-1914* (Cardiff 2011)
Gwent C.H.5	*Gwent County History Volume 5 The Twentieth Century* ed. Chris Williams and Andy Croll (Cardiff 2013)
Merlin	*Monmouthshire Merlin*
Mon. Ant.	*Monmouthshire Antiquary*
N.L.W.	National Library of Wales
P.F.P.	*Pontypool Free Press*
S. Wales M.R.S.	*South Wales and Monmouthshire Record Society*
W.H.R.	*Welsh History Review*

Introduction

1. This reflects a conversation with the late Will Paynter of the N.U.M. at Blaenavon in the late 1970s.
2. House of Lords 12 March 2015, debate on the future of Bletchley Park- Baroness Andrews.

Chapter 1

1. *The Diary of Samuel Pepys* ed. R. Lathan and A.W. Matthews (1970-1983), Vol 3, 112, 165. 14 August 1662.
2. Keith Kissack *Monmouth: The Making of a County Town* (1975), 290-93. I am very grateful to Steve Clarke for this reference.
3. Kissack *ibid* 291; Stephen Clarke and Jane Bray 'Down a cinder mine' *Archaeology in Wales* **44** (2004), 93-5.
4. J.E. Lee *Isca Silurum* (1862), 78, 132; T. Young and P. Guest 'Pont y Clun,

Caergwanaf' *Archaeology in Wales* **44** (2004), *Britannia* **35**, (2004), 263-4, **36**, (2005), 390-91.
5. Knight, J.K., Clarke S. and Owen John, H. 'Medieval ironworking at Trellech: a small salvage excavation, with a list of early bloomery sites in the Monmouth-Trellech area' *Mon. Ant.* **4**, 3-4 (1982), 45-49. Reed et al. *Three late Saxon Iron furnaces;* R. Higham *Making Anglo Saxon Devon* (Exeter 2008), 256-58.
6. On protectionist control of trade and industry in medieval Welsh lordships see R.R. Davies *Lordship and Society in the March of Wales 1282-1400* (Oxford 1978), 234-5. 'By concentrating trade in certain centres he could the more easily control and profit by it' – even to the extent of establishing tollgates on the boundaries of lordships.

7. Dugdale *Monasticon Anglicanum* (1823), 596. W. Rees *South Wales M.R.S.* **4** (1957), 13.

8. *Calendar of Inquisitions Post Mortem* Vol 3, no.371, 245-6 (1295); Vol 5, no.538, 336 (1314).

9. Rees 'Accounts of … lordship of Abergavenny', 75; do *Industry before the Industrial Revolution* 39. *Calendar of Inquisitions Post Mortem Edward III, Vol XII*, no.226, 209. N.L.W. *Badminton Mss 2*, 14776. I am very grateful to Martin Lawler for this reference.

10. N.A. *Ministers Accounts* bundle 890, nos.22-26; *Exchequer Accounts, Various* bundle 485, no.11.

11. Guiseppi 'Some fourteenth century accounts', 145-64. For the excavation of a bloomery site of *c.* 1500-1640 at Rockley Smithies, Yorkshire see D. Crossley and D. Ashurst *Post Medieval Archaeology* **2** (1968), 10-54.

12. N.A. *Durham Auditor's Records* 5.149 Lapsley 'Account Rolls'

13. *Letters and Papers of the Reign of Henry VIII* **XV**, 262 'Bloomery on the King's lands in Glamorgan'.Rees, *Industry before the Industrial Revolution* 143-5.

14. Riden *Charcoal blast furnaces* 13

15. *Exchequer Proceedings Concerning Wales* 27 Elizabeth, 250.

16. Riden *Charcoal blast furnaces* 11-13, 25-6. Rees *Industry* 611.

17. M.P. Doneld *The History of the Company of Mineral and Battery works 1568-1604* (Edinburgh 1961) 86-107. I am very grateful to Neil Phillips for this reference.

18. Knight *Civil War in Monmouthshire* 41 and 186, n.31. Rhys Jenkins 'Iron making in the Forest of Dean' *Trans. Newcomen Society* **6** (1925-6), 42-65. Seventeenth century interest in coke smelting: Pounds and Parker 68-70.

19. Tylecote 'Blast furnace at Coed Ithel', N.L.W. *Badminton Ms 1631*, 12. Survey of the Manor of Porthcasseg 1651 Coed Ithel furnace, including a 'mansion house' (? Catchmays Court), a 'forge house,' a 'coale house' built of timber, 'a way [weigh] house',

'store house' and 'coalyard', Tylecote *Journal of the Iron and Steel Institute* 204 (April 1966).

20. Parr 1973.

21. Riden *Charcoal Blast Furnaces* 15-17. Llewellin 'Iron and wire working'. Nigel Page 'A survey of the charcoal fired iron-working industries of Carmarthenshire and Pembrokeshire' *Post Medieval Archaeology* **41.1** (2007), 180-199. N.L.W. Beaufort Mss 8.575-589 lists, in 1690-1701 Tintern wire-works, Tintern furnace, Upper and Lower forges and Bont Seyson forge, suggesting a complex industrial landscape. In 1788 a traveller noted the cylinder blown furnace 'on a gurgling brook … above the village of Abbey-Tintern', S. Shaw *A Tour in the West of England* (1789), 204.

22. Copy of inscription on memorial to James Pratt N.L.W. *Tredegar Park Mss* 1038; 76/256 (1789); Williams 'Welsh ironworks'.

23. N.L.W. *Tredegar Park Mss* 76/40 and 44-5. In 1753 James Pratt's widow Elizabeth and Jeremiah and Samuel Pratt still had a financial interest, *Tredegar Park Mss* 75

24. Memorial, Crindau chapel, Newport cathedral. Bradney *History V Hundred of Newport* 61.

25. For a possible 'timber famine' and its effects see Brinley Roberts 'Britain's energy crisis in the seventeenth century', *Industrial Revolution and Atlantic Economy* 1-33.

26. N.L.W. *Tredegar Park Mss* 167. There were similar complaints against Pembroke and Lord Herbert of Cardiff for 'cutting of timber in a wood called Glascoed … in order to make coals', with an impressive list of common rights Ifor ap Owen Edwards, *Catalogue of Star Chamber Proceedings Relating to Wales* (Cardiff 1929, P.66/5 (18). Monkswood or Glascoed furnace, Riden *Gazetteer* 25-6. Cyril Hart *Royal Forests: A History of Dean's Woods as producers of timber* (Oxford 1966), 135.

27. Julian Mitchell 'Nathan Rogers and the Wentwood Case', *Welsh History Review* **14.1** (1988), 23-53. Do. 'The Speech Court of Wentwood' *Monmouthshire Antiquary*

6 (1990) 61-67. Knight *Civil War in Monmouthshire* 157-60.

28. Roberts *Industrial Revolution and Atlantic Economy* 6-12.
29. Edward Dudley *Metallum Martis* 1665. In 1619 he began to work a furnace and forges at Pensnet in Worcester and claimed that he obtained a patent from Charles I, made void by the Civil War. Later he worked at Cradley in Worcestershire. His rivals included two Civil War officers, the parliamentarian Captain Buck and Captain John Copley.
30. Tylecote 'Coed Ithel' 150.
31. P.R. Newman *Royalist Officers in England and Wales 1642-1660* (Garland Press, New York and London), no.1596, 419-20. *Calendar of State Papers Domestic 1660-67 Addenda*, 55. Knight *Civil War in Monmouthshire* 142. Roberts *Industrial Revolution*, 12-13.
32. Roberts 'The end of the charcoal iron age' *Industrial Revolution and Atlantic Economy* 60-80. Buxton *Economic Development* 16-19.
33. N.L.W. *Tredegar Park Mss 76/250*. Maryport- Tylecote *Journal of the Iron and Steel Institute* 203 (Sept 1965), 867-874. Chris Evans *Labyrynth* 24, n.21.
34. Atkinson and Baber, 6. *Merlin* 29 August 1840. Coxe *Tour*, introduction, 3. Gray Jones *Ebbw Vale* 43.
35. Gwent Archives D. 397.1664, Pounds and Parker 52, 112-13.
36. William Needham *The Manufacture of Iron* (1831).
37. Brinley Roberts 'Henry Cort and the primacy of Britain' *Industrial Revolution and Atlantic Economy* 100-120. For a detailed description of the process by an informed observer see Svedenstierna *Tour* 52-54.
38. Scrivenor *History of the Iron Trade* 288-9.

Chapter 2
1. Browning *Blaenavon* 90-93. *Mon Ant* **5**, parts 1-2, (1983-4), 64. It is illustrated in *P.F.P.* October 19, 1906.
2. *B.B.C.S.* 14, 88 (N.M.W.49.107). Knight 'Christian origins in south Wales' *Merthyr Historian* **2** (1978), 101-110.

3. Rees *South Wales M.R.S.* **2**, (1950), 75. Do. *Industry Before the Industrial Revolution* **39** (1314). Do. (1950), 123. Falcons, sparrow-hawks 'muskets' and (hen) harriers, many 'from the nests on the mountains'.
4. W. Rees *South Wales M.R.S.* **2** (1950), 119.
5. What follows is based on two typescript letters by Martin Lawler, summarizing his unpublished research.
6. Fox and Raglan *Monmouthshire Houses.*
7. *Monmouthshire Houses* vol 1, 106, 108. *Vernacular Architecture* **36** (2005), 101. Evans *Evolution of Blaenavon* 39-40. Davies *Blaenavon Story* 81. Persondy: Thomas and Lewis *Blaenavon* Vol 3, 36.
8. Gwent Archives JCH 1121-1122. Leases 1696 and 1765, citing earlier ones. They were produced in a lawsuit in 1816, with evidence that the series began under Elizabeth I. Newport Public Library Haines Collection M 250 (672): pamphlet Monmouthshire Assizes Aug 19 1816. N.L.W. Abergavenny Ms 1.
9. R.T. Gunther *Early Science at Oxford* 337-8. N.L.W. Clenennau Mss 2 (E). Knight 'Rural industries'.
10. N.L.W. AB 1, folio 104. Gwent Archives Abergavenny Mss Mon /A/ 20247.
11. N.L.W. Abergavenny Mss 852, 900. Leases 1701 of 'a messuage and thirty acres of land called Blane-Avon' to William Lewis and of the 'hamlet of Blane Avon' to Llywelyn John.
12. Gwent Archives Abergavenny Mss Mon A/2/0004-7. Abergavenny rentals 1746-50. Mon A/2/0259 Perambulation of Abergavenny 1772. Bradney *History of Monmouthshire 2.1 Hundred of Usk* 234-5. The details of the coal leases are from the unpublished work of Martin Lawler, which the author gratefully acknowledges.
13. Wakelin 'Scouring the land'.
14. Bradney *History* I 2b *Hundred of Abergavenny* 466.
15. N.L.W. AB 909. I am very grateful to Martin Lawler for this reference.
16. Jones *Geographical Account* 19.
17. Evans *Labyrinth* 34-5 and 108-9. Elliot *Industrial Development* 27-8.

18. Edmund Jones *A Relation of Apparitions of Spirits in the County of Monmouth and the Principality of Wales* (Newport 1813), 21.

19. Other examples are Jack Bennets Level, Moses Robbins Level and Jim Hoskins Level. It will be noted that virtually all the names are English.

20. Gwent Archives D 2472.1. Harford Memorandum Book, 6. For a similar contract of 1794 see N.L.W. Maybery Mss 1901, Lloyd *Old South Wales Ironworks* 167-8. Gray Jones *Ebbw Vale* 42-6; A.J. Taylor 'Sub contract system'. Ashton and Sykes 1929, chapter 7.

21. Chris Evans *Labyrinth* 15-29. Elsas *Iron in the Making*. Strange *Merthyr Tydfil*.

Chapter 3

1. 1789 lease Gwent Archives D.7.15. Atkinson and Baber, 50 and Table 6, 23.

2. Hill pedigree: Bradney *History* 1, 2b *Hundred of Abergavenny* 410. Hill is sometimes referred to as 'of Oldswinford'. This is the ecclesiastical parish, spanning the county border. Thornton 1.

3. Hadfield *Canals of the West Midlands* 77-9, 100, 138. British Waterways Board Archives, London: Stourbridge Canal Act 1776, 22 George III c. 14; Worcester and Birmingham Canal Act 1791, 31 George III c 59.

4. Monmouthshire Canal Act 1792, 32 George III c 102. *Victoria County History Worcestershire* Vol 3 43.

5. *Gloucester Journal* 29 March 1790. *Holden's Directory* 1809.

6. Court *Rise of the Midland Industries* 220-1.

7. 'Dennis Park and House, Coalbourne Valley, the seat of the late Thomas Hill Esq, now the residence of S. Wheeley Esq.', W. Scott *Stourbridge and its Vicinity* (Stourbridge 1832), 107. 'Fire clay mines, Hill, Waldron and Co'. do. 477.

8. Court *Midland Industries* 115-31. Thornton 1-2.

9. *Gloucester Journal* 25 August 1788.

10. *Stourbridge and its Vicinity* 89, 114. Thornton 1-2, 7. M.V. Herbert *The Hickmans of Oldswinford* (London 1979).

11. N.L.W. Maybery Ms 255, 25 March 1771; Castell Gorfodd Ms 61, 2 April 1776. Gwent Archives D 7. 232: Will of Thomas Hopkins. Thornton 2 and 9, n.12.

12. Coxe *Tour* vol 2, 229. Gwent Archives D 751 201 and 264. Evans *Evolution of Blaenavon* 38.

13. *Gentlemans Magazine* 31 May 1794, 578.

14. Newport Public Library Npt. 1800 (M.350-Gabb file) 24 October 1788.

15. Lloyd *Old South Wales Ironworks* 166-77. Coxe *Tour* vol 2, 250-1. Plan of Nantyglo in 1798-9. Lloyd 167. Gwent Archives D 7 11-12, Lease of Nantyglo (1811) and surrender (1859), do. D 397 Nantyglo and Blaina ironworks.

16. Ince *Knight Family* and *South Wales Iron Industry* 124, Appendix 19, 119-20. Powell *History of Tredegar* 27.

17. Rattenbury 12-13. St Peter's church register (Gwent Archives D Pa 74.1) 3 November 1807: baptism of Elizabeth James, daughter of David and Mary, Varteg Forge. Burials: 1 March 1808 William, son of John Dando, Varteg Works. 2 April 1808 George, son of Moses Piper, Varteg Forge.

18. *Bristol Mercury* 21 January 1843. Sale catalogue Gwent Archives D 751.356 26 April 1844. Archibald Kenrick senior (1760-1835) and junior (1798-1878). G.S. Kenrick (1803 -1848) was the fourth child and second son of Archibald junior. I am grateful to John Owen for valuable discussion of Varteg its output and chronology, from Mineral Statistics. Between 1829 and 1839 Varteg produced 113,000 tons, Blaenavon 85,000. By 1855 the furnaces were 'in a hopeless state of ruin' and in 1865 were robbed of stone by Vipond and Co. to build workers' housing (*Blaenavon Company Minute Book 1* 1864-70, 9 June 1865). For the firm's later history see Church 'Family and failure'.

19. Coxe *Tour* vol 2, 232. Ty Mawr was extended in 1839, presumably by Ashwell, as a datestone on site until recently showed. Sadly, the house is now derelict and vandalised.

20. Gwent Archives D.Pa 74.1: 'Widow of Isaac Bissel of Cradley'.

21. Coxe *Tour* 2, 227-31 and engraving opposite 221.

22. On early competitors of Boulton and Watt see A.E. Musson and E. Robinson 'The early growth of steam power' *Economic History Review* 2nd series 11 (1958-9), 418-39. Cockshutt had been manager of Pontypool ironworks for ten years before moving to Cyfartha. When Crawshay ejected him in 1791 he returned to south Wales, but later removed to Yorkshire to take over the family ironworks at Wortley near Barnsley. Evans *Labyrinth* 63-4.

23. Coxe *Tour* vol 2, 227. *Journeys of Sir Richard Colt Hoare* ed. Thompson 98-9 (27 and 31 August 1798).

24. Coxe *Tour* 228, 230-1. There is a similar description by Colt Hoare *Journeys* 97, Friday 24 August 1798. van Laun *Early Limestone Railways* 71 thinks that Coxe may have been describing the Clydach-Blaenavon Tramroad.

25. van Laun 46-8 and fig 28. Horned sills: van Laun 62 figs 43-4, and Appendix 4, 240-42.

26. Manuscript history of Rugeley by the late Ernest Toy. I am very grateful to John Bennett for this reference.

27. Atkinson and Baber 9 Table 2.

28. Birmingham City Archives Ms 3147/5/673. Wakelin *Blaenavon Ironworks* 37, with an account of the successive blowing engines.

29. Scrivenor *History of the Iron Trade,*126-7: precise figures are 6,042 tons (1807); 7,163 tons (1808); 9,848 tons (1809); 12,254 tons (1810). Map: Gwent Archives Mon/A/2/0273. *The Cambrian* 31 August 1816, quoted John *Industrial Development* 35.

30. Glamorgan Record Office, Neath Abbey Ironworks D/D NAI M /24/2 and M/24/3. Wakelin *Blaenavon Ironworks* 37.

31. Browning *Blaenavon* 31-2. Brute sold his house at Ty Mawdy, Llanfoist to Hill and Hopkins in 1801 (Gwent Archives D.591. 11.43 and 50), possibly marking his move to Blaenavon. 'A certain row of houses built by Aaron Brute, mason, deceased', Gwent

Archives D.751.49. He was buried in November 1818, aged 55. Restoration of his bridge: *C.B.A. Wales Newsletter* **45** (Spring 2013), 4-5. Gwent Archives Llanover D 1210. 1427-68. Evans *Evolution of Blaenavon* 38.

32. Thomas Deakin (1776-1851) Autobiographical note on map of 1837 (Gwent Archives 591.112.27). Obituary: *Merlin* 31 October 1851. Browning *Blaenavon* 64. Long wall working: Morris and Williams 1958, 57-62, Galloway 1904, 247, Elliott *Industrial Development* 33-4. Waste gases: Wilkins 1903, 292-5.

33. Gwent Archives D.Pa 18, 28 March, 18 April 1820. Kenrick *Population of Pontypool* 12-3. He also (*Statistics* 270) notes 'severe battles' in the 1820s between imported Staffordshire men and the 'aborigines' of Monmouthshire.

34. Gwent Archives Quarter Sessions Friendly Society Register 19.19. Browning *Blaenavon* 34.

35. Lowe *Industrial Workers Housing* 9, modified in Lowe 'Stack Square' (1998).

36. *Merlin* 13 October 1832. *Pigot's Directory 1822-3* 'Hampton and Harrison, nail makers, Stourbridge'. Joseph Harrison was Treasurer of the ironmasters quarterly meetings in Newport. *Cambrian* 7 July 1804. Gray Jones *Ebbw Vale* 43.

37. Browning *Blaenavon* 27.

38. Lowe *Industrial Workers Housing* 'Lowe and Anderson Iron Industry Housing Papers'. Gray-Jones *Ebbw Vale* 45-48, 95-6. Browning *Blaenavon* 27. Bunkers Row might also have taken its name from John Bunker 'publican and carpenter' who could have been its speculative builder. He went bankrupt in 1842: *London Gazette* 17 June 1842, issue 20111.

39. Quoted Gray-Jones *Ebbw Vale* 94.

40. Browning *Blaenavon* 82. Kenrick *Population of Pontypool* 35 reported talking to a local schoolmaster: 'I suppose you instruct the boys in their moral duty.' 'Teach them morals' replied the master 'Oh no, that belongs to the girl's school'.

41. From a manuscript history of Rugeley by Ernest Toye. I am very grateful to John Bennett for this quotation. Pevsner *Buildings of England: Staffordshire* 1974, 228.

42. Thornton 4-5, *Cambrian* 24 September 1804.

43. Two letters, 1816 from Ellen Hill to Emma Hodgetts, in possession of Miss K.C. Hodgson of Malvern in 1975. Printed Davies *Blaenavon Story* 28-9.

44. Bradney *History* I, 2b: *Hundred of Abergavenny* 336-346. Evans *Evolution of Blaenavon* 36-7. J. Kyrle Fletcher *The Gwentian Poems of Dafydd Benwyn* (Cardiff 1909). For Einion Sais, an ancestor of Dafydd Gam, see R.R. Davies *Lordship and Society in the March of Wales 1282-1400* (Oxford 1978), 225-6.

45. Newport Reference Library px M250. 672. J.A.H. Evans 'witness and testimony'.

46. 'Notes of antiquarian rambles among the Monmouthshire Hills' *Archaeologia Cambrensis* 1873, 98-101. Letter quoted Davies *Blaenavon Story* 24.

47. David Jones *Before Rebecca* 69-85 (at p.77) (originally published in *Morgannwg* **11** (1967). Powell *History of Tredegar* 33.

48. *Merlin* 31 December 1842, 14 January, 28 April 1843.

49. Hadfield 1967, 174.

50. N.L.W. *Maybery Mss* 797-802, 808-9, 812-3.

51. Rattenbury *Tramroads* 33-45. Van Laun *Early Limestone Railways* 56-60 and figs 38-9.

52. Gwent Archives D 751.53 (May 1818).

53. Gwent Archives D7, 35; D751.81. There is an excellent account of Hill's tramroad and Garnddyrys, with reconstruction drawings by Michael Blackmore, in Barber and Blackmore 1996, 22-37 'Following the iron to Llanfoist wharf'.

54. Hadfield 1967, 176-8. Morris 'Abergavenny and Hereford tramroads'.

Chapter 4

1. Foster *Alumni Oxoniensis* 2, 662. Significantly he gives his origin as Broome, Staffordshire, not Blaenavon. Dyne Steel *Memoir*.

2. Gwent Archives D 591.2, 217; 219-20. *Merlin* 14 November 1829. Anna Tucker 'Old Bank, Abergavenny' *Gwent Local History* **61** (1986), 19-24.

3. *Blaenavon Ironworks Sale Catalogue 1833,* Gwent Archives D.7. 194. On reverse of last page is a pencil note 'Put up at £150,000. Knock down £189,000 by the same person who put it up.' William Crawshay II considered buying the works to set up his son as a partner: N.L.W. *Cyfartha Mss 2*, 733-741.

4. David Jones 'The Scotch Cattle and their black domain' *Before Rebecca* 86-113. Evans *Miners of South Wales* 48-51.

5. *Merlin* 17 September, 1 October 1831, 2 August 1834. R. Challenor and B. Ripley *The Miners Association: A Trade Union in the age of the Chartists* (1968). Evans *Miners of South Wales* 39-47, 53-6.

6. Elsas *Iron in the Making* 12-3 'Minutes of ironmasters meeting'.

7. *Merlin* 28 May 1836.

8. Atkinson and Baber 57-8.

9. Gwent Archives D.7.13, D 7 356. Knight 'Joint Stock Company'.

10. John *Industrial Development* 56. Obituary: *Minutes of the Proceedings of the Institute of Engineers* **66**, 1880-81, 372.

11. Elsas *Iron in the Making; The Times* 18 November 1839, 6. *Annual Register 1839,* 373.

12. Mac Dermot *History of the Great Western Railway* 4, 72-3. Knight 'Joint stock company' 633, n.5. Ince *South Wales Iron Industry* Appendix 2, 173-4.

13. Elliott 80-1.

14. *Merlin* 27 March 1830. They may have been in use earlier. 'A pit for a water machine, 70 yards deep' was constructed at Sirhowy in September 1817. Gray Jones *Ebbw Vale* 85-6. Thomas Evans 'Description of water balance machines' *Trans. Manchester Geological Society* **3** (1862), 334-9, quoted Morris and Williams 70-1. For a photograph of the water balance at Crawshay Bailey's Deep Pit, Nantyglo see Trevor Rowson and Edwin Jones *Old Brynmawr, Nantyglo and Blaina in Photographs* (Barry 1980) pl.109.

15. Lowe *Industrial Housing* 42.

16. Obituary *Minutes of the Proceedings of the Institution of Civil Engineers* **66**, 1880-1881, 372. Gwent Archives D.7.11.

17. R. Cort *A Letter to the Shareholders of the British Iron Company* (1826). Anon *Case ... relative to the frauds practiced on the shareholders of the British Iron Company by some of their agents* (1841); Atkinson and Baber 24, 59-61; Birch 202-5. Colebrook 'History of the British Ironworks'.

18. *Prospectus of the Monmouthshire Iron and Coal Company* (1836): 'Being about to erect a town of considerable magnitude in connection with the Lower Ebbw Vale ironworks, the directors deemed it a proper complement to her present Majesty to call the town by her name'; R. Mushet *Report on the Victoria Ironworks* (Bath 1841).

19. Sale Catalogue: Newport Public Library Px M240. 672. Anon *Plain Facts: History of the Victoria Ironworks from its commencement: Being no 1 of the Bubbles of South Wales.*

20. *Merlin* 1-22 December 1838, *Pontypool Free Press* 15 July 1865. Gwent Archives D.Pa 18, nos 671-677, 11-13 December 1838. Browning *Blaenavon* 45-47. Evans 'Big Pit, Blaenavon' 61.

21. *Merlin* 20 July 1839, from *Mining Journal.*

22. The main source for Ashwell's improvements is the Company Minute Book (Gwent Archives D 751 356).

23. Scrivenor *Comprehensive History; Merlin* 21 May 1842. Scrivenor's other main work *The Railways of the United Kingdom: Statistically Considered* has also been reprinted.

24. J.R.P. Evans 'Ebbw Vale Literary and Scientific Institute: from mutual improvement society to adult education centre 1849-1983' *Gwent Local History* **56**, 1984, 13-21. Anon. *Ebbw Vale Literary and Scientific Institute 1849-1949: A Hundred Years of Endeavour* (Pontypool 1949). Bell and Hopper-Harrison 'Production of pig iron' 74-6. Gray-Jones *Ebbw Vale* 81-2.

25. Wilkins 1906, 292-5. *Merlin* 20 July 1839, 11 June 1853. Savings in coal: Ince *South Wales Iron Industry* 5 and Elliott *Industrial Development* 75, Table 4.1.

26. Between 1830 and 1845 Scotland's market share of pig iron rose from 5% to 25%. *Mining Journal* October - November 1865 confirms that Blaenavon was using hot blast. Regenerative hot blast stove: Harrison 'Production of pig iron' 76-9. Powell *History of Tredegar* 44. Atkinson *Supply of raw materials* 46.

27. Gwent Archives D 751.297. Tombslab in Llanfoist churchyard of Samuel Steele, surgeon, 23rd Dragoons.

28. Dyne Steel *Memoir* and obituary, *Proc. Institution of Civil Engineers* **83** (1897-8), 406-8. van Laun 'Hill Pits'. Wakelin 64. Evans 'Big Pit, Blaenavon', 58-9. Steam locomotives had been in use at Ebbw Vale and Tredegar since 1829-30. Gray-Jones *Ebbw Vale* 76. Powell *History of Tredegar* 40-41.

29. Dyne Steel *Memoir.* Gray-Jones *Ebbw Vale* 80.

30. Mac Dermot 1964, vol 2, 55-67. *Merlin* 1 September 1866.

31. Gwent Archives D 751, 356, Shareholders meeting 28 April 1854. The Mining Inspectors report for 1853 noted (p.163) that the government was using 200 transport vessels 'many of them steamships of the largest size'. Captain Warden *Naval Biographical Dictionary* (1849), 1248. In 1840-1 he led the Royal Naval expedition to Xanthos in Greece to collect 'the Xanthos marbles' for the British Museum.

32. Report of the Committee of Investigation Appointed to Inquire into the Affairs of the Blaenavon Iron and Coal Company in pursuance of a resolution of the shareholders passed at the Annual Meeting held at the Blaenavon Offices on 30 April 1855. The statement on the Varteg lease was misrepresentation. The rent to the company offset some of the ground rent due under the 1806 lease. It was not a direct payment to Lord Abergavenny.

33. *Merlin* 2 May 1850, quoted John *Industrial Development* 57.

34. *Merlin* 11 February 1860. *P.E.P.* September 1859.

35. *Merlin* 29 March, 7 April, 26 May, 16 June, 15 and 22 December 1860, *P.F.P.* 11 February, 16 June, 7 July, 29 December 1860. *Mining Journal* citations: Ince *South Wales Iron Industry* 121-3. When the new mill was opened, the men were given one shilling and sixpence each by the company and went off 'to drink success and prosperity to Blaenavon iron works': *P.F.P.* 7, 21 January 1860.
36. *P.F.P.* 1 February, 28 June 1862.
37. *Mining Journal* 30 October 1869, 821-2.
38. Elliot 'Crumlin Viaduct Works'. The inscription on the 'dogstone', actually of cast iron, reads 'Carlo, a celebrated setter, the property of H.M. Kennard, Crumlin Hall, accidentally shot August 12 1864' with a representation of the dog above.
39. Evans *Evolution of Blaenavon* 44-7. *Merlin* 24 May 1862. *P.F.P.* 24 May 1861, 24 August 1867.
40. Atkinson *Supply of raw materials*.
41. *Monmouth Beacon* 9 July 1839 quoted Elliot 74. Elsas *Iron in the Making* 93, 95, 98. Atkinson *Supply* 48-50.
42. Atkinson and Baber 32-33. Atkinson *Supply* 48. Gwent Archives D 394 D.
43. *Merlin* 13 October 1866, 15 February 1868.
44. Rimmer 'Colonel Bradney'. For a photograph of Bradney with officers of the 2nd Monmouthshires see Rimmer 105, fig 1.
45. G.A. Brett *History of the 2nd Battalion the Monmouthshire Regiment* (new edition 2009). *Merlin* 8 September, 13 October 1860, 25 April 1868. *P.F.P.* 12 January, 16 February 1861. Dixon and Dixon *With Rifle and Pick* 1-8. Dixon *Out Since 14* 1-7.
46. *Merlin* 11 July 1868. Mary-Ann Constantine *The Truth Against the World: Iolo Morganwg and Romantic Forgery* (Cardiff 2007), 153-7.
47. Powell *History of Tredegar* 250. Margaret Escott 'Parliamentary representation' *Gwent County History Vol 4: Industrial Monmouthshire 1780-1914* 273-4. Lovering 2001. *P.F.P.* August 14 -14 November 1868. Of the 240 voters at Blaenavon (each with two votes) 144 voted for Clifford, 54 for Morgan and 52 for Somerset. Most of Clifford's voters presumably cast only one vote.
48. *Merlin* 21, 28 November 1868. *P.F.P.* 28 November 1868. Browning *Blaenavon* 43-4. A butcher, Charles David, also claimed for losses: N.L.W. *Tredegar Mss* 71/649. Powell *History of Tredegar* 78-89. Davies *Blaenavon Story* 60-62.
49. Louise Mitchell 'Re-assessing the anti-Irish riot: popular protest and the Irish in south Wales c.1826-1882' in O'Leary *Irish Migrants* 1-118.
50. Gray-Jones *Ebbw Vale* 170-2. Powell *History of Tredegar* 47, 78-80.

Chapter 5
1. Gwyn A. Williams *The Merthyr Rising* (London 1978, 26.
2. G.S. Kenrick *Population of Pontypool* 23. The exact figures were 61% Welsh, 38% English and 1% Irish. At Tredegar in 1851 there were 72% Welsh, 17.7% English and 8.8% 'other', mostly Irish. Hilling 'Migration' 25, Table 1.
3. *Merlin* 14 January 1837.
4. Collis 'O happy English children'. Johnson 'Educational policy'.
5. On Hugh Seymour Tremenheere (1803-93) see Webb 'A Whig inspector' and O.P. and F.L. Edmonds 1963 and 1965 ed.
6. Kenrick *Journal of the Statistical Society of London* 3, 366-375 and *Population of Pontypool*.
7. Kenrick *Population of Pontypool* 9-10, *Education Enquiry* Vol 2, 602. Elsas *Iron in the Making* 59, Kenrick to J.J. Guest 30 August 1831. In the 1870s 'Coffee taverns' were widespread in south Wales, including Blaenavon. Lambert *Drink and Sobriety* 15.
8. Johnson 'Education policy' 88-100. Tremenheere *Report of the Commission Appointed to Inquire into the state of the population in the Mining Districts* 1847.
9. Kenrick *Population of Pontypool* 9, *Statistics* 368-9. 'Is it true that the government mean to destroy all children under three years of age?'; 'Do you want to send them to Van

Diemen's Land?'; 'The Poor Law only allows us to have three children'.

10. *Merlin* 21 May, 30 July 1942. Morris and Williams 175.

11. *The Times* 5 December 1842, leading article.

12. *Merlin* 5 August 1843.

13. *Merlin* 28 December 1844.

14. Evans *Miners of South Wales* 229-31. *Mining Journal* 1, 22 July 1848.

15. Browning *Blaenavon* 73, Babbidge 'Development of constabulary'. At Merthyr the stocks were originally in the churchyard. Moved to another site, they stayed until *c*.1850. Strange *Merthyr Tydfil* 112.

16. *Merlin* 28 April, 7 July 1832, 9 August 1834, 12 January 1839. On the more turbulent (and colourful) situation in Merthyr see Strange *Merthyr Tydfil* 92-114.

17. *Merlin* 16 November 1839, 15 August 1840.

18. Needham 1831, 31; Kenrick *Statistics* 369.

19. *Morning Chronicle* quoted Strange *Merthyr Tydfil* 27.

20. *Childrens Employment Commission* 616.

21. *Enquiry into the Employment of Females* 616. Dyne Steel *Memoir*.

22. *Childrens Employment Commission* 215, 514.

23. *Enquiry into the Employment of Females* 617. Mary Tanner Gwent Archives D.Pa 74.12 (burial register 1838) and 1841 census Coal Pit, Upper Row 14.

24. Kenrick *Population of Pontypool* 11.

25. *Merlin* 16 January 1858.

26. *Merlin* 30 June 1866.

27. *Childrens Employment Commission* 548. Morris and Williams 212. Gray Jones *Ebbw Vale* 116.

28. *Report of the Commissioners into ... the population in the mining districts* 1847, introduction, Morris and Williams 54-5.

29. On 'immoral' dress among women saltworkers see R. Samuel (ed) *Miners, Quarrymen and Saltworkers* (London History Workshop Series 977), 143.

30. Dyne Steel *Memoir. Mining Journal* 27 May 1843, quoted Morris and Williams 215.

31. Davies *Blaenavon Story* 11. Wakelin 'Scouring the land'. *Merlin* 2 April, 29 August 1857, 31 March 1860, 30 June 1866.

32. Hudson *Munby, Man of Two Worlds*. Davidoff 'Class and gender'.

33. Wren Library, Trinity College Cambridge, Munby Diaries 22 September 1965.

34. *P.F.P.* 28 September, 1 December 1860. *Merlin* 1 December 1860. Browning *Blaenavon* 60. The accidents happened at the height of a religious revival. Overflow crowds packed the chapels for the funeral sermons.

35. Munby *Diaries* 21-22 September 1865.

36. *Childrens Employment Commission* 475. Morris and Williams 211.

37. *Childrens Employment Commission* 616. Kenrick 367, 373. Gray Jones *Ebbw Vale* 117.

38. *Childrens Employment Commission* 610.

39. *Merlin* 6 February 1836, 1-22 December 1838. Gwent Archives D Pa. 74.18 nos.671-677, 11-13 December 1838 Browning *Blaenavon*.

40. *Childrens Employment Commission* 615-6.

41. Quoted Hobsbaum *Labouring Men* (1964).

42. Browning *Blaenavon* 84.

43. Kenrick *Pontypool District* 24, *Statistics* 370. Browning *Blaenavon* 13. *Dowlais Mss* 18 February, 15 June 1818, quoted Birch 246 *Merlin* 8 April 1837. Emigration from south-west Wales Strange *Merthyr Tydfil* 16-19.

44. *Parliamentary Papers* 1893-4 (C. 6894), xxxv, quoted Raphael Samuel (ed) *Village Life and Labour* (History Workshop Series 1975), 3-4.

45. *P.F.P.* 4 August 1860, 18 April 1865. Lesley Walker 'Your fair and sunny land'. Evans *Miners of South Wales* 97.

46. *P.F.P.* 28 November 1874, 28 May 1897.

47. Byron *Don Juan* Canto 1, cxxx 'Bread has been made indifferent) from potatoes' .

48. Gwent Archives Company Minute Book April 1843. Evans *Labyrinth* 166-8. Harris and Co: 6 tons American cheese, 200 sacks and barrels of flour, 5 chests and 7 boxes of tea, 50 casks of butter, 2 tons of bacon, plus clothes and footwear'. Evans 'Evolution of Blaenavon' **44**. *P.F.P.* 18 April 1863. On the Truck system see Evans *Miners of South Wales* 73-85.

49. *Blaenavon Iron and Coal Company Minute Book no 5 1860-64.* Transcript from Adrian Babbidge, Torfaen Museum Trust. *Royal Commission on Truck 1871* quoted Hilton *Truck System* 22. *P.F.P.* 18 April 1863. 'Blaenavon Co. Ltd Provision Store manager M.B. Parker', *Mercer and Crockers Directory 1876.*

50. Wilkins *Old South Wales Ironworks,* 96-8. Hilton 105-6, n.7. Thomas Phillips *Childrens Employment Commission* 543. Crawshay *Report of the Commissioners Appointed to Inquire into the State of the Population in the Mining Districts 1847,* 17.

51. *Royal Commission on Truck,* National Archives H.O. 44/13, quoted Hilton 100, n.6.

52. Evans *Miners of South Wales* 75-77. Brute's Row, Gwent Archives D 751 49.

53. *South Wales Daily News* 9 February 1911. Bailey's payment of a lump sum to a head workman for distribution was not unique. A by-product of the sub-contract system, it was known in Merthyr in the later 18th century. Like other of Bailey's work practices, it may have been an archaic practice, disued elsewhere.

54. Evans *Labyrinth* 79. Powell *History of Tredegar Truck Commission* lii. Hilton *Truck System* 135. Morris and Williams 230. Gwent Archives D 591. 112. Powell *History of Tredegar* 64, 71.

55. Gwent Archives D 591. 112 (1873)

56. W.J. Davies *Nineteenth Century Token Coinage* (1906, reprinted 1969), R. Dalton and S.H. Hamer *The Provincial Token Coinage of the Eighteenth Century* (1910, reprinted 2011).

57. *New London Magazine* December 1787. The Priestfield, Wolverhampton token of 1811 has a view of a three furnace ironworks with parallels to Blaenavon. The Wilkinson tokens have a number of reverse types, including Vulcan and a workman operating a forge hammer.

58. Browning *Blaenavon* 84.

Chapter 6

1. Johnson 'Educational policy' 105-6. Evans *Labyrinth* 162-3. Lambert 19.

2 Kenrick *Population of Pontypool* 18, *Statistics* 371.

3. Davies *Blaenavon Story* 115-16. For a pictorial survey of surviving Blaenavon pubs see Thomas and Lewis *Blaenavon* vol 3, 64-70, figs 90-102. *P.F.P.* 28 May 1859.

4 I am extremely grateful to Yolanda Stanton for kindly sending me full details of the Blaenavon pub checks.

5. Browning *Blaenavon* 34-6.

6. This paragraph is based on Thomas and Lewis *Blaenavon* 61-2. Gwent Archives D 591. 30.12 (1875) and D 591.30.71 (1884).

7. Monmouthshire Quarter Sessions List 1836-41. Knight 'Oddfellows', Evans *Labyrinth* 163-5.

8. Kenrick *Population of Pontypool* 12, 24, *Statistics* 373. O'Leary 50-3.

9. *Merlin* 8 June 1833.

10. Dot Jones 1984, 1985. Gwent archives Bythway 309. An Odd Women's Lodge opened in Blaenavon in 1861 (*P.F.P.* 24 August 1861). *Rules of Loyal Friendship Lodge of Odd Women, Prince of Wales Inn Blaenavon* (1865). *Merlin* 23 March 1867. Faithful Friends female benefit society of Ebbw Vale: Gray Jones *Ebbw Vale* 63.

11. Gwent Archives *Quarter Sessions Friendly Society Rules* 0019.19.0022.18. Will of Samuel Hopkins: Gwent Archives D 751 297.

12. *Merlin* 5 November 1831, 10 March 1832.

13. *Merlin* 30 June 1860. For a detailed list of Tredegar benefit societies see Powell *History of Tredegar* 185-90.

14. Browning *Blaenavon* 27, 35. When the Ancient Britons of Tredegar paraded in 1866 'The quaint dresses, long beards etc afforded considerable amusement to the lookers on': *Merlin* 13 October 1866.

15. Dot Jones 20.

16. O'Leary 'Cult of respectability'. Browning *Blaenavon* 35-36.

17. For a typical Whitsun Sunday School procession of 1905 with banners see Thomas and Lewis *Blaenavon* Vol 3, 30.

18. *Merlin* 21 January 1860. *P.F.P.* 10 November 1861.
19. *Merlin* 10 October 1879. *P.F.P.* 21 February 1896. J.J. Morgan *The '59 Revival in Wales* (Mold 1909), 107. Gray Jones *Ebbw Vale* 151-3.
20. Browning *Blaenavon* 70-1.
21. *P.F.P.* 26 November, 17 December 1886.
22. *Merlin* 21 January 1860, *P.F.P.* November 10 1861.
23. *P.F.P.* 27 July 1861, 2 May 1863.
24. *Merlin* 10 February 1866, *P.F.P.* 1 May 1880, 2 April 1886. The limitation of the Mutual Improvement Society to 'respectable tradesmen' may be indicated by a letter to the *P.F.P.* from a 'working man' in the year after its foundation. Dr Steel had died from a fall from his horse and was commemorated by a fine monument in the church. The 'working man' suggested that a reading room would have been a more fitting memorial. *P.F.P.* 4 September 1867.
25. E.T. Davies *Religion in the Industrial Revolution* 143-4. Powell *History of Tredegar* 215-16. Evan Owen *Workmen's Libraries in Glamorgan and Monmouthshire* (Cardiff 1895).
26. Jack Jones *Rhondda Roundabout* 147. Dorothy Donaldson 'The penny collector' *Gwent Family History Society Journal* (2013), 111.
27. Bailey *Leisure and Class in Victorian England* 132. Parry and Keen *Blaenavon in Old Picture Postcards,* 64. One of Arthur Morrison's *Martin Hewitt Investigator* stories 'The Loss of Sammy Crockett' (*Strand Magazine* April 1894) tells of two rival pub landlords with entries for a race and a crooked bookmaker who kidnapped the favourite.
28. Prescott *Spellbound People* 9-31 'From Football to Rugby'. Beck 'Leisure and sport'. Browning *Blaenavon* 43-4.
29. *Funeral to Festival* 189-93.
30. *Funeral to Festival* 176-9.
31. Martin Johnes *Soccer and Society in South Wales 1900-1939* (Cardiff 2002). *Studies in Welsh History,* **20,** 148. G. Williams 'How amateur was my valley? professional sport and national identity in Wales 1890-1914' *British Journal of Sports History* 2, no.3 (1985), 248.
32. *Funeral to Festival* 179-183.
33. Lewis *Ken Jones.*

Chapter 7

1. Williams, G. *The Welsh Church from Conquest to Reformation* (Cardiff 1962), 457.
2. Knight 'Nonconformity of the gentry'.
3. Bradney *History* II, 2a *Hundred of Abergavenny* 177.
4. Bassett, T.M. *The Welsh Baptists* (Swansea 1977), 14-16; White B.R. 'John Miles and the structure of the Calvinist Baptist Mission to south Wales 1649-1660' in Mansel J. (ed) *Welsh Baptist Studies* (Cardiff 1976), 35-76.
5. White 76, citing Josuah Thomas *The History of the Baptist Church in Wales c.1796* Bristol Baptist College Library Ms Z dz folios 93 ff.
6. A characteristic example occurs in Charles Parry's manuscript *History of Ebbw Vale* (1870); Ms in library of Ebbw Vale Scientific and Literary Institution, photo-copy in possession of the author. In 1859 Joseph Saunders recalled how he had come to Ebbw Vale in 1802. On Sunday morning he asked his landlady 'if she knew of any religious man in that place'. She directed him to someone 'living in one of the houses above us'. The two men journeyed to Sirhowy Baptist Chapel. From this came prayer meetings of Baptists and Independants in Ebbw Vale. Eventually, the Independants moved to the carpenter's shop in the ironworks.
7. Horeb Church Book *A Church Record: A Synopsis of the State and Transactions of a Christian Church* (1847); in possession of the Minister and deacons of Horeb Baptist Church, typescript in possession of the author. For another manuscript history see Revd William Jones (1835-1911) *The Church at Horeb Blaenavon* National Library of Wales Minor Deposits 1209 B.
8. Bassett 1977 125-9. Evans *Evolution of Blaenavon* 40.

9. Young, D. *Origins and History of Methodism in Wales and the Borders* (1893) 125-29: '... one of their great debaters, called Aaron Brut of Blaenavon, who entered the house of Richard Evans at the close of Mr Jones's sermon, openly and flatly contradicting him'. In 1831, the South Wales Association of the Calvinists, meeting in Tredegar, ruled that 'no member of the Union of Colliers, Miners and Firemen would be tolerated as a church member'. Oliver Jones *Early Days of Sirhowy and Rhymney* 64.

10. N.A. RG4/1250, cited Evans Evolution of Blaenavon 41 (Penuel register). Map, 29 September 1819 Gwent archives Mon/A/202 and 203 Browning *Blaenavon* 54-6, 63-4.

11. Browning *Blaenavon* 61-62. *Merlin* 13, 20 August 1864.

12. 'Notes of antiquarian rambles among the Monmouthshire hills' *Arch. Camb.* 1873, 98-101. Gwent Archives D.Pa. 74.48, taking down of Capel Newydd. Jones and Williams *Religious Census*.

13. Browning *Blaenavon* 59. D.C. Jenkins (ed) *The Diary of Thomas Jenkins of Llandeilo 1826-1870* (Bala 1976).

14. W. Scott *Stourbridge and its Vicinity* (Stourbridge 1832), 89. M. Midgley (ed) *Victoria County History : County of Stafford V* (1959), 58-72.

15. Gwent Archives D.Pa.74.

16. Dyne Steel *Memoir* Browning *Blaenavon* 59; *P.F.P.* 24 July 1885.

17. E.T. Davies *Religion in the Industrial Revolution* 99-140.

18. Gwent Archives D.Pa 74.48. *P. F.P* 3 March 1911.

19. Gwent Archives D. 942.75 Baptismal register, Blaenavon circuit, 1829-76. D 942.76-78 Reports of Quarterly Meetings 1830-1837. In December 1830, T. Griffiths was excluded for selling beer on the sabbath.

20. R. Pyke *The Early Bible Christians* (London 1941). T. Shaw *The Bible Christians* (London 1965).

21. *P.F.P.* 12 January, 21 September 1861. *Merlin* 21 September 1861. Gwent Archives D 942 72-75 (Accounts, minutes and baptisms 1891-1939).

22. J.L. Morgan *The 1859 Revival in Wales* (Mold 1909), 102-7. *P.F.P.* 9 March 1861. Browning *Blaenavon* 60.

23. *Merlin* 13 June 1829. Kenrick *Statistics* 344. O'Leary *Irish in Wales*.

24. Anon *Franciscan Missions* 45. Browning *Blaenavon* 33-4. E.T. Davies 187-191. Lambert *Drink and Sobriety* 16.

25. *Franciscan Missions* 46, *Merlin* 22 May 1868. On Torreggiani (1830-1904) see C.J. Duffy *Australian Dictionary of Biography* (1976) 6.

26. *Franciscan Missions* 42-4. There is a memorial to Mary Peterson in Trevethin churchyard. Her friend died on 2 August 1870 and was buried in Chiselhurst.

27. *Merlin* 13 July 1867. Stephen Hughes 'Thomas Thomas 1817-88 The first national architect of Wales' *Arch. Camb.* 152 (2003), 151. Thomas was also architect of Bethlehem Independent Chapel (Hughes 142, *Merlin* 13, 20 August 1864). Thomas Rees and Scotch Cattle: *Merlin* 26 July 1834, 17 January 1835.

28. E.T. Davies *Religion in the Industrial Revolution* 70-71. Bradney *Hundred of Abergavenny* 355, *Memorandum* (on) *the decline of the Welsh language*.

29. *P.F.P.* 18 May 1867.

30. *P.F.P.* 21 January 1881.

31. Knight 'Brought forth in a high place' 128-9. Baptist churches, with their autonomous organization were prone to similar disputes. There were others at Horeb in 1860, described by the *P.F.P.* as 'a most unseemly brawl', when the minister resigned and at Ebenezer in 1877 when he survived. *P.F.P.* 17, 24 March 1860, 27 October, November 1877. D.P. Jenkins *A Short History of King Street (Bethel) English Baptist Chapel* (1978).

32. *P.F.P.* 8 December 1880, 14 August, 20 November 1885, 12 February 1886. Thomas and Lewis vol 3, 95-6.

33. Browning *Blaenavon* 87.

34. Pryce Population and language, Appendix 1, 183. This left 3,336 without religious affiliation, though presumably the Roman

Catholic community, not otherwise mentioned, should be subtracted.

35. D. Ben Rees *Chapels in the Valley* (Ty Ffynnon Press 1975) 185-210 provides a perceptive analysis.

36. Jeremy Morris 'Religion' 245-8.

37. Morris 246-7.

Chapter 8

1. Pounds and Parker *Coal and Steel* 59-61, 116. Barraclough 'setting of the stage' 3.

2. 'Henry Bessemer' G. Tweedale *D.N.B.* Vol 5 514-7. Pounds and Parker 116-23.

3. Carpenter 'Percy Carlyle Gilchrist' 19.

4. Carpenter 19-20.

5. Birnie *Memoir* 30.

6. 'Sidney Gilchrist Thomas' J.K. Almond *D.N.B.* Vol 54, 373-5. Birnie *Memoir*. Lilian Gilchrist Thomas *An Invention and its consequences*.

7. W.H. Brock *D.N.B.* Vol 22, 221-2. Carpenter 'Percy Carlyle Gilchrist'. Reese Edwards *British Steelmaker* November 1951. Marion Walker Alcaro *Walt Whitman's Mrs G : A Biography of Ann Gilchrist* (Fairleigh University Press, New Jersey 1991). A plaque in Marine Parade, Lyme Regis commemorates Percy Gilchrist's birth close by.

8. Almond 'Cleveland and the basic process' 12-3. Barraclough 'British steel trade' 9 and 'Setting of the scene' 8.

9. Sidney Gilchrist Thomas to Percy Gilchrist August 1876, Birnie 58.

10. Sidney Gilchrist Thomas to Percy Gilchrist 20 Dec. 1876, Birnie 89.

11. Percy Thomas to Sidney Gilchrist Thomas 19 October 1877, Birnie 103-4.

12. Sidney Gilchrist Thomas to Elizabeth Burton December 1877, Birnie 107

13. Barraclough 'British steel trade' 9-10.

14. Hempstead 186. Denner 'Pursuit of crochets' 6.

15. Sidney Gilchrist Thomas to Elizabeth Burton December 1878, Birnie 126.

16. Pounds and Parker 120-6. Sidney Gilchrist Thomas to E.P. Martin January 1880, Birnie 151.

17. Elliot p.76. Denner, p.6.

18. Brian Ll, James (ed) *G. T. Clark: Scholar Ironmaster in the Victorian Age* (Cardiff 1998).

19. A Hutchinson Presidential address *Journal Iron and Steel Institute* 135.1 (1937), 73 quoted Almond 'Making steel' 177.

20. Almond 187-9. *The Times* 14 March 1879.

21. Andrew Carnegie 'An American Four-in hand in Britain (Doubleday Doran, New York 1983). 83-7. J.F. Wall *Andrew Carneige* (Oxford 1970), 500-504. Denner 'Pursuit of crochets' 5.

22. R.L. Rudolf *Banking and Industrialization in Austria Hungary 1873-1914* (Cambridge 2008), 52-3. For an illustration of the casket see *Gathering the Jewels* (http://www.gtj.org.uk) GTJ 31588.

23. Thomas and Lewis *Blaenavon* 84-85. There is a bust of Sidney Gilchrist Thomas in the garden of the Basic Slag Research Institute in the German steelmaking city of Essen.

24. Carpenter 'Percy Carlyle Gilchrist'; and *The Engineer* 20 December 1935, 650-651.

Chapter 9

1. *Merlin, P.F.P.* and *Star of Gwent* all with long accounts 6 August 1870. *P.F.P.* 6 October 1871.

2. *P.F.P.* 6 June, 10 October 1874, 14 February 1908.

3. Gwent Archives D 2133,2. Atkinson and Baber 13-15, 59.

4. *Merlin* 12 January 1872, 31 March 1871. Morris and Williams 202-3. Obituary: do. 12 January 1872. The song 'Crawshay Bailey had an engine' was already being quoted as 'that old song that used to be sung here' by Sir Joseph Bailey at a Conservative meeting in Nantyglo in 1891. *South Wales Times* and *Star of Gwent* 4 September 1891. Alan Jones 'The Crawshay Bailey estate' *Gwent Local History* **80** (Spring 1996), 31-40. Elliot *Industrial Development* 88.

5. Evans *Miners of South Wales* 85-93.

6. C. Fisher and J. Smethurst 'War on the law of supply and demand. The Amalgamated Association of Miners and the Forest of Dean colliers 1869-1875' in R. Harrison (ed)

Independent Collier (Harvester Press 1978), 114-55. A Dalziel *The Colliers strike in south Wales: Its causes, progress and settlement* (Cardiff 1872). Evans *Miners of South Wales* 101-14.

7. J.H. Morris and L.J. Williams 'The South Wales sliding scale 1874- 79: An experiment in industrial relations' *Industrial South Wales 1750-1914* ed W.E. Minchinton (1969). Reuben Price: *P.F.P.* 28 November 1863. Powell *History of Tredegar* 82-87.

8. *Merlin* 4, 25 January 1878.

9. *P.F.P.* 17 January 1880. An example from Sweden may be seen on the Wikipedia Blaenavon website.

10. *Merlin* 25 August, 22 September 1882, 11 May 1883. Photograph of the Blaenavon Bessemer shop: Parry and Keen plate 6.

11. *P.F.P.* 16 April 1886. Wakelin 13.

12. Drower 1985. James *Freemasonry in Monmouthshire* 150-56. Morris L. Bierbrier *Who was Who in Egyptology* (4th ed, Egypt Exploration Society, 2012), 294. Kennard was also associated with an important Coptic papyrus containing Biblical texts, (B.L. Or 7651, now TM 107945), which he presented to the British Museum.

13. Effects of McKinley tariff: *P.F.P* 14 January 1910.

14. J. Medwar and D. Pyke *Hitlers Gift: Scientists who fled Nazi Germany* (2000), 3-5.

15. Elliot 73. Powell *History of Tredegar* 122-5. Robb *British Culture* 190-92.

16. The Black Pins, Pwllaca, Ballsis (or Three Quarter Ball), Soap Vein and Bottom Vein: Browning *Blaenavon* 20-21. In the final phase, only the latter was worked. Ironstone mining ended at Tredegar in *c.*1875 Powell *History of Tredegar* 87.

17. Letter, J.W. Thatcher to Cartwright, 22 November 1922 (photocopy in writer's possession).

18. E.P. Martin Presidential address *Journal of the Iron and Steel Institute* 51, 1895. Elliot 83-4. L.J. Williams in Lloyd Jones *G.T. Clark,* 61.

19. Barber and Blackmore 31-2. There is a photograph of the Queen Victoria in Grabar. Around 1840 there was a Star Inn at Garnddyris, though this may have been an earlier name for the Queen Victoria. *London Gazette* 17 July 1842.

20. Abergavenny Steam Society *Garnddyrys* (no date).

21. Barber *Exploring Blaenavon* 189-92 and information from Martin Lawler.

Chapter 10

1. *Johns' Directory* 1891. Davies *Blaenavon Story* 82-3, 90. Ince gives 1900 as the date for the end of the Old Side furnaces. They may have been abandoned after the strike before being dismantled in 1911. In their final years they were using ore from Gelli Isaf, Aberdare: Wilkins 210.

2. O'Leary *Irish in Wales* 156. For Blaenavon men in the Crimea and Boer War see Davies *Blaenavon Story* 91-2. W.E.A. *Funeral to Festival* 210-3. Furnace 2 in the Old Works may have been put briefly into blast in 1904-6.

3. Happily, the Blaenavon Band still flourishes. Founded in the 1890s as the Blaenavon Town Silver Band it was for many years supported by Big Pit, becoming the Blaenavon Colliery Workman's Band. When Big Pit closed in 1980 it became the Blaenavon Town Band. Lewis and Thomas *Blaenavon Through the Ages* 105.

4. Gwent Archives D 480.102. Davies *Blaenavon Story* 116.

5. *P.F.P.* March 1911: raising money to replace 'the corrugated edifice'. Parry and Keen plate 12.

6. *P.F.P.* 21 August 1914, 8 January 1915.

7. Parry and Keen pl.14, *Old Ebbw Vale in Photographs* 118, pl.112. For an interview with a woman brickyard worker from Buckinghamshire see Raphael Samuel *Village Life and Labour* 114. 'William Burgoyne, contractor and brickmaker', *Mercer and Crockers Directory 1876*. 'John Burgoyne, brickmaker', *Slaters Directory 1880*. Losses: Gwent Archives D 751.357.

8. Interview, Mrs Howells, Brickyard Cottage, by Martin Lawler 17 May 1978. The

photographer may have been Raymond Cook 'draper and photographer'. For his portrait, with his camera, see Thomas and Lewis *Blaenavon Through the Years* Vol *3*, 64.

9. *P.F.P.* 7 May, 17 September 1915. Thomas and Lewis *Blaenavon* Vol 3, 116-19.

10. Strong *First World War* 3-4. The 1st Battalion were recruited from Newport, the 2nd from Pontypool, Blaenavon and Usk, the 3rd from the Abergavenny area. According to a local tradition, the outbreak of war also saw the end of the Monmouthshire Canal. The boatmen brought the last boat as far as Fourteen Locks outside Newport, where it ran aground, the men then abandoned ship and enlisted. The boat was visible into the 1970s.

11. Dixon *Out Since 14* 281-2, 292-3. *Blaenavon and the First World War* 31-2.

12. Brett *History* 39-40. A plate opposite p.40 shows 'snipers cottage' and a group photograph of the mining party. *London Gazette* 20 June 1915, 6126. Dixon and Dixon *With Rifle and Pick* 70-83. Dixon *Out Since 14,* 286. Strong 4-5.

13. Dixon and Dixon 211-2, 215. *Blaenavon and the First World War* 33, 124.

14. Dixon *Out Since 14* 240, 282-3.

15. For a full roll call of the town's war dead see *Blaenavon and the First World War* 123-34.

16. W.G. Sweet 'A Memoir of the final advance and march into Germany 1918' *Gwent County History* **66** (1989), 9-36. W.E.A. *Funeral to Festival* 162-70.

17. Becket and Simpson *Nation Under Arms* 202-6.

18. Chris Williams *Capitalism, Community and Conflict* 27-30.

19. Becket and Simpson 202-6. Simmonds 137, fig 5.2. Marwick *Women at War.*

20. Robb *British Culture* 42-5. Parry and Keen, pl.13. *Blaenavon and the First World War* 62-5, 71.

21. Becket and Simpson 118, Simmonds 56-9, 68-9. *Funeral to Festival* 84-8.

22. Marwick 34. Idris Davies 'I was born in Rhymney' *Selected Poems of Idris Davies* (1953) 46 from *Tonypandy and Other Poems* (1945).

23. Kirby *British Coalmining Industry* 24-8.

24. Chris Williams *Capitalism, Community and Conflict* 63-4. Beddoes 'Munitionettes' 189-90. Ex war workers were entitled to 25 shillings a week 'out of work donation' for 13 weeks. R.M. Jones 'Wales and British politics' 92.

25. *South Wales News* 15 May, 12 June 1926, cited Francis and Smith *The Fed* 56-7.

26. Kirby 24-8, Gray-Jones *Ebbw Vale* 193-8. Ward, Stephanie *Unemployment and the State in Britain: The Means Test and Protest in 1930s South Wales and North East England* (Manchester, 2013).

27. *P.F.P.* 1 May, 12 June 1908.

28. Roy Jenkins *Churchill* (2001), 123. R.M. Jones 'Wales and British Politics' 88-92.

29. The account has since been published and the original preserved in Gwent Archives. James Daniel Matthews, with notes by John Evans 'the miner's bravery will count at Judgement Day: an eyewitness account of the Milfraen Pit explosion', *Gwent Local History* **93** (Autumn 2002), 40-50.

30. R. Westlake *First World War Graves and Memorials in Gwent* Vol 1 (2001), 41-3, Vol 2 (2002), 29-33. *Funeral to Festival* 106-10.

31. Gwent Archives D Pa 74.

32. Francis and Smith *The Fed* 270-4.

33. Beck 'Leisure and sport' 459.

34. For the plot of the novel see *Gwent C.H. 5*, 288-9.

35. Ridgwell 'South Wales and the cinema' 601

36. Berry *Wales and Cinema* 129-30.

37. Davies *Blaenavon Story* 99. Pincombe *Gwent C.H. 5* 107. W.E.A. *Funeral to Festival* 76-84 and 244-5. I am very grateful to Viscount Grimston for information on Jim Forrester.

38. Berry *Wales and Cinema* 137-40.

39. W.E.A. *Funeral to Festival* 80-4.

40. B.B.C. Wales News Channel 10 May 2010. Carolyn Spiller 'Evacuees in Gwent' *Gwent County History* **69** (Autumn 1990), 32-7. *Funeral to Festival* 246-92.

41. Doyleruish 107. *Famine to Festival* 289.

42. High duty alloys: Gwent Archives D 480/164-5 D.A. Thomas 'War and the economy: the south Wales experience' Baber

and Williams 255. 'Gathering the Jewels' website Gtj 01262.

43. Roberts 'Mining town in wartime'.
44. Eric Turner *Funeral to Festival* 289. Gwent Archives D 480. 168 and information from Francis Keene. The Pullido family were established Blaenavon residents rather than refugees from the Spanish Civil War. They may have been part of the influx of Spanish immigrants to south Wales associated with iron ore imports.
45. Gwent Archives D 480 168.
46. Wakelin *Blaenavon Ironworks* 53. *Antiquaries Journal* **28** (1948), 28 and information from Professor Grimes.
47. Information Mrs Maisie House, 16 June 1986 and entry in visitors book, Whistle Inn, Doyleruish 78-81.
49. *Funeral to Festival* 234-7.

Chapter 11
1. Newport Public Library q. 417.8.900. Alexander Cordell *Life among the Ironworkers of Garndyrus and Blaenavon 1810-1836* (Blaenavon Community Heritage Museum 2009).
2. Williams *A Forgotten Army* 258.
3. Thomas and Lewis *Blaenavon* vol 3, 30-2, Olive Philips *Monmouthshire* (1951), 113.
4. *Funeral to Festival* 93-106.
5. James Kegie *Blaenavon Central Area: A Housing Study* (Blaenavon Urban District Council 1970).
6. I am very grateful to Jeremy Lowe for this account of his work.
7. John Evans Big Pit.
8. For the Blaenavon 'Pyramids' see Thomas and Lewis *Blaenavon* figs 109,113.
9. *The Independent* 1 December 2000.
10. *The Welsh World Heritage Experience; Blaenavon and Big Pit.*
11. Kelleher 'Identifying, recording and restoring'.
12. Bernard Wasserstein 'Glasgow in the 1950s' *Ultimate Adventures with Britannia* ed. William Roger Louis (London and Auste, Texas 2005), 19-31.

GENERAL INDEX

INDEX OF PERSONAL NAMES

Usk Castle, Priory and Town
edited by Jeremy K. Knight & Andy Johnson
216 pages, with over 120 b/w and 20 colour illustrations
Hardback   ISBN 978 1906663 01 8   £17.50
Paperback ISBN 978 1906663 02 5   £12.95

The Norman borough (or town) of Usk was established around its castle and priory and these are at the heart of this book. Through a series of chapters, the contributors explore Usk through the history of its inhabitants, and that of the buildings which still make up the town, as well as the archaeology of former times. The contributors include John and Jan Barrow, Madeleine Gray, Rosemary and Henry Humphreys, Jeremy K. Knight, Professor W. Manning, Geoffrey Mein, Frank Olding, Sian Rees, Peter Rennie, Keith Underwood and Professor Chris Given Wilson.

A Guide to Slow Travel in the Marches
by Les Lumsdon
Paperback, 240 pages, 30 colour & 100 b/w photos, 20 maps ISBN 978 1906663 53 7   £10

The Guide is structured around eight towns – Welshpool, Oswestry, Shrewsbury, Church Stretton, Ludlow, Hereford, Llandrindod Wells and Abergavenny – which act as bases for exploration and for which there is a guided walk, with tours from each using trains and buses. There are also suggestions for cycle rides and walks. The guide also suggests places to eat and imbibe. The section for each location includes a list of extras such as farmers' markets, local activities and festivals, as well as a selection of useful local publications and websites. The book is also supported by its own website which will help keep information up to date.

Three Chevrons Red
The Clares: A Marcher Dynasty in Wales, England and Ireland
by Paul Davies
Paperback, 368 pages, full colour, over 130 illustrations ISBN 9781906663803   £15

Seven hundred years ago one of the greatest dynasties of the Middle Ages was brought to a premature end on a Scottish battlefield. Gilbert de Clare, earl of Gloucester and Hertford, Marcher baron of Glamorgan and lord of Clare, lay among the corpses at Bannockburn. The young earl was the last male heir of a family that had ruled in Britain since the Norman Conquest, and had gained properties and titles stretching from East Anglia to the shores of western Ireland. For two and a half centuries the Clares set about amassing wealth and privileges until they became one of the richest and most powerful dynasties in the land. As Marcher lords and leading magnates the Clares were involved in the politics and wars of the Welsh border, of Ireland, of the government in England and finally and fatally in that of Scotland. This book explores the history of the family – of earls and clerks, of jousters and warriors, of cosmopolitan men of the world and xenophobic land-grabbers, of marriages arranged for family gain and the occasional triumph of love nurtured in secret liaisons, of war and of diplomacy, of women who stood their ground and enjoyed their widowhood. With many photographs, maps and reconstruction drawings.